Scott Foresman - Addison Wesley

Another Look

Reteaching Masters

Grade 4

Scott Foresman - Addison Wesley

Editorial Offices: Menlo Park, California • Glenview, Illinois
Sales Offices: Reading, Massachusetts • Atlanta, Georgia • Glenview, Illinois
Carrollton, Texas • Menlo Park, California

http://www.sf.aw.com

Overview

Another Look (Reteaching Masters) provide additional teaching options for teachers to use with students who have not yet mastered key skills and concepts covered in the student edition. A pictorial model is provided when appropriate, followed by worked-out examples and a few partially worked-out exercises. These exercises match or are similar to the simpler exercises in the student edition.

For Learn lessons and Explore lessons, the masters provide an alternative approach to the lesson development. This approach simplifies or clarifies the concept presented on the student edition page.

For Problem Solving and Decision Making lessons, the masters provide additional problems with problem solving hints or problems that focus on the skills needed for the student edition lesson.

ISBN 0-201-3125409

Printed in the United States of America

1 2 3 4 5 6 7 8 9 10 – BW – 01 00 99 98 97

Contents

Name ______________________________

Another Look
1-1

Pictographs and Bar Graphs

This **bar graph** shows the number of skyscrapers in some major cities. The **pictograph** shows the same data.

How many skyscrapers are there in Chicago, IL?

To find the data on the bar graph, follow the bar next to Chicago. It ends at 50, so there are __50__ skyscrapers in Chicago.

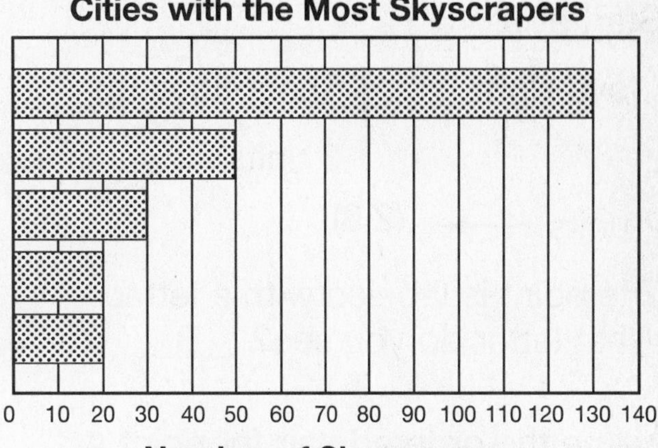

To find the data on the pictograph, find Chicago on the left. There are 5 symbols next to Chicago. Each symbol shows 10 skyscrapers. Count 1 ten for each symbol. 10. . . 20. . . 30. . . 40. . . 50. . . . Chicago has __50__ skyscrapers.

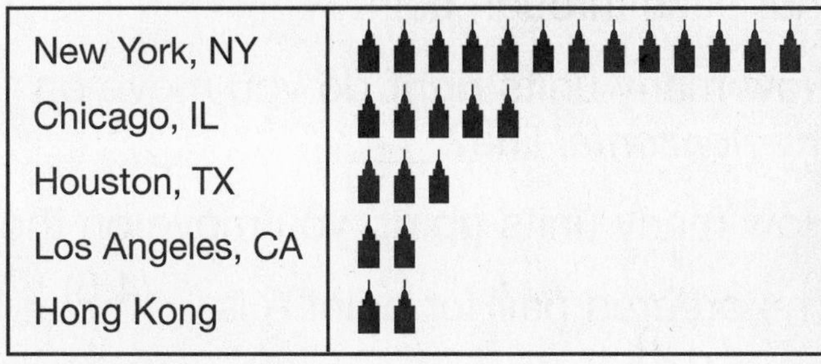

Use the graphs to answer the questions.

1. Which city has about 30 skyscrapers? ______________

2. Do Chicago, Houston, Los Angeles, and Hong Kong all together have more skyscrapers than New York? ______________

3. Which cities have fewer than 50 skyscrapers?

____

4. Suppose your town has 20 skyscrapers. How many symbols would you draw in the pictograph? ______________

Name ______________________

Another Look 1-2

Ordered Pairs

Ordered pairs can help you find a location on a coordinate grid.

An ordered pair gives you directions.

Give the letter of the point named by (2,3).

Start at 0.

Move **right** 2 units → Then move **up** 3 units ↑ (2,3)

The point is labeled with a letter.
What letter do you see? B

Name the ordered pair for point A.

Find the horizontal and vertical lines that pass through point A.

How many units **right** do you move on the *horizontal* line? 4

How many units **up** do you move on the *vertical* line? 6

The ordered pair for point A is (4,6)

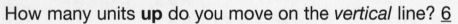

Coordinate Grid

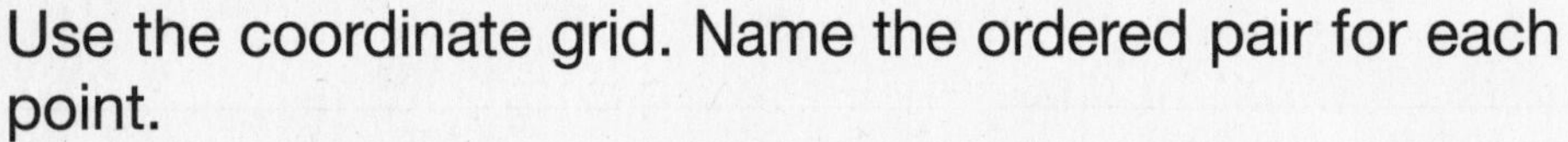

Use the coordinate grid. Name the ordered pair for each point.

1. C ________ **2.** E ________ **3.** J ________

Give the letter of the point named by each.

4. (6,2) ________ **5.** (9,1) ________ **6.** (3,9) ________

7. (7,5) ________ **8.** (10,8) ________ **9.** (2,1) ________

Name ______________________________

Reading Line Graphs

You can read **line graphs** to get information. This line graph shows the number of students that were absent each month.

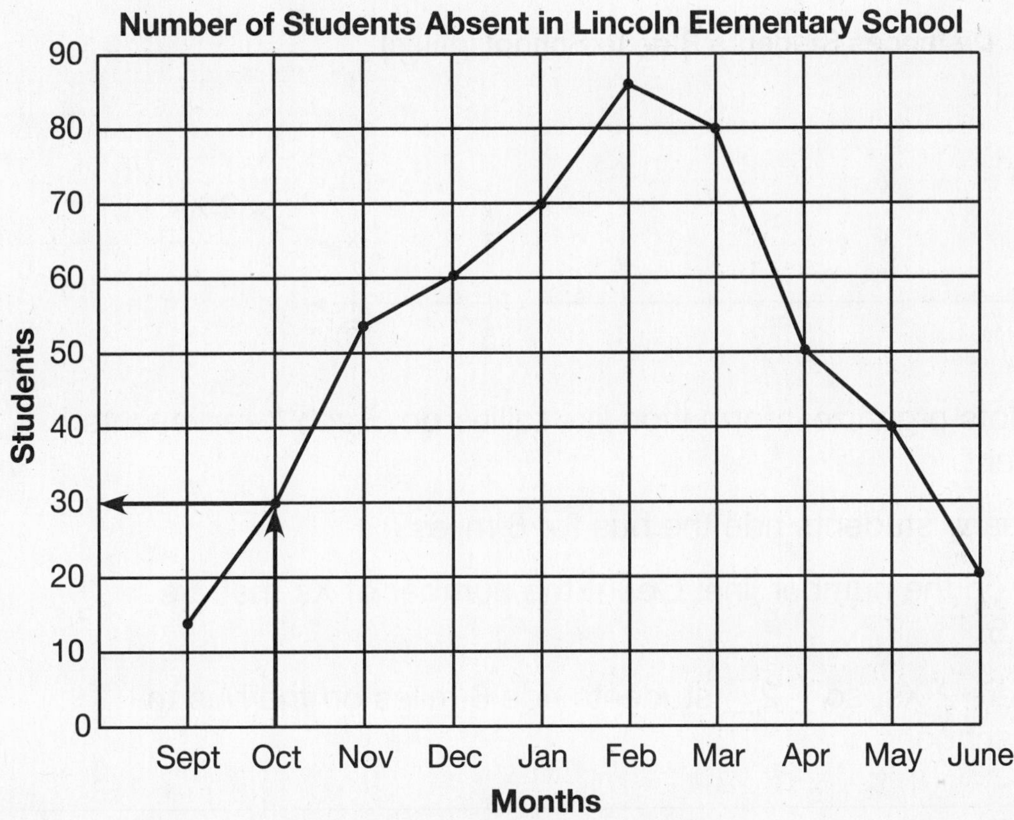

About how many students were absent in October?

Find October on the bottom axis.

Use your finger to trace a straight line from October until you reach a point on the graph. Then trace a line over to the data on the left axis to find the number of students absent.

About __30__ students were absent in October.

---

1. About how many students were absent in December? ____________
2. About how many students were absent in March? ____________
3. In which month were about 50 students absent? ____________
4. In which month were about 40 students absent? ____________

Name ______________________

Reading Line Plots

Line plots show data along a number line. This line plot shows the distances students ride the bus to get to school.

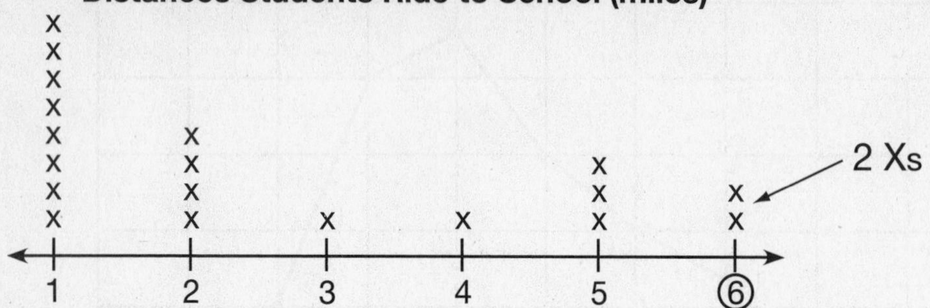

Line plots organize information like tallies do. Each X represents 1 student.

How many students ride the bus for 6 miles?

Find 6 on the number line. Count the number of Xs that are above 6.

There are 2 Xs, so 2 students ride 6 miles on the bus to get to school.

---

1. How many students ride the bus for 2 miles? ______
2. How many students ride the bus for 5 miles? ______
3. How far do most students ride the bus? ______
4. A **cluster** is a large group of Xs around 1 or more numbers. Where do the data on this line plot form a cluster? ______
5. Which two distances do the same number of students ride? ______
6. What is the difference in the greatest and least distances students ride on the bus? ______

Name ______________________________

Another Look
1-5

Reading Stem-and-Leaf Plots

This stem-and-leaf plot shows the number of points scored by the Green Bay Packers in their games during the 1995 season.

The numbers in the stem are tens digits.

The numbers in the leaf are ones digits.

Stem	Leaf
1	4 4 6 0
2	7 4 4 4 4 4
3	0 8 5 1 5 4

← Shows 14, 14, 16, and 10 points.

You can use the stem-and-leaf plot to find the greatest number of points the Green Bay Packers scored in one game in 1995.

First look for the greatest tens digit in the stem. 3

Then look for the greatest one digit in its leaf. 8

The greatest number of points scored by the Green Bay Packers in 1995 was 38 points.

---

1. What was the least number of points scored by the Green Bay Packers in 1995? ____________
2. In how many games did the Packers score 14 points? ____________
3. What would you say is a typical score for the Green Bay Packers? ____________
4. In how many games did the Green Bay Packers score more than 25 points? ____________
5. What was the difference in points between Green Bay's best and worst scores? ____________

Name ______________________________

Another Look
1-6

Analyze Word Problems: Introduction to Problem Solving Guide

This bar graph shows the lengths of the world's longest rivers.

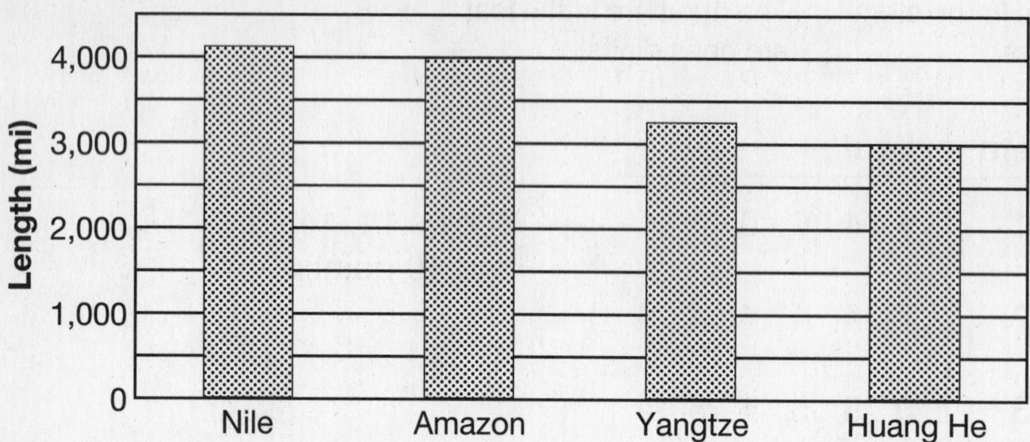

Find the difference in length between the longest and shortest rivers in the bar graph.

Step 1 Find the data in the bar graph.

The Nile is the longest river and is about 4,000 miles long. The Huang He is the shortest river and is about 3,000 miles long.

Step 2 Determine the operation to use.

Subtract the 2 lengths to find the difference.

Step 3 Find the answer.

4,000 miles − 3,000 miles = 1,000 miles

The Nile is 1,000 miles longer than the Huang He.

Find the total length of the Amazon and the Huang He rivers.

1. What is your first step?

____

2. What operation will you use? __________

3. Solve the problem.

____

Name ______________________

Analyze Word Problems: Choose an Operation

A dog breeder has 8 dogs. Then one of his dogs has 5 puppies. How many dogs does he have now? Decide what operation you will use.

Do you put together two groups (add) or compare two groups (subtract)?

The dog breeder wants to know how many animals he has all together. So, you are putting together the dogs and the puppies.

How many dogs does the breeder have now? 13 dogs

Which number sentence would you use to solve each of the following?

1. The dog breeder spends \$7 a day on dog food. How much does she spend in 2 days? ________

   A. \$7 + \$7 = ▩ **B.** \$7 − \$7 = ▩

2. Last year a dog license cost \$10. This year it costs \$14. How much more is a license this year? ________

   A. \$10 + \$14 = ▩ **B.** \$14 − \$10 = ▩

3. The dog breeder has 12 puppies for sale. He sells 5 puppies one weekend. How many puppies are left? ________

   A. 12 + 5 = ▩ **B.** 12 − 5 = ▩

4. One puppy sells for \$25. Another sells for \$40. How much do their sales total? ________

   A. \$40 − \$25 = ▩ **B.** \$40 + \$25 = ▩

Name ______________________________

Another Look 1-8

Exploring Making Bar Graphs

In your book you learned how to show data using a bar graph. Here is another way to draw the bars to show the data.

To draw a bar that shows the number of students who own Birds look at the scale for Students. You need to draw a bar that goes up to the line for 6.

Draw an arrow to the bar for birds.

Animal	Number of Students Who Own Animals
Bird	6
Cat	9
Dog	10
Pony	2
Gerbil	3

How can you draw a bar to show that 9 students own cats? The scale does not show odd numbers.

Since 9 is between 8 and 10, make the top of the bar halfway between 8 and 10.

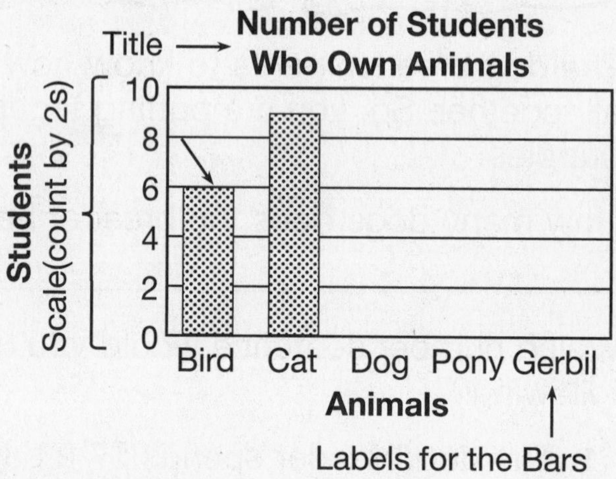

1. Complete the graph above.

   a. Draw the bar for the number of students who own dogs.
   b. Draw the bar for the number of students who own ponies.
   c. Draw the bar for the number of students who own gerbils.

2. Complete the bar graph to show the data in the table below.

Student	Hours Spent on Pet Care Weekly
Anika	9
Corine	14
Martin	16
Priscilla	4

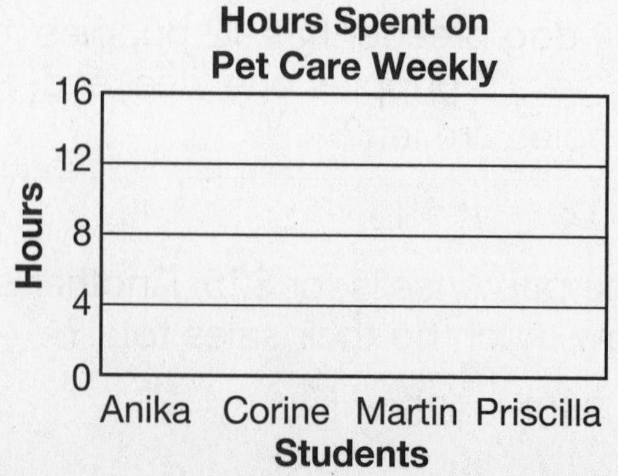

Name ______________________________

Another Look
1-9

Exploring Making Line Plots

In your book, you showed data from a tally table on a line plot. You can show data from other tables on a line plot.

Look at the data in the table.

Miles Run	Days
2	2
3	4
4	5
5	3
6	2

To show on a line plot the number of days that Freda ran 4 miles, you need to make 5 Xs above the 4.

How can you show that Freda ran 2 miles on each of 2 days?

Since each X represents 1 day, make 2 Xs above the 2.

Complete the line plot.

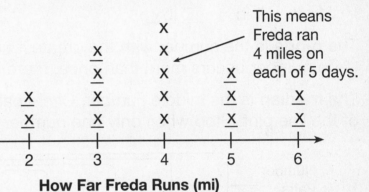

This means Freda ran 4 miles on each of 5 days.

1 2 3 4 5 6

How Far Freda Runs (mi)

---

1. Complete the line plot to show the data in the table.

Weight (lb)	Number of Puppies
3	5
4	3
5	2
6	0
7	1

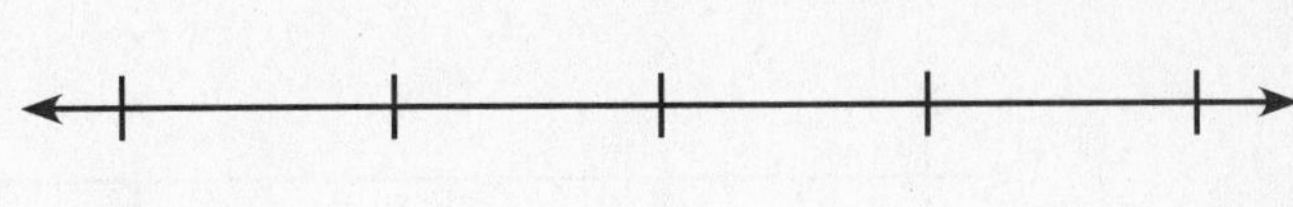

Label: ______________________

Name ______________________

Another Look
1-10

Exploring Range, Median, and Mode

In your book you explored range, median, and mode by arranging data cards. Here is another way to find range, median, and mode.

Suppose these are the weights (in pounds) of 9 cats.

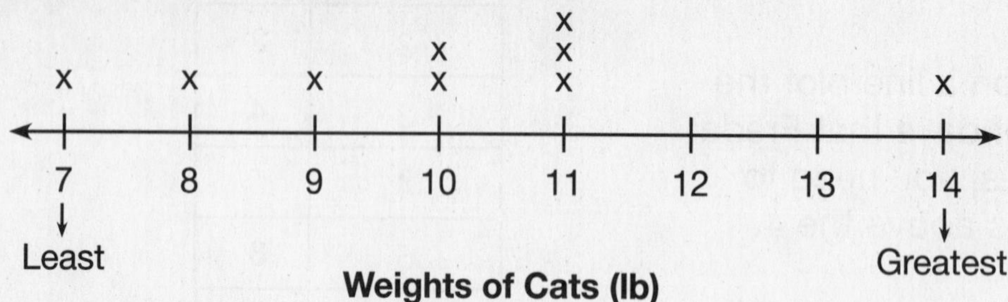

Weights of Cats (lb)

The **range** is the difference between the least and greatest weights.

14 lb − 7 lb = 7 lb

The **mode** is the number with the greatest number of X's.
(If no number occurs more than once, there is no mode.) 11 lb

The **median** is the middle number. Circle pairs of X's—one from each side of the line plot. Stop when only one number remains.

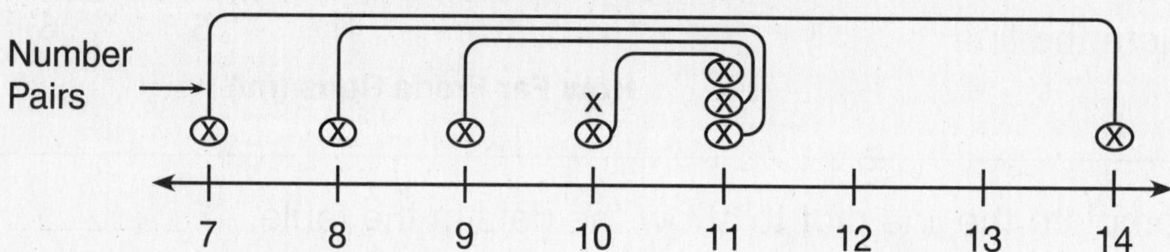

The median is 10 lb.

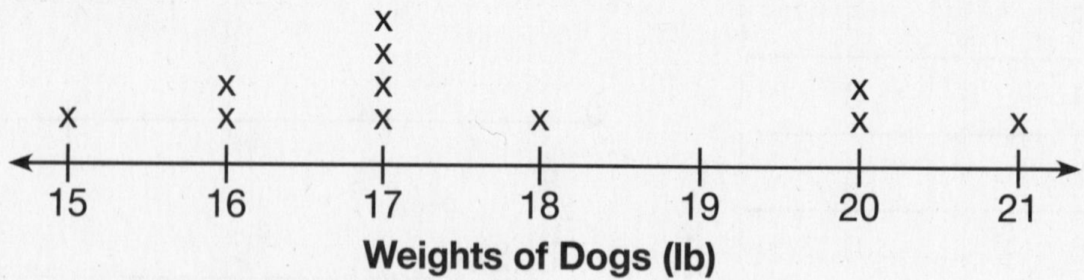

Weights of Dogs (lb)

Use the line plot of dog weights (in pounds) for **1–3**.

1. Find the range of the weights. ________ − ________ = ________

2. Find the mode of the weights. ________

3. Find the median weight. ________

Name ____________________

Another Look
1-11

Exploring Algebra: What's the Rule?

In your book you explored finding a rule for number pairs by playing "Guess My Rule." Here is another way to find the rule for number pairs.

In	3	5	8	4
Out	7	9	12	

Step 1 Look at the first pair of numbers, 3 and 7.
Think: What can you do to 3 to get 7?
You can add 4 to 3 to get 7.

Step 2 Check your rule with the next pairs of numbers.
Since $5 + 4 = 9$ and $8 + 4 = 12$, the rule checks.

Step 3 Write your rule in words. Write the operation and the number.

add 4

Write your rule with a variable. Use a letter in the place of the In number, then follow with the operation sign and the number.

$n + 4$

Step 4 Use your rule to complete the table. $4 + 4 = 8$

Answer the questions, then complete the table.

In	8	10	11	6	9	14
Out	5	7	8			

1. What can you do to 8 to get 5? ________
2. What can you do to 10 to get 7? ________
3. Write the rule in words. ________
4. Write the rule using a variable. ________
5. Use the rule to complete the table.

Name ______________________

Another Look 1-12

Analyze Strategies: Guess and Check

Every morning, Rosie meets Tammi on their way to school. The girls walk a total of 11 blocks. They meet after Rosie walks 3 blocks. How far does each girl live from school?

Guesses		Sum	Difference
Rosie	Tammi	11	3
8	3	11	5
6	5	11	1
7	4	11	3

Rosie walks 3 blocks further than Tammi each day.

Guess: Find any two numbers whose sum is 11. 8 + 3 = 11

Write your guess in the table.

Check: What is the difference between the two numbers? 8 − 3 = 5

What should the difference be between the numbers? 3

Keep guessing until you find the pair that works.

How far does Rosie walk? 7 blocks Tammi Lee? 4 blocks

Use the table to record your guesses. Keep guessing until you find a pair that works.

1. Sam earned \$8 in two days for helping his neighbor. On Friday he earned \$2 more than on Saturday. How much did he earn each day?

Friday ____________

Saturday ____________

Guesses		Sum	Difference
Friday	Saturday	\$8	\$2

2. Millen swam a total of 30 yards in two tries. The second time she swam 10 yards farther than the first time. How far did she swim each time?

1st time ____________

2nd time ____________

Guesses		Sum	Difference
First Time	Second Time		

Name ______________________

Another Look
2-1

Place Value Through Thousands

You can use place-value blocks to model a number.

Expanded form: 2,000 + 100 + 50 + 6

Standard form: 2,156

Word name: two thousand, one hundred fifty-six

Greater numbers can be written in the same three ways.

Expanded form: 100,000 + 20,000 + 8,000 + 700 + 60 +1

Standard form: 128,761

Word name: one hundred twenty-eight thousand, seven hundred sixty-one

---

Write each number in standard form. Then write the word name for the number.

1.

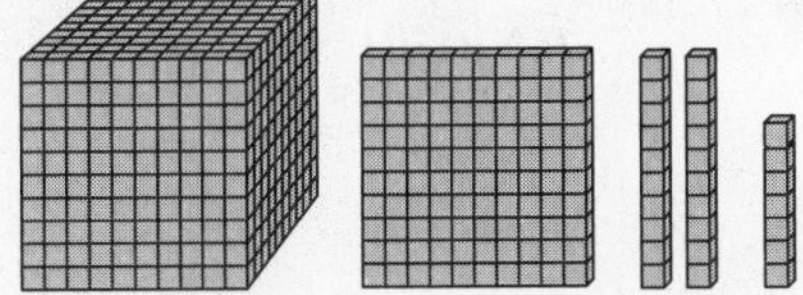

Standard Form: ______________________

Word Name: ______________________

2.

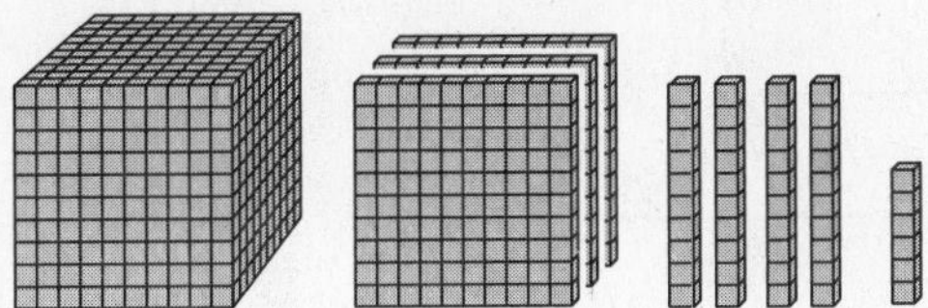

Standard Form: ______________________

Word Name: ______________________

3. 7,000 + 200 + 10 + 1

Standard Form: ______________________

Word Name: ______________________

Name ______________________________

Another Look
2-2

Exploring Place-Value Relationships

In your book, you used place-value blocks or pictures to explore number patterns. Here is another way to explore place-value patterns.

Example 1

How many tens are in 500?

Draw a line to the right of the digit in the tens place.

50|0

Read the number to the left of the line.

There are 50 tens in 500.

Example 2

How many hundreds are in 6,000?

Draw a line to the right of the digit in the hundreds place.

60|00

Read the number to the left of the line.

There are 60 hundreds in 6,000.

Write how many.

1. How many tens are in 400? ________
2. How many hundreds are in 9,000? ________
3. a. How many tens are in 6,000? ________

   b. How many hundreds are in 6,000? ________
4. a. How many tens are in 700? ________

   b. How many hundreds are in 700? ________
5. a. How many tens are in 1,400? ________

   b. How many hundreds are in 1,400? ________
6. a. How many tens are in 1,800? ________

   b. How many hundreds are in 1,800? ________

Name ______________________________

Another Look
2-3

Place Value Through Millions

You can use pictures to help you understand place value.

Millions | Thousands | Ones

Commas are used in greater numbers, to break them into periods. The numbers in each period are written on separate crayons.

9 million | 371 thousand | 560

Standard form: 9,371,560

Write the word name by writing the number on each crayon in words. Then follow with the period name.

Word name: nine million, three hundred seventy-one thousand, five hundred sixty

Write each number in standard form. Then write its word name.

500 million | 300 thousand

1. Standard form: ______________________________

Word name: ______________________________

____

12 million | 502 thousand

2. Standard form: ______________________________

Word name: ______________________________

____

Write each number in word form. Use the crayons to help you.

___ million | ___ thousand

3. 6,117,500 ______________________________

____

4. 20,019,007 ______________________________

Name ___________________________

Another Look
2-4

Analyze Strategies: Make an Organized List

Kevin is buying two notebooks. How many choices does he have?

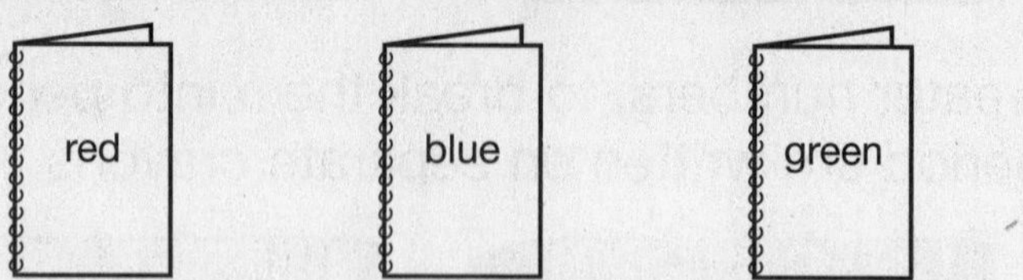

Make an organized list. (Remember green-yellow is the same as yellow-green.)

red (r)	rr	rb	rg	ry
blue (b)	bb	bg	by	
green (g)	gg	gy		
yellow (y)	yy			

Count the entries. How many choices are there? 10

---

1. Margo is getting dressed for school. She can wear a yellow or red shirt. She can wear blue or white pants. How many different outfits can she wear?

a. List all the possible combinations. Her shirts come in yellow or red. Her pants come in blue or white.

yellow (y)	
red (r)	

b. Count the choices. How many outfits can she wear? ____________

2. Andrew can have juice, milk or lemonade to drink for lunch. He can have a sandwich, rice, or pasta for lunch. Make an organized list to find the number of lunch choices Andrew has. ____________

Name ______________________________

Another Look
2-5

Comparing Numbers

You can use a place-value chart to compare numbers.

Compare 14,260 and 14,306. Find which is greater.

Thousands Period			Ones Period		
hundreds	tens	ones	hundreds	tens	ones
	1	4	2	6	0
	1	4	3	0	6

Begin at the left. Compare.

How many ten thousands does 14,260 have? 1

How many ten thousands does 14,306 have? 1

How many thousands does 14,260 have? 4

How many thousands does 14,306 have? 4

How many hundreds does 14,260 have? 2

How many hundreds does 14,306 have? 3

14,306 __>__ 14,260 because 14,306 has more hundreds than 14,260. 14,306 > 14,260

Compare. Write >, <, or =.

1. 3,210 ◯ 3,401

Thousands Period			Ones Period		
hundreds	tens	ones	hundreds	tens	ones
		3	2	1	0
		3	4	0	1

2. 52,348 ◯ 51,348

Thousands Period			Ones Period		
hundreds	tens	ones	hundreds	tens	ones
	5	2	3	4	8
	5	1	3	4	8

Name ______________________________

Another Look
2-6

Ordering Numbers

You can use a number line to order numbers. Order these numbers from greatest to least:

21,359; 22,491; 19,389

Step 1 Draw a number line.

Step 2 Put the numbers on the number line.

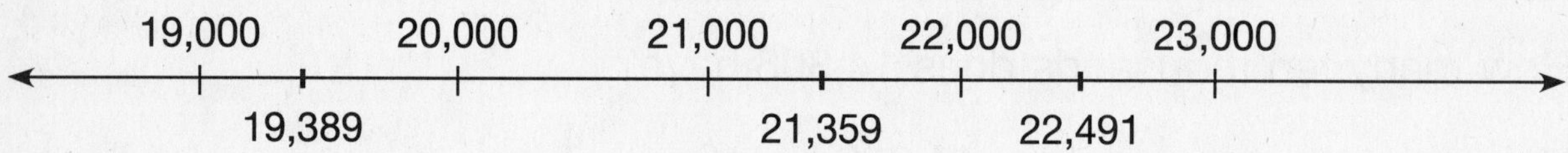

Step 3 To order the numbers from greatest to least, move from right to left on the number line.

In order from greatest to least, the numbers are: 22,491; 21,359; 19,389

---

1. Order the numbers from greatest to least. Use the number line to help.

78,111; 75,981; 76,980; 77,398

____

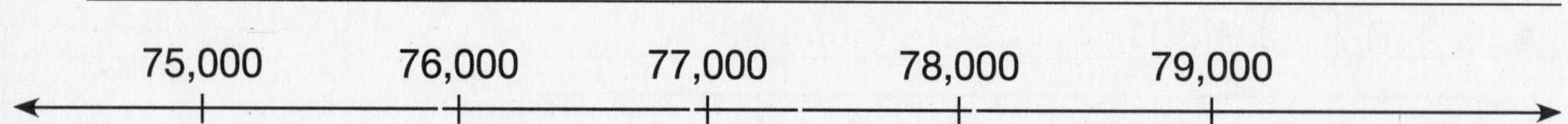

2. Order the numbers from least to greatest (left to right on the number line).

152,000; 155,281; 153,892; 154,389

____

Name ____________________

Exploring Rounding

In your book you used halfway numbers on number lines to help you round numbers. Here is another way to round numbers.

Each box shows two numbers and the number halfway between them. Write the **number to be rounded** above or below the halfway number. The number next to your written answer is the rounded number.

Example: Round 178 to the nearest hundred: 200

178	**200**
- - - - - - - - - -	(150)
	100

178 is greater than 150, so 178 is closer to 200 than 100. 178 rounded to the nearest 100 is 200.

---

1. Round 318 to the nearest hundred: ______

	400
- - - - - - - - - -	(350)
	300

2. Round 6,235 to the nearest hundred: ______

	6,300
- - - - - - - - - -	(6,250)
	6,200

3. Round 145 to the nearest hundred: ______

	200
- - - - - - - - - -	(150)
	100

4. Round 8,769 to the nearest thousand: ______

	9,000
- - - - - - - - - -	(8,500)
	8,000

5. Write the halfway number in the box. Then round 478 to the nearest hundred. ______

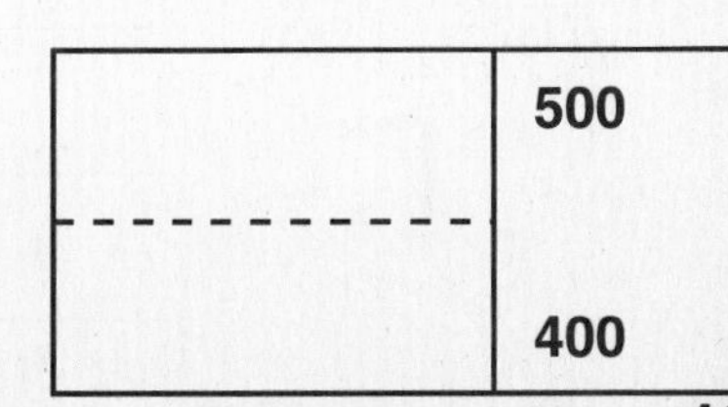

	500
- - - - - - - - - -	
	400

Name ______________________

Telling Time

Read the time on one clock and show it on the other.

Here is the analog clock:

Here is the digital clock:

8:15

The longer hand shows the minutes. It is __15__ minutes after the hour.
The shorter hand points to the hour. The shorter hand is pointing to __8__.

You can read the time in 2 ways.

One way: Tell how many minutes after the hour it is.
It is eight-fifteen.

Another way: Tell how many minutes until the next hour.
It is forty-five minutes before nine.

---

1. Here is the analog clock:

Draw the digital clock:

2. Here is the analog clock:

Draw the digital clock:

Write each time two ways.

3.

____

____

____

4.

6:20

____

____

____

 Use with pages 74–75.

Name ______________________________

Another Look
2-9

Exploring Time: Exact or Estimate?

It takes about : 1 second to blink your eyes.

1 minute to walk a block.

1 hour to do homework.

1 day to drive across Texas.

1 week for a plant to sprout.

Using this data as reference, you know that you cannot tie your shoe in 1 second. You may not need a full minute either. You can probably tie your shoe in a few seconds. So the most reasonable unit of time to tie your shoe is seconds.

Fill in the blanks with one of the following units of time: seconds, minutes, hours, days, weeks, months, or years.

1. A weekend lasts for 2 __________.

2. A cup of hot chocolate lasts for about 5 __________.

3. You can keep library books for 2 or 3 __________.

4. Each night, most people sleep for 8–10 __________.

5. Most television commercials last for about 20 __________.

6. I threw a ball in the air and I caught it in 2 __________.

7. I rode my bike for 30 __________.

8. Recess lasts 20 __________.

9. Movies are usually about 2 __________ long.

10. My summer vacation from school lasts 2 __________.

11. I have been going to this school for 3 __________.

12. I put my sweater on in about 5 __________.

13. Your hair grows about an inch in 4 __________.

14. Dentists like to check your teeth every 6 __________.

Name ________________________________

Another Look
2-10

Elapsed Time

Departure Time	Arrival Time
Boston 1:00	Cleveland 4:10

How long does it take to fly from Boston to Cleveland?

Use a clock to help you.

From 1:00 P.M. until 4:00 P.M. is 3 hours.
Count 10 minutes from 4:00 P.M. until 4:10 P.M.

It takes <u>3 hours and 10 minutes</u> to fly from Boston to Cleveland.

Write each elapsed time. Use a clock to help you.

1. 9:15 P.M. to 10:30 P.M.

9:00 P.M. to 10:00 P.M. is ________ hour(s).

:15 to :30 is ________ minutes

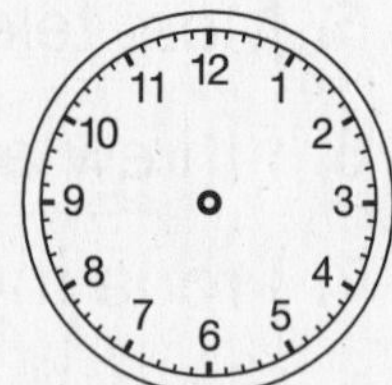

____

2. 5:15 P.M. to 8:30 P.M.

5:00 P.M. to 8:00 P.M. is ________ hour(s).

:15 to :30 is ________ minutes.

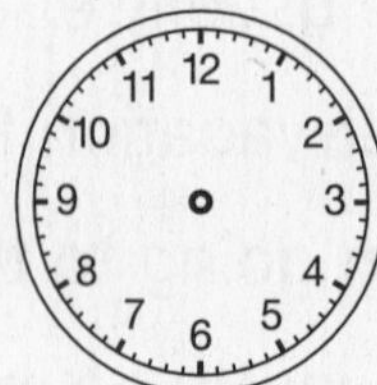

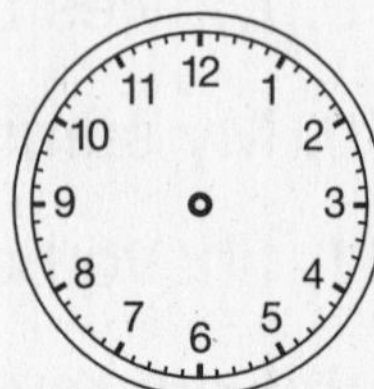

____

3. 1:00 P.M. to 10:30 P.M. ____________________

4. 8:30 P.M. to 9:15 P.M. ____________________

5. 7:20 A.M. to 10:05 A.M. ____________________

6. 10:15 A.M. to 1:00 P.M. ____________________

Name ______________________

Another Look
2-11

Exploring the Calendar

Use the calendar to answer each question.

July						
Sun.	Mon.	Tues.	Wed.	Thur.	Fri.	Sat.
				1	2	3
4	5	6	7	8	9	10
11	12	13	14	15	16	17
18	19	20	21	22	23	24
25	26	27	28	29	30	31

How many Fridays are in this month?

Count the squares under Friday. There are 5.

Write the date of the third Wednesday.

Count the first 3 Wednesdays and write the date. July 21

Write the day of the week of July 7th.

Find the number 7 and look at the top of the column to see the day of the week. Wednesday

1. How many Mondays are in July? ______
2. How many Wednesdays? ______
3. How many Thursdays? ______
4. Write the dates of these days.
   a. the fourth Tuesday ______
   b. the second Monday ______
   c. the fifth Friday ______
5. Write the days of the week of these dates.
   a. July 18th ______
   b. July 1st ______
   c. July 10th ______

Name ______________________

Another Look
2-12

Decision Making

Your Drama Club is performing four stories for Drama Night:

"The Harvest Moon"	20 minutes
"Thanksgiving in Hawaii"	15 minutes
"The Fourth of July Surprise"	18 minutes
"Presidents for Breakfast"	12 minutes

1. Your job is to make a schedule for the evening. Your drama teacher will welcome everyone with a 2-minute speech.

Drama Night

Time	Event
7:30 P.M.	Welcome: Ms. Chan, Our Director
________	______________________
________	______________________
________	______________________
________	______________________

2. What time should the evening end? ________

3. You want to have the refreshment stand ready for when the show has finished. What time should you finish setting it up? Explain.

____

4. A friend is meeting you afterwards. What time should you arrange to meet? Why?

____

Name ______________________________

Another Look
3-1

Exploring Addition and Subtraction Patterns

In your book you used patterns to help you add and subtract mentally. Here is another way using place-value blocks.

Use place-value blocks to find the sum of 60 and 30.

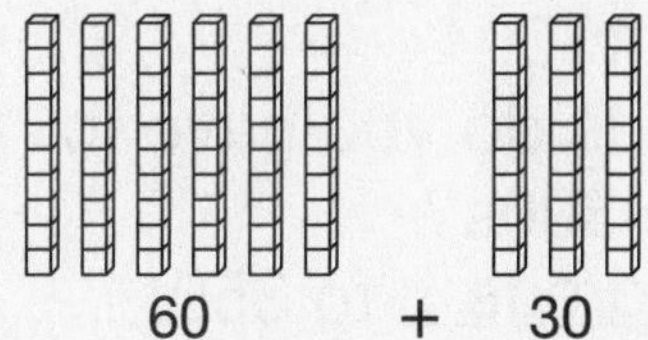

The place-value blocks help you see that 60 + 30 = __90__.

You can also use place-value blocks to find the difference between 400 and 200.

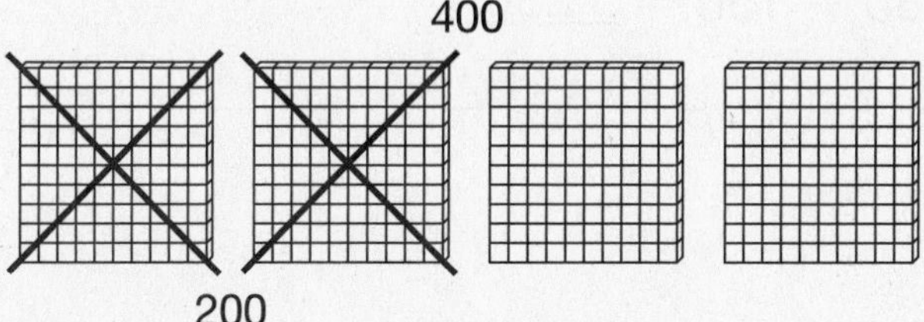

The place-value blocks help you see that 400 − 200 = __200__.

Use place-value blocks to help find each sum or difference. Check with a calculator.

1. 70 + 20 = __________
700 + 200 = __________
7,000 + 2,000 = __________

2. 70 − 20 = __________
700 − 200 = __________
7,000 − 2,000 = __________

3. 40 + 60 = __________
400 + 600 = __________
4,000 + 6,000 = __________

4. 60 − 40 = __________
600 − 400 = __________
6,000 − 4,000 = __________

5. 90 + 50 = __________
900 + 500 = __________
9,000 + 5,000 = __________

6. 90 − 50 = __________
900 − 500 = __________
9,000 − 5,000 = __________

Name ______________________________

Another Look
3-2

Exploring Adding and Subtracting on a Thousand Chart

In your book you used counters on a thousand chart to add and subtract. Here is another way to use a thousand chart.

Find 300 − 100.

Put your finger on 100.
How many hundreds do you have to move to get to 300?
You move 2 hundreds.

300 − 100 = <u>200</u>

Find 380 − 150.

Put your finger on 150.
How many hundreds do you have to move to get to the 300s?
You move <u>2 hundreds</u> to 350.

How many tens do you have to move to get from 350 to 380?
You move <u>3 tens</u>.

380 − 150 = <u>230</u>

Add or subtract. Use a thousand chart.

1. 840 − 310

a. Start at 310. How many hundreds do you have to move to get to the 800s? ________

b. How many tens do you have to move to get from 810 to 840? ________

c. The difference is ________ hundreds and ________ tens.

d. 840 − 310 = ________

2. 130 + 290

a. Put your finger on 290. Move up 1 hundred. On what number did your finger land? ________

b. Move up 3 tens. On what number did your finger land? ________

c. 130 + 290 = ________

3. Find 620 − 210. ________

4. Find 330 + 210. ________

Name ______________________________

Another Look
3-3

Estimating Sums and Differences

You can use a number line to help you estimate sums and differences.

Estimate 248 + 457.

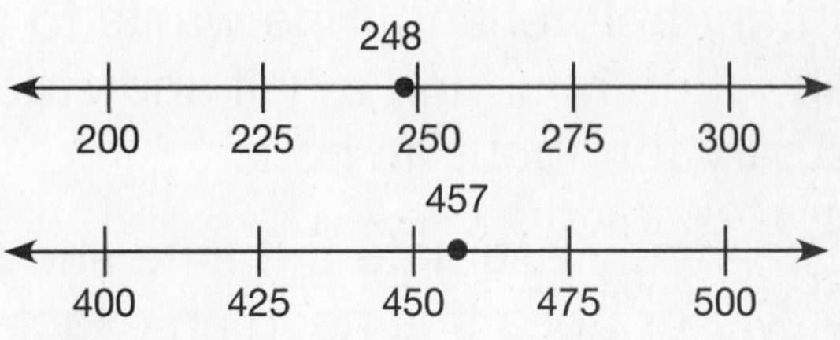

Is 248 closer to 200 or 300?
Since $248 < 250$, it is closer to 200.

Is 457 closer to 400 or 500?
Since $457 > 450$, it is closer to 500.

Estimate the sum by adding the rounded addends.

200 + 500 = 700

Estimate by rounding to the nearest hundred.

1. 548 − 160

a. Is 548 closer to 500 or 600?

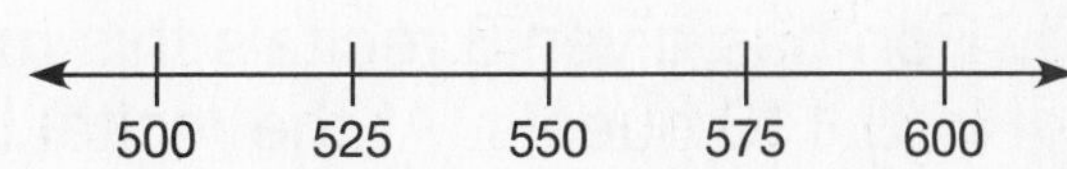

____

b. Is 160 closer to 100 or 200?

____

100 125 150 175 200

c. ____ − ____ = ____

2. 814 − 335

____ − ____ = ____

3. 329 + 221

____ + ____ = ____

4. 624 + 919

____ + ____ = ____

5. 735 + 589

____ + ____ = ____

6. 911 − 732 ________

7. 852 − 499 ________

8. 328 + 271 ________

9. 729 − 356 ________

10. 615 − 138 ________

11. 521 + 411 ________

12. 298 − 157 ________

13. 362 + 621 ________

14. 417 + 388 ________

Name ______________________

Another Look
3-4

Analyze Word Problems: Exact or Estimate?

Cindy has a dentist's appointment at 4:00. She plans to go shopping and then to the library beforehand. She wants to shop for about an hour and a half and study at the library for about an hour.

Travel Time	
Home → Store	20 min.
Store → Library	18 min.
Library → Dentist	13 min.

Can Cindy estimate the time she should leave, or does she need an exact answer?

Cindy does not know exactly how long she will be shopping or studying, so she doesn't have to leave the house at an exact time. Since she wants to make sure she's at the dentist by 4:00, she should overestimate.

For each problem, tell if you need an exact answer or an estimate.

1. Ron has given 3 recitals this month. At his last recital, he had 118 guests. At the recital before that, he had 180 guests. 165 people came to the first recital. About how many guests have come to Ron's recitals?

Exact or estimate? ______________

2. Karen is the owner of City Diner. She is planning to bake pies for the upcoming week. Last week 57 people ordered pie. One pie serves 8 people.

a. How many pies should Karen bake?

Exact or estimate? ______________

b. What is the greatest number of people Karen can serve if she bakes 8 pies?

Exact or estimate? ______________

3. Ann has $3.40. She would like to buy a juice which costs $0.75 and a sandwich which costs $2.55. Does she have enough?

Exact or estimate? ______________

Name ______________________________

Another Look 3-5

Adding

You can use place-value blocks to add numbers.

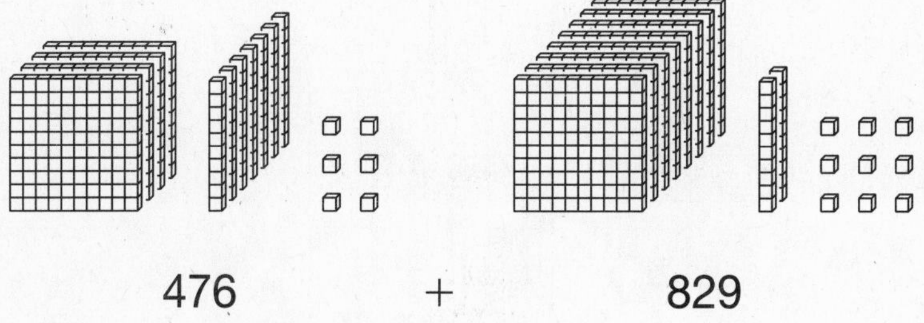

476 + 829

6 ones + 9 ones = 15 ones

Regroup 15 ones as 1 ten and 5 ones

1 ten + 7 tens + 2 tens = 10 tens

Regroup 10 tens as 1 hundred

1 hundred + 4 hundreds + 8 hundreds = 13 hundreds

$$\begin{array}{r} {}^{1\,1} \\ 476 \\ +\,829 \\ \hline 1{,}305 \end{array}$$

Use the place value blocks to find each sum.

1.

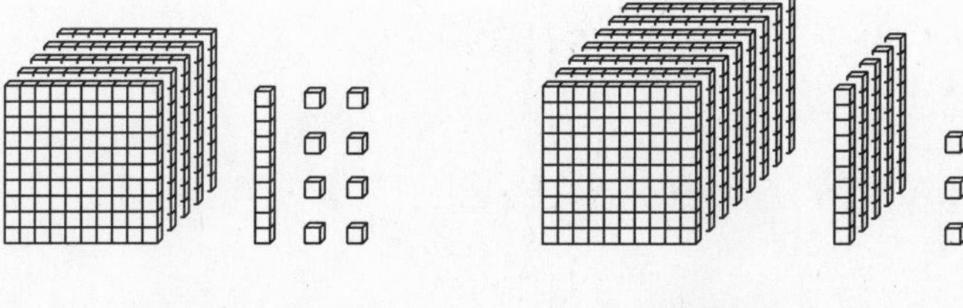

518 + 853 = ________

2.

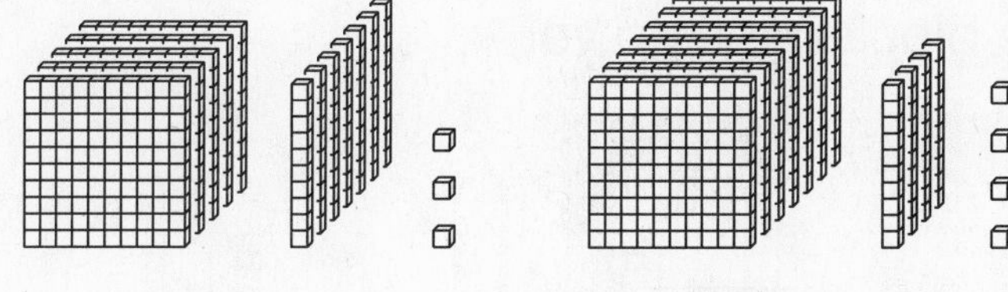

573 + 744 = ________

3.

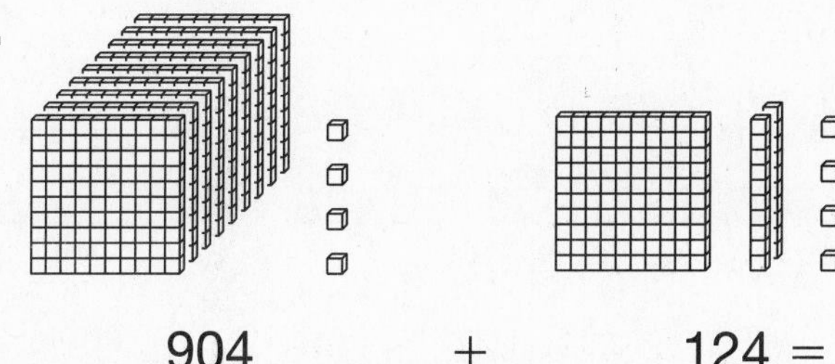

904 + 124 = ________

Name ______________________________

Column Addition

You can use place-value blocks to help you add 327 + 256 + 332.

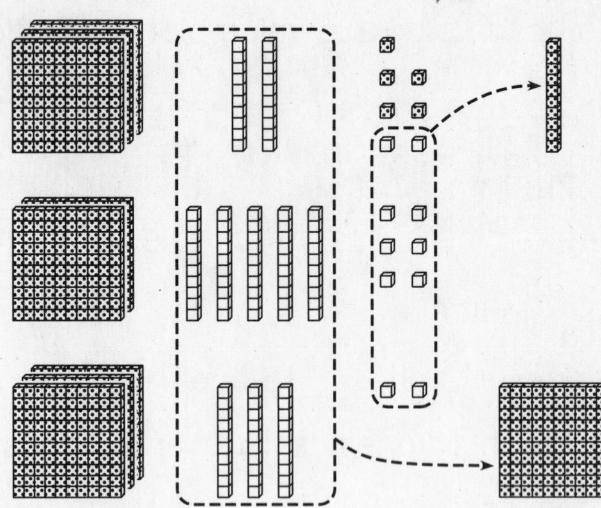

Count the ones.
Regroup 10 ones
to make 1 ten.

```
    1
  3 2 7
  2 5 6
+ 3 3 2
-------
      5
```

Count the tens.
Regroup 10 tens
to make 1 hundred.

```
  1 1
  3 2 7
  2 5 6
+ 3 3 2
-------
    1 5
```

Count the hundreds.

```
  1 1
  3 2 7
  2 5 6
+ 3 3 2
-------
  9 1 5
```

327 + 256 + 332 = 915

Find each sum. Use place-value blocks to help you.

1.

```
   335
   521
+   67
------
```

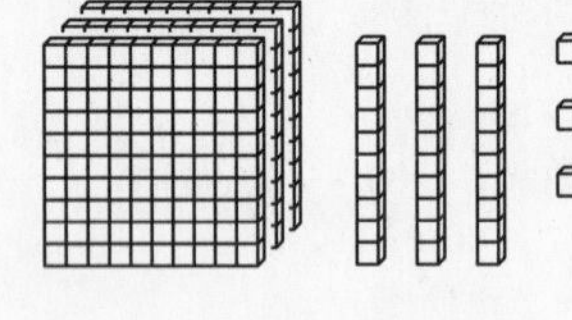
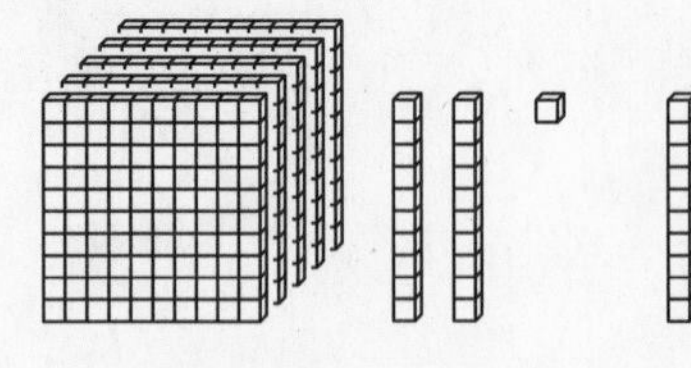
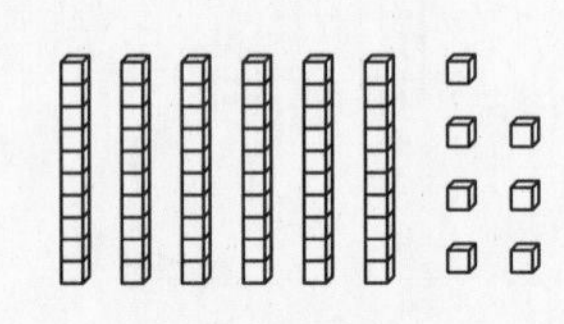

2. 59 + 92 + 65 = __________

3. 986 + 134 + 522 = __________

4. 63 + 28 + 49 = __________

5. 832 + 214 + 488 = __________

Name ______________________________

Another Look 3-7

Subtracting

If a digit in the top number is less than the digit in the same place in the bottom number, regrouping is necessary. Sometimes it's helpful to regroup before subtracting.

Find 332 − 145.

Compare the ones. Since $2 < 5$, you must regroup.

```
  2 12
 3 3̸ 2̸
− 1 1 5
```

Compare the tens. $2 > 1$. Regrouping is not necessary. Subtract the ones, the tens, and the hundreds.

```
  2 12      12 ones − 5 ones = 7 ones
 3 3̸ 2̸      2 tens − 1 ten = 1 ten
− 1 1 5     3 hundreds − 1 hundred = 2 hundred
  2 1 7
```

Subtract. Regroup before subtracting to help find the difference.

1. 419 − 287

a. Compare ones. Do you need to regroup? ________

b. Compare tens. Do you need to regroup? ________

c. 419 − 287 = ________

2. 565 − 178

3. 726 − 329

4. 487 − 198

5. 4,621 − 1,580

6. 5,644 − 4,589

7. 8,211 − 1,566

8. 9,213 − 4,865

9. 4,329 − 1,202

10. 6,413 − 2,127

Name ______________________________

Another Look
3-8

Subtracting with Middle Zeros

Sometimes it's helpful to regroup before subtracting.

Find 1,003 − 317.

Compare the ones. Since 3 < 7, you must regroup.

Look for the first non-zero digit to the left of the 3. It is the 1 in the thousands place. One thousand is the same as 100 tens.

You can regroup 100 tens as 99 tens and 10 ones.

```
  99 13
 1,003
− 3 1 7
```

Subtract the ones, the tens, and the hundreds.

```
  99 13     13 ones − 7 ones = 6 ones
 1,003      9 tens − 1 ten = 8 tens
− 3 1 7     9 hundreds − 3 hundreds = 6 hundreds
```

Find each difference.

1. 2,005 − 836

a. Compare the ones. Since 5 < 6, you must regroup. The first non-zero digit to the left of the 5 is __________.

b. 2 thousands is the same as __________ tens.

c. You can regroup __________ tens as __________ tens and __________ ones.

d. 2,005 − 836 = __________

2. 800 − 452

a. Compare the ones. Do you need to regroup? __________

b. 800 − 452 = __________

3. 3,008 − 1,589 = __________

4. 8,006 − 927 = __________

Name ______________________________

Another Look
3-9

Analyze Word Problems: Multiple-Step Problems

Crystal has 436 stamps in her stamp collection. Daryl has 213 stamps in his collection. Kathie has 221 stamps in her collection. Who has more stamps, Kathie and Daryl together or Crystal?

Find the total number of stamps that Kathie and Daryl have together.

$$\begin{array}{rl} 221 & \text{(Kathie's stamps)} \\ +\,213 & \text{(Daryl's stamps)} \\ \hline 434 & \text{(Kathie and Daryl's total)} \end{array}$$

Compare the total to Crystal's number of stamps.

434 stamps (Kathie and Daryl) $<$ 436 stamps (Crystal)

Crystal has more stamps than Kathie and Daryl together.

---

1. There are 346 students in the third grade. There are 662 students in fourth grade and 309 students in fifth grade. How many more students are there in the fourth grade than in the third and fifth grades combined?

a. How many students are in the third and fifth grades combined? ____________

b. How many students are in the fourth grade? ____________

c. What is the difference between the number of fourth grade students and the number of students in the third and fifth grades? ____________

2. On Thursday, 113 people attended the school play. On Friday, 152 people attended. On Saturday, 270 people attended. Did more people see the play on Saturday or on Thursday and Friday combined? ____________

Name ________________________________

Another Look
3-10

Using Mental Math

Follow these steps to mentally add 57 and 42:

First add the tens. $5 + 4 = 9$

Then add the ones. $7 + 2 = 9$

Write the total as a 2-digit number.

Follow these steps to mentally subtract 53 from 78:

First subtract the tens. $7 - 5 = 2$

Then subtract the ones. $8 - 3 = 5$

Write the difference as a 2-digit number. $78 - 53 = 25$

To add or subtract 3-digit numbers (without regrouping) mentally, add or subtract the hundreds first, then follow the same steps.

Add or subtract mentally.

1. 546 + 213

a. 5 + 2 = ☐

b. 4 + 1 = ☐

c. 6 + 3 = ☐

546 + 213 = ________

2. 74 − 31

a. 7 − 3 = ☐

b. ☐ − 1 = ☐

c. 74 − 31 = ________

3. 676 + 223 = ________

4. 417 + 82 = ________

5. 89 − 42 = ________

6. 288 − 164 = ________

7. 213 + 424 = ________

8. 679 − 322 = ________

9. 876 − 431 = ________

10. 527 + 332 = ________

Name ______________________

Another Look 3-11

Choosing a Calculation Method

Mental Math	Paper and Pencil	Calculator
47,000 − 5,000 42,000	27,515 + 8,021 35,536	50,070 − 27,589 22,481
Use mental math when there are a lot of zeros in both numbers.	Use paper and pencil when you only need to regroup once or twice.	Use a calculator when there is a lot lot of regrouping to do.

Which method is most appropriate to solve each problem?

Write *mental math*, *paper and pencil*, or *calculator*.

1. 57,211 + 5,314 ______________

2. 90,000 − 87,923 ______________

3. 59,000 − 18,000 ______________

Find each sum or difference. Tell which calculation method you used.

4. 72,000 − 12,000 ______________

5. 43,900 + 11,327 ______________

6. 42,397 + 56,998 ______________

7. 92,187 − 41,023 ______________

8. 14,000 + 7,000 ______________

9. 64,127 − 5,238 ______________

Name ____________________

Another Look
3-12

Counting Money

Counting by 5s, 10s, and 25s can help you count change. Here are some examples.

Example 1 Count nickels by 5s and dimes by 10s.

Say: "10, 20, 30, 40, 45, 50, 55."

You have 55 cents.

Example 2 Count quarters by 25s.

Say: "25, 50, 75, 85, 95, 105, 115, 120."

You have 120 cents.

To write any amount with a dollar sign, put a decimal point to the left of the digit in the tens place.

55 cents is the same as $0.55.

120 cents is the same as $1.20.

Write each amount. Use a dollar sign and decimal point.

1. ____________

2. ____________

3. ____________

4. ____________

Solve.

5. Which is more: 3 quarters and 2 dimes, or 2 quarters and 3 dimes?

____

6. Which is less: 5 nickels and 3 dimes, or 1 quarter and 2 dimes?

____

Name ________________________________

Adding and Subtracting Money

You can use play money to help you add and subtract money amounts.

$$\begin{array}{r} \$12.52 \\ +\ 7.67 \\ \hline \end{array}$$

Start by adding the coins. Count the quarters, then the dimes, then the nickels, then the pennies: "25, 50, 75, 100, 110, 115, 116, 117, 118, 119."

Exchange the coins for dollars. 119 cents is the same as 1 dollar and 19 cents.

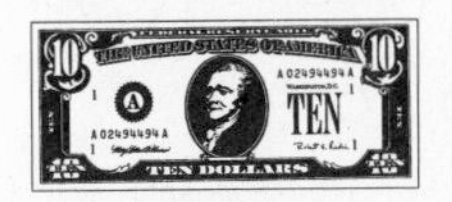

Write the amount left in coins after the decimal point.

Count the bills. Count "10, 15, 16, 17, 18, 19, 20."

Write the amount in bills in front of the decimal point.

$12.52 + $7.67 = $<u>20.19</u>

Add or subtract. Use play money to help you.

1. $$\begin{array}{r} \$4.13 \\ +\ 5.95 \\ \hline \end{array}$$

2. $$\begin{array}{r} \$7.13 \\ +\ 2.27 \\ \hline \end{array}$$

3. $$\begin{array}{r} \$10.82 \\ -\ 6.41 \\ \hline \end{array}$$

4. $$\begin{array}{r} \$6.13 \\ -\ 2.79 \\ \hline \end{array}$$

5. $$\begin{array}{r} \$19.32 \\ +\ 8.74 \\ \hline \end{array}$$

6. $$\begin{array}{r} \$6.27 \\ -\ 4.82 \\ \hline \end{array}$$

7. $$\begin{array}{r} \$12.36 \\ +\ 7.55 \\ \hline \end{array}$$

8. $$\begin{array}{r} \$15.47 \\ +\ 9.08 \\ \hline \end{array}$$

9. $$\begin{array}{r} \$3.11 \\ -\ 1.49 \\ \hline \end{array}$$

Name ________________________________

Another Look 3-14

Exploring Making Change

In your book you used play money or drew pictures to make change. Here is another way to make change.

You just bought school supplies that cost $11.42. You gave the store clerk a twenty-dollar bill. How much change should you receive?

Subtract mentally.

Subtracting whole dollar amounts is easier to do mentally. Add an amount of change that will make the purchase price a whole dollar amount.

$20.00	+	0.58	→	20.58
− 11.42	+	0.58	→	− 12.00
				$8.58

Write the change for each purchase.

1. Amount given: $70 — $70.00 + ________ → ________

Amount due: $67.98 — − 67.98 + 0.02 →

change: ________

2. Amount given: $20.00 — $20.00 + ________ → ________

Amount due: $15.77 — − $15.77 + ________ →

change: ________

3. Amount given: $50.00

Amount due: $36.82

____

4. Amount given: $20.00

Amount due: $6.52

____

5. Amount given: $25.00

Amount due: $21.42

____

6. Amount given: $10.00

Amount due: $8.58

____

Name ____________________

Exploring Algebra: Balancing Number Sentences

In your book you used workmats to balance number sentences. Here is another way to balance number sentences.

$6 + n = 9$

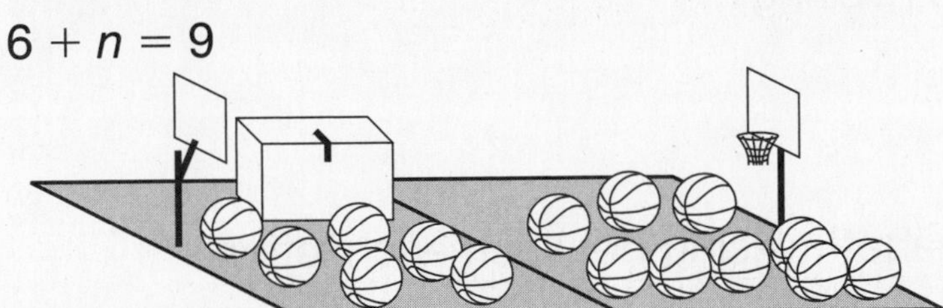

The basketball team has been practicing. They used the same number of basketballs on each side of the court. How many basketballs are in the box?

You can change the picture to solve the problem. Draw Xs over six basketballs on each side of the court.

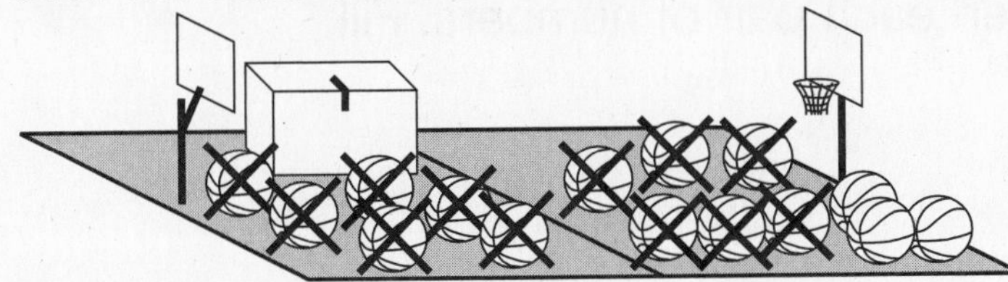

You took 6 basketballs away from both sides of the basketball court. So, the number of basketballs on either side should be the same. How many basketballs are in the box? 3

---

1. How many basketballs are in the box? ______

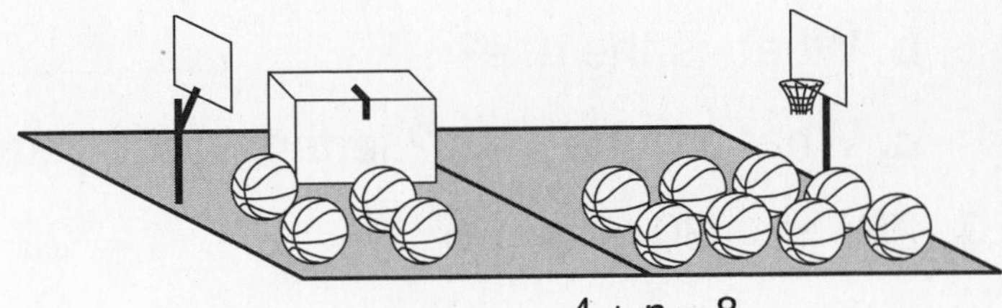

$4 + n = 8$

2. How many tennis balls are in the box? ______

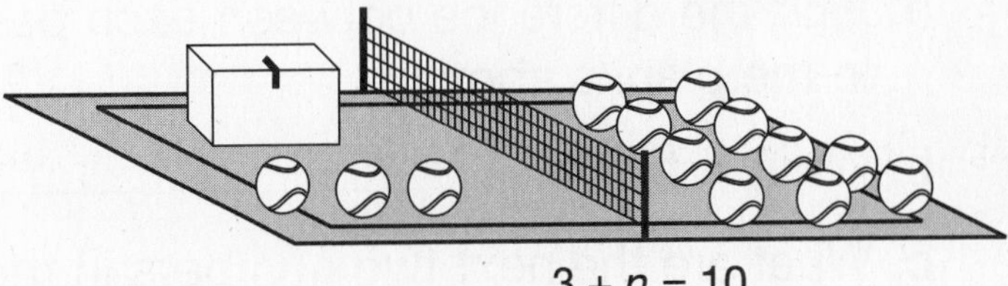

$3 + n = 10$

Draw pictures to show each number sentence. Then find the value of n.

3. $n + 8 = 16$ $n =$ ______

4. $9 + n = 11$ $n =$ ______

Name ______________________

Analyze Strategies: Look for a Pattern

This row of letters follows a pattern:

A E I M Q

What letters of the alphabet are missing?

A bcd E fgh I jkl M nop Q

What is the pattern?

There are 3 letters of the alphabet missing between each letter.

What are the next 2 letters? Q rst U vwx Y

1. 4 10 16 22 28

___ ___ ___ ___

a. Find the difference between each pair of numbers. Fill in the blanks above.

b. What is the rule?

____

c. What are the next two numbers in the pattern? ___, ___

2. Z W T Q N

___ ___ ___ ___

a. Fill in the blanks to show which letters are missing.

b. What is the rule? ______________________

c. What are the next 2 letters in the pattern? ___, ___

3. 28 30 25 27 22

___ ___ ___ ___

a. Find the difference between each pair of numbers. Fill in the blanks above.

b. What is the rule? ______________________

c. What are the next two numbers in the pattern? ___, ___

Name ______________________________

Another Look
4-1

Reviewing the Meaning of Multiplication

You can use addition to help you multiply.

Adding 3 to itself 4 times is the same as multiplying 4 times 3.

$4 \times 3 \quad = \quad 3 + 3 + 3 + 3 \quad = \quad 12$

You can draw pictures to show multiplication.

Show 4×3 using groups.

Draw a group of 3 counters 4 times so that you have 4 groups in all.

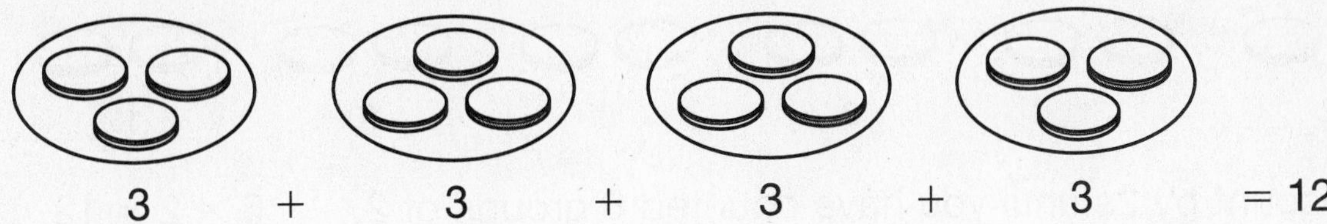

$3 \quad + \quad 3 \quad + \quad 3 \quad + \quad 3 \quad = 12$

$4 \times 3 = 12$

1.

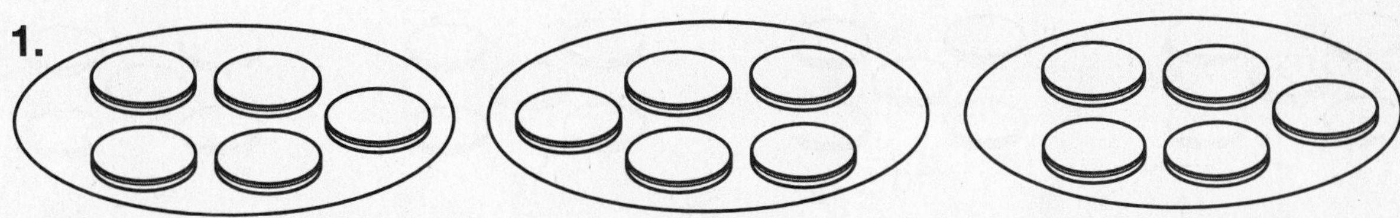

a. ______ + ______ + ______ = ______

b. ______ × ______ = ______

2.

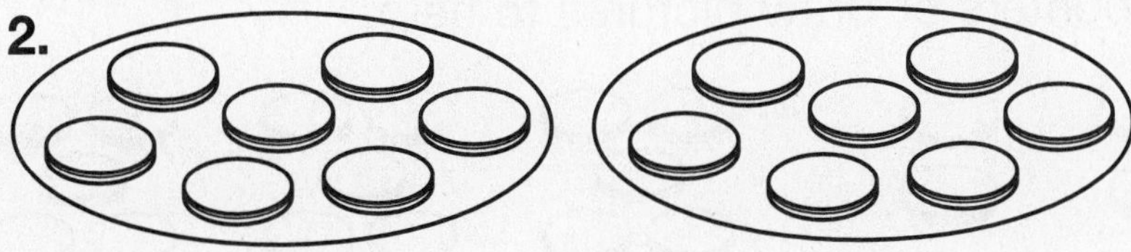

a. ______ + ______ = ______

b. ______ × ______ = ______

3. a. Draw a picture to show 5×4.

b. $5 \times 4 =$ ______

Name ______________________________

Exploring Patterns in Multiplying by 0, 1, 2, 5, and 9

In your book you used a hundred chart to find multiplication patterns. Here is another way to explore patterns in multiplying by 0, 1, 2, 5, and 9.

You can use counters and patterns to help you multiply.

Skip counting by 2s with counters can help you multiply by 2.
Find 6 × 2.

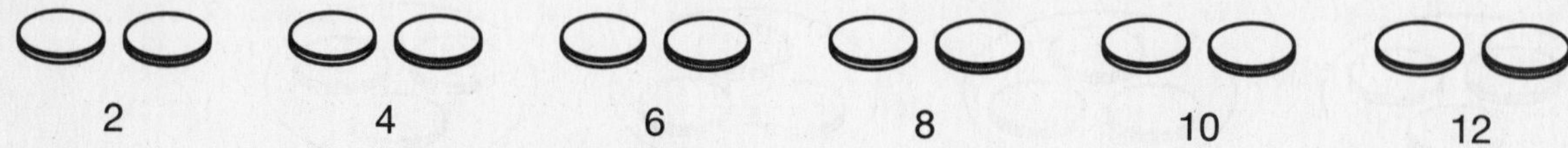

Skip count by 2s until you have counted 6 groups of 2. 6 × 2 = 12

Skip counting by 5s with counters can help you multiply by 5.
Find 4 × 5.

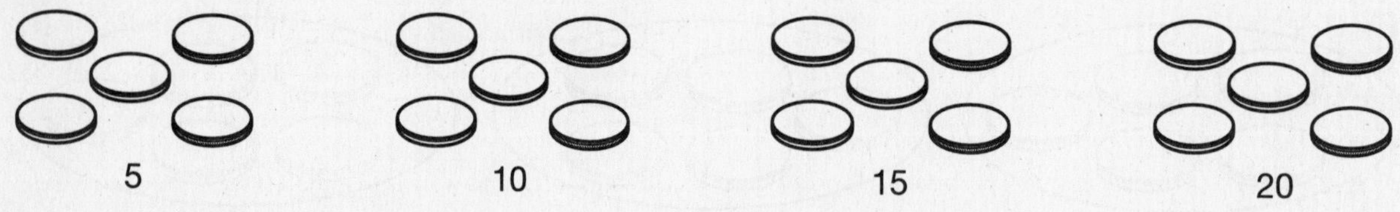

Skip count by 5s until you have counted 4 groups of 5. 4 × 5 = 20

Find each product. Use counters or draw pictures to help.

1. 4 × 2 = ________

2. 3 × 5 = ________

3. 9 × 1 = ________

4. 5 × 4 = ________

5. 2 × 8 = ________

6. 9 × 5 = ________

7. 1 × 7 = ________

8. 0 × 6 = ________

Name ______________________

Another Look 4-3

Multiplying with 3 and 4 as Factors

You can use triangles and squares to help you multiply by 3 and 4.

Find 3×7.

Draw 7 triangles. Each triangle has 3 sides. Count the number of sides in all the triangles. The total number of sides will equal the product of 3 and 7.

$3 + 3 + 3 + 3 + 3 + 3 + 3 = 21$.

$7 \times 3 = 21$

Find 4×8.

Draw 8 squares. Each square has 4 sides. Count the number of sides in all the squares. The total number of sides will equal the product of 4 and 8.

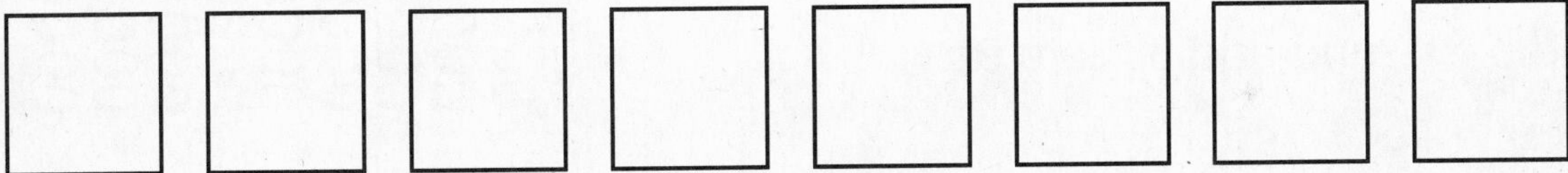

$4 + 4 + 4 + 4 + 4 + 4 + 4 + 4 = 4 \times 8 = 32$

$8 \times 4 = 32$

Find each product. Draw triangles and squares to help you.

1. 3×6

$3 \times 6 =$ ______

2. 4×7

$4 \times 7 =$ ______

3. $3 \times 8 =$ ______

4. $3 \times 9 =$ ______

5. $4 \times 9 =$ ______

6. $4 \times 3 =$ ______

Name ______________________________

Multiplying with 6, 7, and 8 as Factors

You can use 5s to help you multiply by 6s, 7s, and 8s.

Find 6×4.

Find 5×4 and add 1 more 4.

$5 \times 4 = 20$ $\quad$ $20 + 4 = 24$

$6 \times 4 = 24$

5
×4
20
+4
24

Find 7×6.

Find 5×6 and add 2 more 6s.

$5 \times 6 = 30$ $\quad$ $30 + 6 = 36$ $\quad$ $36 \times 6 = 42$

$7 \times 6 = 42$

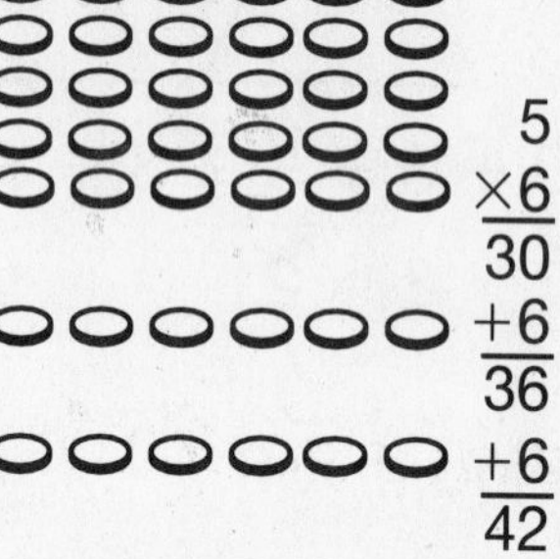

Find 8×9.

Find 5×9 and add 3 more 9s.

$5 \times 9 = 45$ $\quad$ $45 + 9 = 54$

$54 \times 9 = 63$ $\quad$ $63 + 9 = 72$

$8 \times 9 = 72$

5
×9
45
+9
54
+9
63
+9
72

Find each product. You may use counters or draw pictures to help.

1. Find 6×9.

$5 \times 9 =$ ____ $\quad$ ____ $+ 9 =$ ____ $\quad$ $6 \times 9 =$ ____

2. Find 7×4.

$5 \times 4 =$ ____ $\quad$ ____ $+ 4 =$ ____ $\quad$ ____ $+ 4 =$ ____ $\quad$ $7 \times 4 =$ ____

Name ______________________________

Exploring Patterns in Multiples of 10, 11, and 12

In your book you used a multiplication table to explore patterns multiples of 10, 11, and 12. Here are some patterns that can help you find these multiples.

Find 10 × 6.
When you multiply a number by 10, add **0** to the end of the number being multiplied by 10.
10 × 6 = 6**0**

Find 11 × 5.
When you multiply a number less than 10 by 11, write the number being multiplied by 11 in the tens and the ones places.
11 × **5** = **55**

When you multiply a number by 12, find the multiple of 10, then add twice the number.
Find 12 × 4.
First find 10 × 4 = 40.
Then add 2 × 4 = 8. 40 + 8 = 48
12 × 4 = 48.

Find each product. Use the patterns above to help.

1. Find 2 × 12.

a. 10 × ☐ = ☐

b. 2 × ☐ = ☐

c. ☐ + ☐ = ☐

d. 2 × 12 = ☐

2. Find 9 × 11.

a. 10 × ☐ = ☐

b. 9 × ☐ = ☐

c. ☐ + ☐ = ☐

d. 9 × 11 = ☐

3. 11 × 8 = ________

4. 10 × 11 = ________

5. 12 × 5 = ________

6. 10 × 12 = ________

7. 10 × 6 = ________

8. 3 × 10 = ________

9. 4 × 11 = ________

10. 6 × 12 = ________

11. 11 × 6 = ________

12. 12 × 4 = ________

Name ______________________________

Another Look
4-6

Decision Making

Andrew wants to buy his mother a gift that costs $24. He has 4 weeks to save for the gift. To earn the money for the gift, Andrew can work the following jobs.

Day	Job	Number of Hours	Pay
Monday	Babysitting	2	$4 per hour
Wednesday	Clipping shrubs	1	$3 per hour

How can Andrew earn the money for the gift in 4 weeks?

How much money will Andrew make babysitting each week?
$2 \times \$4 = \$8$

How long will it take to earn $24? $\$24 \div \$8 = 3$ weeks

How much money will Andrew make clipping shrubs each week?
$1 \times \$3 = \$3$

How long will it take to earn $24? $\$24 \div \$3 = 8$ weeks

Andrew can babysit for 3 weeks to earn the money he needs to buy the gift.

Monica wants to buy new sneakers for school track meets. The first meet is in 8 weeks. The sneakers cost $48. Monica could work on Tuesdays watering plants for 2 hours for $3 per hour. She could work on Fridays walking a dog for 2 hours for $4 per hour. How can Monica earn $48 in 8 weeks?

1. a. How much would Monica earn in a week watering plants? __________

b. How many weeks will it take to earn $48? __________

2. a. How much would Monica earn in a week walking the dog? __________

b. How many weeks will it take to earn $48? __________

3. How much would Monica earn in 8 weeks walking the dog each week? __________

Name ________________________________

Another Look
4-7

Reviewing the Meaning of Division

You can use counters to help you think about division in 3 different ways.

Find 18 ÷ 6.

Place 18 counters on your desk.

Example 1 Think of division as sharing. Imagine you are sharing the counters with 6 people.

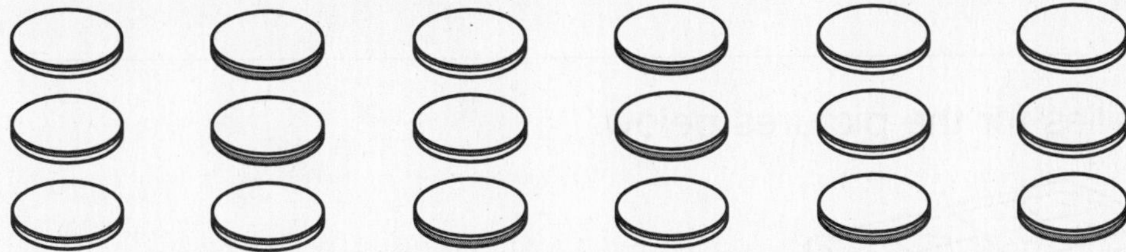

How many counters would each person receive? __3__ So, 18 ÷ 6 = __3__

Example 2 Think of division as repeated subtraction.

Take away 6 counters from the 18 counters until you have 0. Count how many times you took away 6.

18 − 6 = 12   12 − 6 = 6   6 − 6 = 0

You took away 3 groups of 6. So, 18 ÷ 6 = __3__.

Example 3 Think of division as the opposite of multiplication.

Think: What number times 6 equals 18?

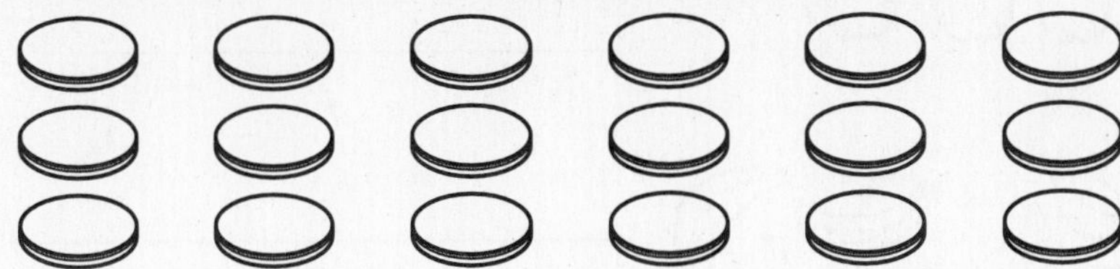

3 × 6 = 18 So, 18 ÷ 6 = __3__.

Find each quotient. Use the examples above to help.

1. 28 ÷ 4 = ________   **2.** 36 ÷ 6 = ________

3. 27 ÷ 3 = ________   **4.** 20 ÷ 5 = ________

Name ______________________________

Exploring Multiplication and Division Stories

In your book you explored multiplication and division by writing stories. Here is another way to explore division and multiplication. Think about objects in groups.

Lila has 2 packs of baseball cards. There are 8 cards in each pack. Write the fact family for this problem.

$2 \times 8 = 16$

$8 \times 2 = 16$

$16 \div 2 = 8$

$16 \div 8 = 2$

Write the fact families for the pictures below.

1. 

____

____

____

____

2. 

____

____

____

____

3.   

____

____

____

____

Name ______________________________

Another Look
4-9

Dividing with 2, 5, and 9

You can use counters to help you divide by 2, 5, and 9.

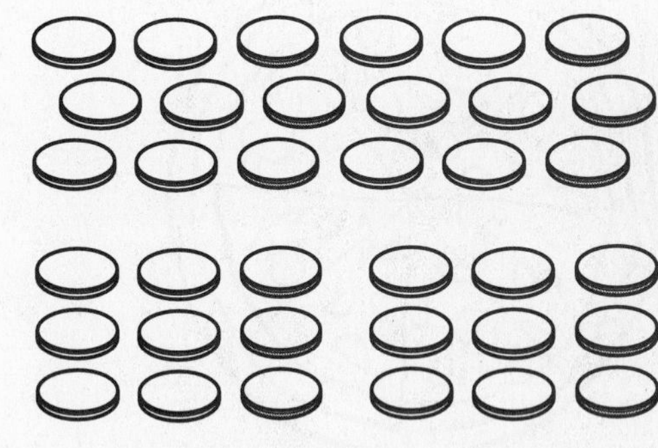

Example 1 Find 18 ÷ 2.
Place 18 counters on your desk.

Divide the counters into 2 equal groups.

How many counters are in each group?

9

So, 18 ÷ 2 = 9.

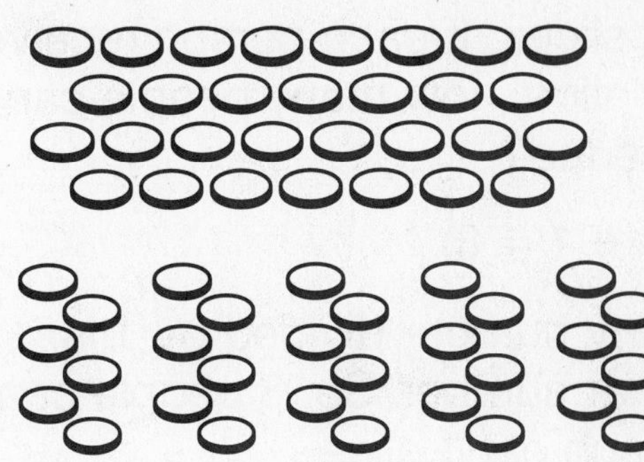

Example 2 Find 30 ÷ 5.
Place 30 counters on your desk.

Divide the counters into 5 equal groups.

How many counters are in each group?

6

So, 30 ÷ 5 = 6.

Find each quotient. Use counters to help.

1. 27 ÷ 9

a. How many counters do you need to start with? ______

b. Divide the counters into ______ equal groups.

c. Draw the groups of counters in the space below.

d. 27 ÷ 9 = ______

2. 14 ÷ 2 = ______ **3.** 25 ÷ 5 = ______ **4.** 36 ÷ 9 = ______

Name ______________________________

Another Look
4-10

Special Quotients

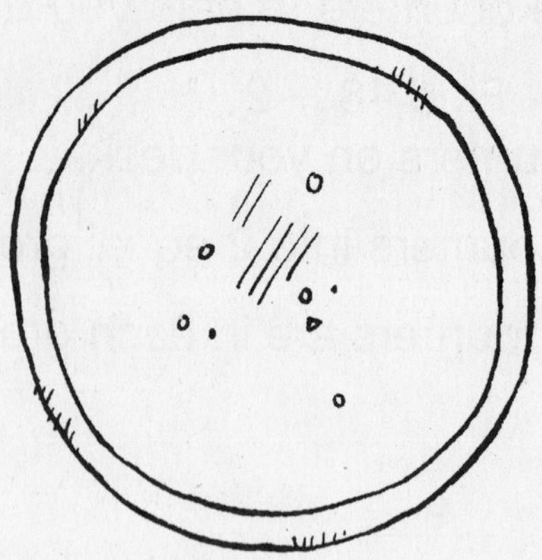

A full pizza has been divided into 8 slices. If each person receives 1 slice, how many people can be fed?

$8 \div 1 = 8$

Any number divided by 1 is that number. So, 8 people can each eat 1 slice.

Everyone wants a second slice, but there is no more pizza left. How many people will receive a second slice?

$0 \div 8 = 0$

0 divided by any number (except 0) equals 0. It doesn't matter how many people want a second slice. There is no more pizza left to be divided.

Use what you know about dividing with 0s and 1s to find each quotient.

1. $7 \div 7 =$ ________ **2.** $7 \div 1 =$ ________

3. $0 \div 4 =$ ________ **4.** $9 \div 1 =$ ________

5. $6 \div 6 =$ ________ **6.** $0 \div 1 =$ ________

7. $4\overline{)4}$ **8.** $1\overline{)2}$ **9.** $3\overline{)0}$

10. $1\overline{)7}$ **11.** $1\overline{)10}$ **12.** $5\overline{)5}$

13. $6\overline{)0}$ **14.** $1\overline{)4}$ **15.** $3\overline{)3}$

Name ______________________

Another Look
4-11

Dividing with 3 and 4

It's easier to divide by 3 or 4 if you know your multiplication facts.

$3 \times 1 = 3$	$4 \times 1 = 4$
$3 \times 2 = 6$	$4 \times 2 = 8$
$3 \times 3 = 9$	$4 \times 3 = 12$
$3 \times 4 = 12$	$4 \times 4 = 16$
$3 \times 5 = 15$	$4 \times 5 = 20$
$3 \times 6 = 18$	$4 \times 6 = 24$
$3 \times 7 = 21$	$4 \times 7 = 28$
$3 \times 8 = 24$	$4 \times 9 = 36$
$3 \times 10 = 30$	$4 \times 10 = 40$

To solve $9 \div 3$, find a multiplication fact that has a product of 9 and a factor of 3.

Since $3 \times \boxed{3} = 9$, $9 \div 3 =$ __3__.

Complete each statement.

1. Since $3 \times \square = 12$, $12 \div 3 = \square$.
2. Since $4 \times \square = \square$, $12 \div 4 = \square$.
3. Since ______________, $32 \div 4 = \square$.
4. Since ______________, $27 \div 3 = \square$.
5. Since ______________, $18 \div 3 = \square$.
6. Since ______________, $24 \div 4 = \square$.
7. Since ______________, $24 \div 3 = \square$.
8. Since ______________, $8 \div 4 = \square$.
9. Since ______________, $20 \div 4 = \square$.
10. Since ______________, $21 \div 3 = \square$.
11. Since ______________, $36 \div 4 = \square$.
12. Since ______________, $28 \div 4 = \square$.
13. Since ______________, $16 \div 4 = \square$.
14. Since ______________, $15 \div 3 = \square$.

Name ______________________________

Another Look 4-12

Dividing with 6, 7 and 8

You can use multiplication facts to help you divide by 6, 7, or 8.

To find 18 ÷ 6, think 6 times what number equals 18.

6 × ☐ = 18

$6 \times 1 = 6$

$6 \times 2 = 12$

$6 \times 3 = 18$

To solve 18 ÷ 6, find a multiplication fact that has a product of 18 and a factor of 6.

Since 6 × 3 = 18, 18 ÷ 6 = __3__.

Complete each statement.

1. Since 6 × ☐ = 24, 24 ÷ 6 = ☐.
2. Since 8 × ☐ = ☐, 24 ÷ 8 = ☐.
3. Since ______________, 21 ÷ 7 = ☐.
4. Since ______________, 48 ÷ 6 = ☐.
5. Since ______________, 35 ÷ 7 = ☐.
6. Since ______________, 64 ÷ 8 = ☐.
7. Since ______________, 12 ÷ 6 = ☐.
8. Since ______________, 28 ÷ 7 = ☐.
9. Since ______________, 56 ÷ 8 = ☐.
10. Since ______________, 54 ÷ 6 = ☐.
11. Since ______________, 40 ÷ 8 = ☐.
12. Since ______________, 49 ÷ 7 = ☐.
13. Since ______________, 36 ÷ 6 = ☐.

 Use with pages 178–179.

Name ______________________________

Exploring Even and Odd Numbers

In your book you used counters to explore even and odd numbers. Here is another way to explore even and odd.

Is 17 odd or even?

Below are 17 stars. Draw a ring around each pair of stars. If there are no stars left over, 17 is even. If there is one star left over, 17 is odd.

17 is an ___odd___ number.

---

1. Is 8 even or odd? __________

2. Is 9 even or odd? __________

3. Is 11 even or odd? __________

4. Is 16 even or odd? __________

Name ______________________________

Another Look 4-14

Exploring Factors

In your book you used rectangles to find factors. Here is another way to explore factors.

To find *all* the factors for a number, make an organized list of multiplication sentences. Write sentences until your factors start to repeat. (Ignore any sentences that won't work.) Then list the factors.

Find all the factors of 48.

$48 = 1 \times 48$
2×24
3×16
4×12
~~5 ×~~
6×8
~~7 ×~~
8×6 (← STOP! Repeat of 6×8).

The factors of 48 are 1, 2, 3, 4, 6, 8, 12, 16, 24 and 48.

The factors of 48 are 1, 2, 3, 4, 6, 8, 12, 16, 24, and 48.

---

1. Find all the factors of 15.

15 = 1 × □
~~2 × □~~
3 × □
~~4 × □~~
5 × □

____

2. Find all the factors of 24.

____

3. Find all the factors of 56.

____

4. Find all factors of 32.

____

Name ______________________________

Analyze Word Problems: Too Much or Too Little Information

To solve a word problem, look carefully at the information. Does it give you enough information to find the answer?

Example Julie bought milk, cereal, and juice today. How much did she spend if the milk cost $1.85 and the cereal cost $4.25.

a. What does the problem tell you? the cost of the milk and cereal

What does it leave out? the total cost; the cost of the juice

b. Can you figure out the answer? Explain. No. I don't know how much the juice cost so I can't figure the total cost.

---

1. Central Middle School has 450 students in 7th, 8th, and 9th grade. There are 185 students in the 7th grade and 115 students in the 8th grade. How many students are in the 9th grade?

a. What does the problem tell you? ______________________________

____

____

What does it leave out? ______________________________

b. Can you figure out the answer? Explain. ______________________________

____

____

2. Central High School has 215 students in 10th grade and 158 students in 11th grade. How many students are in 10th, 11th, and 12th grade?

a. What does the problem tell you? ______________________________

____

What does it leave out? ______________________________

____

b. Can you figure out the answer? Explain. ______________________________

____

Name ______________________________

Compare Strategies: Guess and Check/Draw a Picture

Together, Janie and Howard brought 15 fruit tarts to a party. If Howard brought 3 more tarts than Janie, how many fruit tarts did they each bring?

JANIE | HOWARD

You can solve the problem by drawing a picture. First write the names “Janie” and “Howard”. Draw 1 tart under “Janie” and 4 tarts under “Howard.” Howard has 3 more tarts than Janie, but the picture doesn't show 15 tarts.

Now add one tart to Janie's and one tart to Howard's until you have 15 tarts in all.

This drawing shows that Janie brought 6 tarts and Howard brought 9.

JANIE | HOWARD

Marla and Ahmed brought 18 beach shells to show and tell. If Marla brought 4 more shells than Ahmed, how many did they each bring?

1. What do you need to find out?

____

2. Draw a picture to show the number of shells each person brought to show.

3. How many shells did Ahmed bring? __________

4. How many shells did Marla bring? __________

Name ______________________________

Multiplying Tens

Place-value blocks can help you multiply.

Example 1 Find 3 × 4.

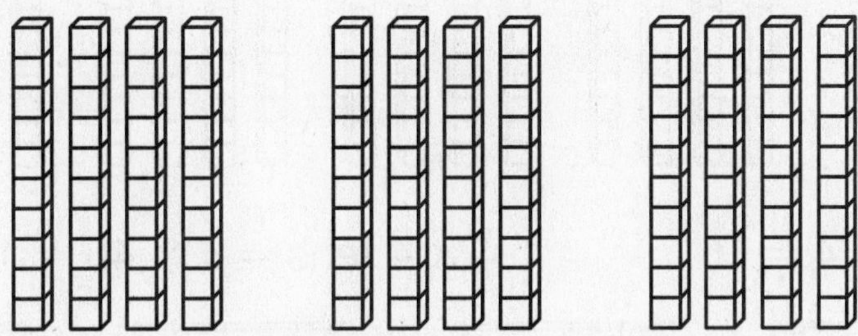

The place-value blocks show 3 groups of 4 tens.

3 × 4 tens = 12 tens = 120

3 × 40 = 120

Example 2 Find 4 × 50.

4 × 5 tens = 20 tens = 200

Use place-value blocks to help you find each product.

1. 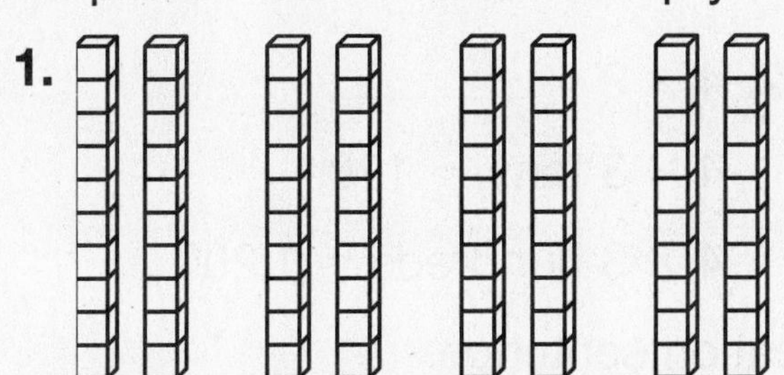

a. 4 × _____ tens = _____ tens

b. 4 × 20 = _____

2. 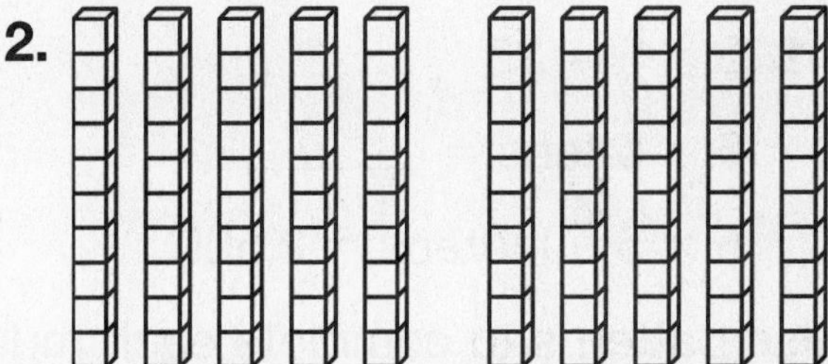

a. 2 × _____ tens = _____ tens

b. 2 × 50 = _____

3. a. 4 × 4 tens = _____ tens

b. 4 × 40 = _____

4. a. 6 × 3 tens = _____ tens

b. 6 × 30 = _____

5. 5 × 10 = _______ **6.** 8 × 70 = _______ **7.** 7 × 70 = _______

8. 40 × 7 = _______ **9.** 30 × 8 = _______ **10.** 80 × 7 = _______

11. 3 × 50 = _______ **12.** 20 × 6 = _______ **13.** 9 × 6 = _______

Name ___________________________

Another Look
5-2

Exploring Multiplication Patterns

In your book you multiplied using patterns. Here is another way to multiply.

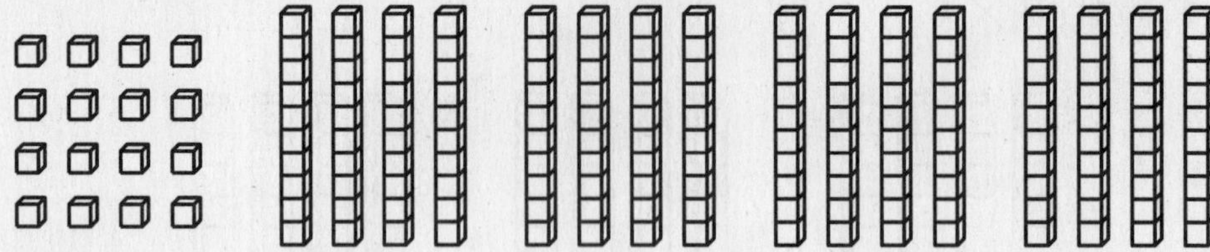

4 × 4 ones = 4 × 4 = 16 4 × 4 tens = 4 × 40 = 160

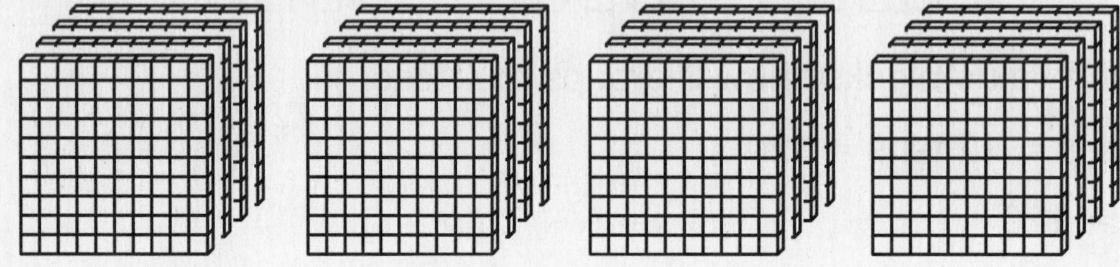

So, 4 × 4 hundreds = 4 × 400 = 1,600

Complete each multiplication sentence. Think of place-value blocks and look for patterns.

1. 5 × 5 = 25

5 × 5 tens = ________

5 × 5 hundreds = 2,500

2. 4 × 3 = ________

4 × 3 tens = 120

4 × 3 hundreds = 1,200

Use patterns to complete each multiplication sentence.

3. 4 × 80 = ________

________ × 800 = 3,200

4 × ________ = 32,000

4 × ________ = 320,000

4. 3 × ________ = 150

3 × 500 = ________

3 × ________ = 15,000

3 × ________ = 150,000

Find each product.

5. 6 × 400 = ________

6. 3 × 200 = ________

7. 5 × 700 = ________

8. 8 × 2,000 = ________

9. 4 × 3,000 = ________

10. 6 × 5,000 = ________

Name ______________________________

Another Look 5-3

Estimating Products

Estimate.

Example 1 3×12

Round 12 to nearest multiple of 10.

Think of the multiples of 10.

0, 10, 20, 30, 40, 50, 60, 70, 80, ...

↑

12

Which number is nearest to 12?

Replace 12 in the problem with 10.

$3 \times \not{1}\not{2}$

↓

$3 \times 10 = 30$

Example 2 4×570

Round 570 to nearest multiple of 100.

570 is closer to 600.

Replace 570 with 600.

$4 \times \not{5}\not{7}0$

↓

$4 \times 600 = 2{,}400$

Write the nearest multiple of ten for each number.

1. 83 ________ **2.** 46 ________ **3.** 57 ________ **4.** 48 ________

Write the nearest multiple of 100 for each number.

5. 120 ________ **6.** 280 ________ **7.** 940 ________ **8.** 350 ________

Estimate each product by rounding each two-digit number to the nearest multiple of 10. Round each three-digit number to the nearest multiple of 100.

9. 2×93

$2 \times$ _____ = _____

10. 37×7

_____ $\times 7 =$ _____

11. 6×49

$6 \times$ _____ = _____

12. 5×14

____

13. 42×5

____

14. 85×4

____

15. 47×8

____

16. 26×9

____

17. 7×81

____

Name ______________________________

Exploring Multiplication with Arrays

In your book you used place-value blocks to multiply. Here is another way to multiply. Drawing a rectangular array on grid paper can help you find the product. Here is how you can use an array to find the product of 3 × 25.

a. Draw a rectangle 25 boxes wide and 3 boxes long.

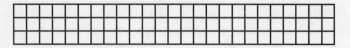

b. Outline groups of ten boxes in each row.

c. How many ones are there? 15

d. How many tens are there? 6

e. How many ones boxes are there in all? 75

Draw an array to help you find each product. Use a separate sheet of grid paper.

1.
$$\begin{array}{r} 23 \\ \times\ 6 \\ \hline 18 \\ +\ 120 \\ \hline \end{array}$$

a. How many ones are there? ________

b. How many tens are there? ________

c. How many ones boxes in all? ________

2.
$$\begin{array}{r} 37 \\ \times\ 8 \\ \hline \\ + \quad \\ \hline \end{array}$$

a. How many ones are there? ________

b. How many tens are there? ________

c. How many ones boxes in all? ________

3.
$$\begin{array}{r} 28 \\ \times\ 3 \\ \hline \\ + \quad \\ \hline \end{array}$$

a. How many ones are there? ________

b. How many tens are there? ________

c. How many ones boxes in all? ________

Name ______________________

Another Look
5-5

Multiplying 2-Digit Numbers

Step 1 Multiply the ones.

$$\begin{array}{r} 73 \\ \times\ 7 \\ \hline 21 \end{array}$$ $7 \times 3 = \underline{21}$

$$\begin{array}{r} 24 \\ \times\ 9 \\ \hline 36 \end{array}$$ $9 \times 4 = \underline{36}$

Step 2 Multiply the tens.

$$\begin{array}{r} 73 \\ \times\ 7 \\ \hline 21 \\ 490 \\ \hline \end{array}$$ 7×7 tens $= 49$ tens or 490

$$\begin{array}{r} 24 \\ \times\ 9 \\ \hline 36 \\ 180 \\ \hline \end{array}$$ 9×2 tens $= \underline{180}$

Step 3 Add.

$$\begin{array}{r} 73 \\ \times\ 7 \\ \hline 21 \\ 490 \\ \hline 511 \end{array}$$

$$\begin{array}{r} 24 \\ \times\ 9 \\ \hline 36 \\ 180 \\ \hline 216 \end{array}$$

Step 4 Estimate to check the answer.

73×7 is close to $\underline{70} \times 7$.

$70 \times 7 = 490$

511 is close to 490, so the answer is reasonable.

24×9 is close to $\underline{20} \times 9$.

$20 \times 9 = 180$

180 is close to 216, so the answer is reasonable.

Complete. Show your ones and tens products.

1. $\begin{array}{r} 23 \\ \times\ 3 \\ \hline \end{array}$

2. $\begin{array}{r} 21 \\ \times\ 4 \\ \hline \end{array}$

3. $\begin{array}{r} 44 \\ \times\ 3 \\ \hline \end{array}$

4. $\begin{array}{r} 59 \\ \times\ 5 \\ \hline \end{array}$

5. $\begin{array}{r} 33 \\ \times\ 2 \\ \hline \end{array}$

6. $\begin{array}{r} 64 \\ \times\ 8 \\ \hline \end{array}$

7. $\begin{array}{r} 24 \\ \times\ 4 \\ \hline \end{array}$

8. $\begin{array}{r} 54 \\ \times\ 6 \\ \hline \end{array}$

Name ______________________________

Another Look
5-6

Multiplying 3-Digit Numbers

Breaking numbers apart can make them easier to multiply.

Find the product of 547 and 4.

You can break 547 into hundreds, tens, and ones.

Step 1 547 = 500 + 40 + 7

Step 2 Multiply each part by 4.

$4 \times 7 = 28$

$4 \times 40 = 160$

$4 \times 500 = 2{,}000$

Step 3 Add. 2,188

Find each product. Break numbers apart to help you.

1. 566 = 500 + 60 + 6
× 4

$4 \times 6 =$ ______

$4 \times 60 =$ ______

$4 \times 500 =$ ______

______

2. 601 = 600 + 1
× 5

$5 \times 1 =$ ______

$5 \times 600 =$ ______

______

3. 789 = 700 + 80 + 9
× 3

$3 \times 9 =$ ______

$3 \times 80 =$ ______

$3 \times 700 =$ ______

______

4. 342 = 300 + 40 + 2
× 8

$8 \times 2 =$ ______

$8 \times 40 =$ ______

$8 \times 300 =$ ______

______

Name ____________________

Another Look 5-7

Decision Making

A group of sea otters is called a raft. Several rafts of sea otters live off the coast of California. Scientists who study sea otters often tag a few otters of different ages in each raft. They often tag 1 of 10 otters in each raft. They make conclusions based on what they notice about the tagged otters.

$$\begin{array}{r} 65 \text{ otters} \\ \times\ 7 \text{ rafts} \\ \hline 455 \end{array}$$

Seven rafts had 65 sea otters each.

How many otters are there all together? 455

How many tens are there in 455? 45 tens

How many sea otters will be tagged? 45

---

1. In another area, there are 8 rafts with 82 sea otters in each raft.
   - **a.** How many otters are there all together? ________
   - **b.** How many tens are there? ________ tens
   - **c.** How many sea otters will be tagged? ________

2. By one island, there are 6 rafts of 72 sea otters.
   - **a.** How many otters are there all together? ________
   - **b.** How many tens are there? ________ tens
   - **c.** How many sea otters will be tagged? ________

3. How many otters will be tagged in each of the following:
   - **a.** 5 rafts of 42 ________
   - **b.** 4 rafts of 53? ________
   - **c.** 7 rafts of 25? ________

Name ____________________

Another Look
5-8

Choosing a Calculation Method

Place-value blocks can help you find the product of 3 and 1,032.

```
  1,032
×     3
      6 = 3 × 2 ones
     90 = 3 × 3 tens
  3,000 = 3 × 1 thousand
  3,096
```

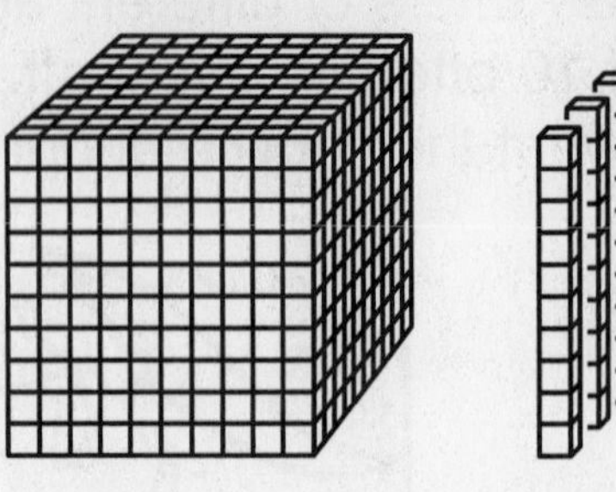

Or, you can multiply using a short cut. Multiply each digit in 1,032 by 3. Write your answer.

```
  1,032
×     3
  3,096
```

A calculator can be helpful for harder problems.

2,378 × 9 = 21,102

Multiply by drawing place-value blocks.

1. 1,223 × 3

____

2. 1,120 × 4

____

Multiply. Use place-value blocks if needed. Try using the short-cut method, or use a calculator.

3. 1,025 × 3

4. 2,432 × 4

5. 2,056 × 6

6. 3,127 × 7

Name ______________________________

Multiplying Money

Draw a picture to help you find the product of $1.40 × 3.

How many dimes do you need to have 3 stacks of $1.40?

$$\begin{array}{r} \$1.40 \\ \times \quad 3 \\ \hline \$4.20 \end{array}$$ (42 dimes)

Complete each problem.

1. $2.35 × 2 = $_.70

2. $1.09 × 4 = $_._6

3. $4.50 × 3 = $__.50

4. $2.23 × 6 = $__._8

Multiply.

5. $3.45 × 4

6. $5.50 × 5

7. $8.04 × 2

8. $4.33 × 7

9. $7.15 × 3

10. $1.13 × 6

11. $6.60 × 5

12. $3.97 × 4

13. $4.23 × 4

14. $2.74 × 7

15. $1.85 × 3

16. $5.05 × 9

Name ____________________

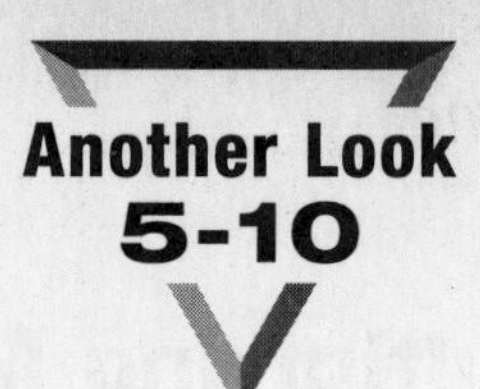

Mental Math: Special Products

Here is a way to solve problems mentally when one number is even. Cutting an even number in half and doubling the other number can help you do mental math.

$6 \times 15 =$

Half of 6 is: 3

Double 15 is: 30

$3 \times 30 = 90$

If one number is still too large, you can keep cutting it in half to make it easier, but don't forget to double your other number! Try 13×16.

Double		Half
26	×	8
52	×	4
104	×	2 = 208

Use mental math to solve these problems. If necessary, cut one number in half and double the other.

1. 4×18 ________ **2.** 6×35 ________

3. 8×42 ________ **4.** 45×4 ________

5. 25×6 ________ **6.** 49×4 ________

7. 22×8 ________ **8.** 44×6 ________

9. 4×36 ________ **10.** 55×8 ________

11. 6×27 ________ **12.** 4×29 ________

13. 32×4 ________ **14.** 54×8 ________

15. 43×6 ________ **16.** 34×4 ________

Name ________________________________

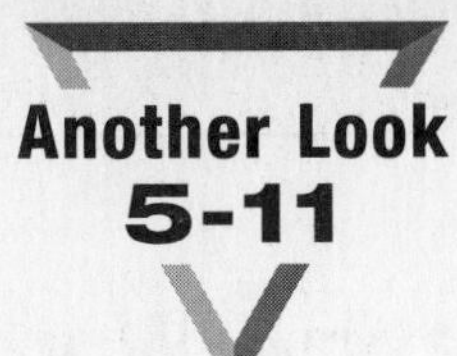

Multiplying 3 Factors

Here is a way you can find the product when there are 3 factors. Multiply the least numbers or use the easy facts first. Use parentheses to show what to multiply first.

$5 \times 9 \times 3 = (5 \times 3) \times 9$

$\downarrow$

$15 \times 9 = 135$

Write each product. Multiply the least numbers first and use parentheses.

1. $6 \times 2 \times 8$

____

2. $5 \times 7 \times 3$

____

3. $4 \times 9 \times 2$

____

4. $3 \times 6 \times 4$

____

5. $9 \times 5 \times 7$

____

6. $4 \times 1 \times 8$

____

7. $3 \times 7 \times 2$

____

8. $5 \times 2 \times 6$

____

Name ____________________

Another Look 5-12

Analyze Word Problems: Multiple-Step Problems

How much money would you need to buy 4 loaves of bread and 3 boxes of cereal?

Grocery Items

loaf of bread – $2.25
box of cereal – $4.29
bar of soap – $1.69

What do you know? You need: 4 loaves of bread at $2.25 each
3 boxes of cereal at $4.29 each

What do you need to find out? The total cost of the groceries

How can you find the cost of 4 loaves of bread? Multiply 4 × $2.25.
How can you find the cost of 3 boxes of cereal? Multiply 3 × $4.29.
How can you find the total cost? Add.

Step 1 Multiply.

	bread	**cereal**
	$2.25	$4.29
	× 4	× 3
	$9.00	$12.87

Step 2 Add. $9.00 + ______

What's the answer? You need $ 21.87 to buy the groceries.

How can you check if your answer makes sense?

Estimate. $2 × 4 = $8
$4 × 3 = + $12
$20

---

1. What is the total cost of 4 bars of soap, 3 loaves of bread, and 5 boxes of cereal?

a. What is the cost of 4 bars of soap? ______

b. What is the cost of 3 loaves of bread? ______

c. What is the cost of 5 boxes of cereal? ______

d. What is the total cost of all of the groceries above? ______

5. How much change would you receive if you paid for 2 bars of soap with a $5 bill? ______

Name ____________________

Analyze Strategies: Make a Table

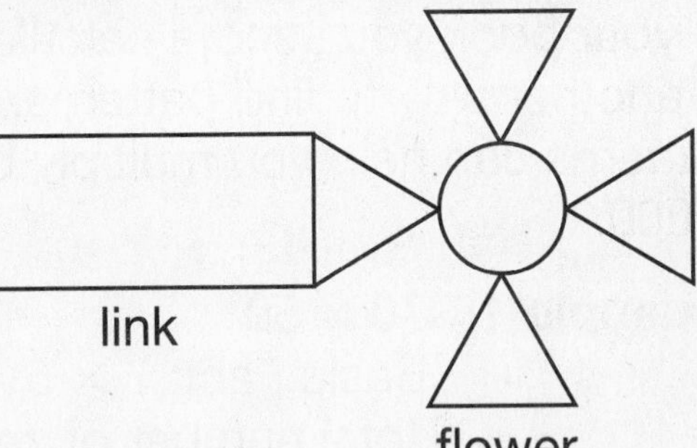

How many pattern pieces do you need to make a bracelet with 3 flowers?

Understand What do you know? There are 5 pieces in a flower. There are 11 pieces in a 2-flower bracelet.

What do you need to find out? How many pieces are there in a 3-flower bracelet?

Plan Make a table to organize the data.

Solve Fill in the table. You can use power polygons or draw a picture to help you see a pattern. Complete the table to find the pattern.

Number of Flowers	Number of Pieces
1	5
2	
3	

When there are 3 flowers, there are 17 pieces in all.

Look Back How can you check your answer? Possible answer: Draw a picture.

Use the pattern above to answer the questions.

1. If you continue the pattern until you have a 4-flower bracelet, how many pieces will you need? ______

2. If your bracelet has 6 flowers, how many pieces will it have in all? ______

Name ______________________________

Another Look
6-1

Exploring Multiplication Patterns

In your book you used a calculator to explore patterns. Here is another way to find patterns. Basic fact and place-value patterns can help you multiply by multiples of 10; 100; or 1,000.

Example 1 70 × 50
Basic Fact: 7 × 5 = 35
Total number of zeros in factors: 2
Therefore, 70 × 50 = 3,500 (35 = basic fact; 2 zeros)

Example 2 700 × 500
Basic Fact: 7 × 5 = 35
Total number of zeros in factors: 4
Therefore, 700 × 500 = 350,000 (35 = basic fact; 4 zeros)

Use patterns to find each product.

1. 30 × 70

a. Find the product of the basic fact: 3 × 7 = ____________

b. Count the number of zeros in the factors. ____________

c. Write the final product. ____________

2. 600 × 500

a. Find the product of the basic fact: 6 × 5 = ____________

b. Count the number of zeros in the factors. ____________

c. Write the final product. ____________

3. 80 × 30 = ____________

4. 900 × 300 = ____________

5. 40 × 500 = ____________

6. 800 × 500 = ____________

7. 20 × 700 = ____________

8. 300 × 600 = ____________

9. 400 × 400 = ____________

10. 200 × 800 = ____________

Name ______________________

Another Look
6-2

Estimating Products

Estimate the product of 43 and 57.

Step 1 Round each number to the nearest ten.

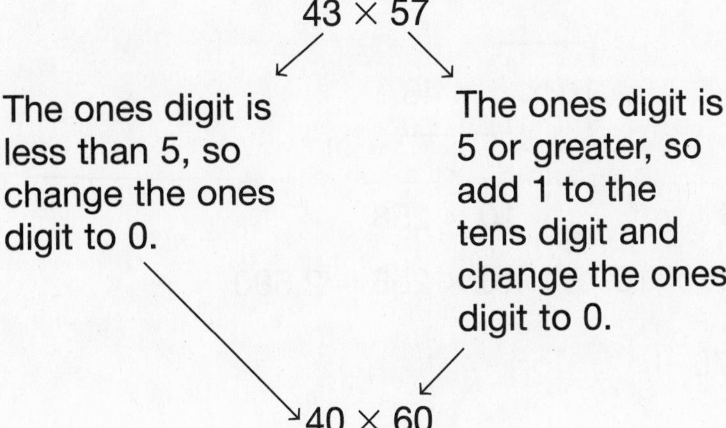

43 × 57
The ones digit is less than 5, so change the ones digit to 0.
The ones digit is 5 or greater, so add 1 to the tens digit and change the ones digit to 0.
40 × 60

Step 2 Multiply. 40 × 60 = 2,400

Estimate the product.

1. 36 × 82
   ↓ ↓
   40 × 80 = ______

2. 68 × 32
   ↓ ↓
   70 × 30 = ______

3. 93 × 75
   ______ × ______ = ______

4. 36 × 57
   ______ × ______ = ______

5. 34 × 65
   ______ × ______ = ______

6. 66 × 42
   ______ × ______ = ______

7. 38 × 67
   ______ × ______ = ______

8. 78 × 23
   ______ × ______ = ______

9. 48 × 58
   ______ × ______ = ______

10. 14 × 18
    ______ × ______ = ______

11. 93 × 26
    ______ × ______ = ______

12. 77 × 44
    ______ × ______ = ______

Name ______________________________

Another Look
6-3

Multiplying by Multiples of 10

You can break apart each multiple of 10 to help you multiply.

Example 1 60×43

Think: 60 is 10×6 — $10 \times 6 \times 43$

Multiply. $6 \times 43 = 258$ — 10×258

Multiply by the product of 10. $10 \times 258 = 2{,}580$

Example 2 40×78

$10 \times 4 \times 78$

$10 \times 312 = 3{,}120$

Find each product.

1. 30×48

a. $10 \times$ ______ $\times 48$

b. $10 \times$ ______ $=$ ______

2. 50×78

a. $10 \times$ ______ $\times 78$

b. $10 \times$ ______ $=$ ______

3. 86×20

4. 24×40

5. 64×70

6. 73×50

7. 51×60

8. 32×90

Name ______________________________

Exploring Multiplication with 2-Digit Factors

In your book you multiplied using place-value blocks. Here is another way to show multiplication.

Draw rectangles on grid paper to show partial products.

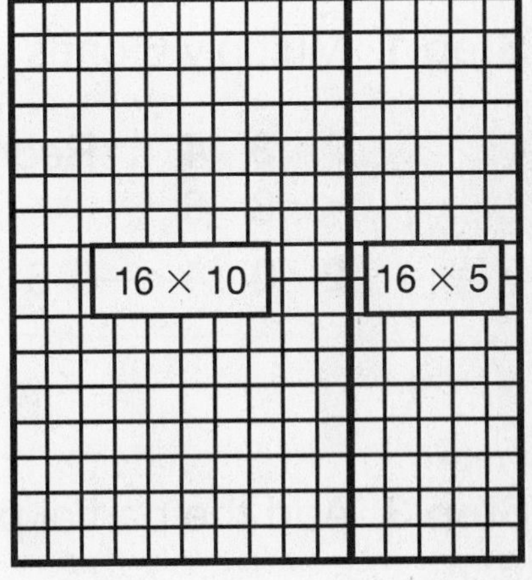

$$\begin{array}{lr} & 16 \\ & \times\ 15 \\ \hline 16 \times 5 \longrightarrow & 80 \\ 16 \times 10 \longrightarrow & 160 \\ \hline 16 \times 15 \longrightarrow & 240 \end{array}$$ Add.

---

1. Draw lines to show the multiplication. Find 11 × 16.

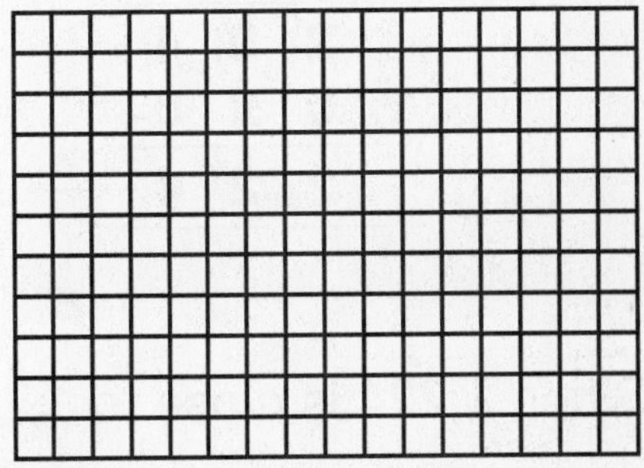

$$\begin{array}{lr} & 11 \\ & \times\ 16 \\ \hline 11 \times 6 \longrightarrow & \square\square \\ 11 \times 10 \longrightarrow & \square\square\square \\ \hline & \square\square\square \end{array}$$

2. $$\begin{array}{lr} & 18 \\ & \times\ 32 \\ \hline 18 \times 2 \longrightarrow & \square\square \\ 18 \times 30 \longrightarrow & \square\square\square \\ \hline & \square\square\square \end{array}$$

3. $$\begin{array}{lr} & 18 \\ & \times\ 43 \\ \hline 18 \times 3 \longrightarrow & \square\square \\ 18 \times 40 \longrightarrow & \square\square\square \\ \hline & \square\square\square \end{array}$$

Find each product.

4. $\begin{array}{r} 32 \\ \times\ 15 \\ \hline \end{array}$

5. $\begin{array}{r} 73 \\ \times\ 32 \\ \hline \end{array}$

6. $\begin{array}{r} 46 \\ \times\ 55 \\ \hline \end{array}$

Name ______________________

Multiplying with 2-Digit Factors

Multiply 34 × 36.

Step 1 Multiply 6 ones and 34.

```
    3 4    Regroup.
  × 3 6
  -----
  2 0 4 ← 6 × 34
```

Step 2 Multiply 3 tens and 34.

```
      3 4    Regroup.
    × 3 6
    -----
    2 0 4
  1 0 2 0 ← 30 × 34
```

Step 3 Add the partial products.

```
      3 4
    × 3 6
  -------
    2 0 4
  1 0 2 0
  -------
  1 2 2 4 ← 204 + 1,020
```

Step 4 Check by estimating.

34 × 36
↓ ↓
30 × 40 = 1,200

Since 1,224 is close to 1,200, the answer is reasonable.

Complete.

1.

```
      2 4
    × 1 7
  -------
          ← 7 × 24
          ← 10 × 24
  -------
```

2.

```
      4 2
    × 5 3
  -------
          ← 3 × 42
          ← 50 × 42
  -------
```

3. 76 × 23

4. 63 × 34

5. 45 × 25

6. 56 × 43

Name ______________________________

Another Look
6-6

Estimating Greater Products

Estimate 37 × 592

Step 1 Round each number to its greatest place.

37 × 592
↓ ↓
40 × 600

Step 2 Multiply the non-zero digits.

40 × **6**00 4 × 6 = 24

Step 3 Count the zeros in the factors.

40 × 600
↑ ↑↑
3 zeros

Step 4 Write them after the product in **Step 2.**

24,**000**

The product of 37 × 592 is about 24,000.

Estimate each product.

1. 489 × 73

a. Round: 500 × ______

b. 5 × ______ = ______

c. ______ zeros in the factors

d. 500 × ______ = ______

2. 365 × 47

a. Round: ______ × ______

b. 4 × ______ = ______

c. ______ zeros in the factors

d. 400 × ______ = ______

3. 683 × 28

______ × ______ = ______

4. 835 × 62

______ × ______ = ______

5. 176 × 38

______ × ______ = ______

6. 342 × 78

______ × ______ = ______

7. 491 × 87

______ × ______ = ______

8. 947 × 52

______ × ______ = ______

Name ____________________

Choosing a Calculation Method

The table below shows 3 ways of thinking about different calculation methods.

Method	When to Use It	Examples
Paper and pencil	to work out a long problem on your own	2,700 × 19 24,300 27,000 51,300
Calculator	to get a quick but accurate answer to check your figures from the long method	2,700 × 19 = 51,300
Estimation	to make sure your answer is reasonable	2,700 × 19 = 51,300 3,000 × 20 = 60,000 The answer is reasonable.

Find each product. Tell which method you used.

1. $\begin{array}{r} 373 \\ \times\ 21 \\ \hline \end{array}$

Method: ____________

2. $\begin{array}{r} 407 \\ \times\ 18 \\ \hline \end{array}$

Method: ____________

3. $\begin{array}{r} 6{,}000 \\ \times\ 30 \\ \hline \end{array}$

Method: ____________

4. $\begin{array}{r} 243 \\ \times\ 61 \\ \hline \end{array}$

Method: ____________

5. $\begin{array}{r} 162 \\ \times\ 25 \\ \hline \end{array}$

Method: ____________

6. $\begin{array}{r} 278 \\ \times\ 40 \\ \hline \end{array}$

Method: ____________

Name ______________________

Another Look
6-8

Decision Making

Len is making snacks and drinks for his friends to take to the beach. He only has $\frac{1}{2}$ hour to get the food ready. He wants to take 3 different items. Here is a list of possible choices and the time they take to get ready.

- cheese sandwiches: 10 minutes
- fruit punch: 10 minutes
- chips and dip: 10 minutes
- tuna sandwiches: 15 minutes
- drink mix: 5 minutes
- trail mix: 5 minutes
- fruit salad: 5 minutes
- frosted cake: 15 minutes

Len asked himself the following questions to help him make his decision:

What are my top 6 choices in order?
tuna sandwiches, cake, fruit punch, drink mix, chips and dip, fruit salad

How long will my top 3 choices take to prepare?
40 minutes

Should I take only my top 2 items?
No, drinks are important to have at the beach.

Len decides to bring tuna sandwiches, chips and dip, and drink mix.

____

1. Which sandwiches are fastest to make? How much time could Len save?

____

2. What drink is the fastest to make? How much time could Len save?

____

3. What 3 items could Len bring that would take the least time to make?

____

4. If you want to take two different kinds of sandwiches, what else would you have time to prepare in the 30 minutes?

____

Name ______________________________

Another Look
6-9

Multiplying Money

You can multiply money in the same way you multiply whole numbers.

To multiply $7.89 and 15, multiply the whole numbers 789 and 15.

$$\begin{array}{lr} & 789 \\ & \times \quad 15 \\ 789 \times 5 \;= & 3945 \\ 789 \times 10 = & 7890 \\ \hline & 11835 \end{array}$$

Place a dollar sign in front of the answer and a decimal point to the left of the tens digit.

$7.89 × 15 = $118.35

Find the product of the whole number amount and place the dollar sign and decimal point.

1. $4.47 × 11

$$\begin{array}{rl} 447 & \\ \times \quad 11 & \\ \hline \square & \leftarrow 447 \times 1 \\ \square & \leftarrow 447 \times 10 \\ \hline \square & \end{array}$$

$4.47 × 11 = ____________

2. $36.19 × 47

$$\begin{array}{rl} 3619 & \\ \times \quad 47 & \\ \hline \square & \leftarrow 3619 \times 7 \\ \square & \leftarrow 3619 \times 40 \\ \hline \square & \end{array}$$

$36.19 × 47 = ____________

3. $6.31 × 15

4. $59.80 × 4

5. $15.11 × 6

Name ______________________

Another Look 6-10

Analyze Word Problems: Overestimating and Underestimating

Asking a series of questions can help you decide when to overestimate and when to underestimate.

Jasmine invites 22 friends to a party. She plans to spend about $0.45 per person on favors. Should she overestimate or underestimate the total cost of favors?

How many people are expected at the party?
22 friends plus Jasmine, 23 people in all

How much does Jasmine plan to spend? $0.45 per person

How do you figure the total cost?
Multiply the cost of favors per person by the number of people.

What will happen if she underestimates?
She may not plan for enough money.

What if she overestimates?
She will have money left over.

Should she overestimate or underestimate?
She should overestimate. She can round the cost per favor to a greater amount, $0.50.

$23 \times \$0.50 = \$11.50$

Jasmine will need about $11.50 for favors.

1. The captain is planning a kick-off meeting for her 16-member team. She plans to buy a headband for each person. The headbands cost $0.57 each. Should she overestimate or underestimate the total cost? Explain. How much money should she take when she goes shopping?

____

____

Name ______________________

Another Look 6-11

Analyze Strategies: Draw a Picture

A filled auditorium has 6 rows with 15 seats per row. José is seated in row 5. How many people are in front of José? How many in all?

Here is a picture to help you.

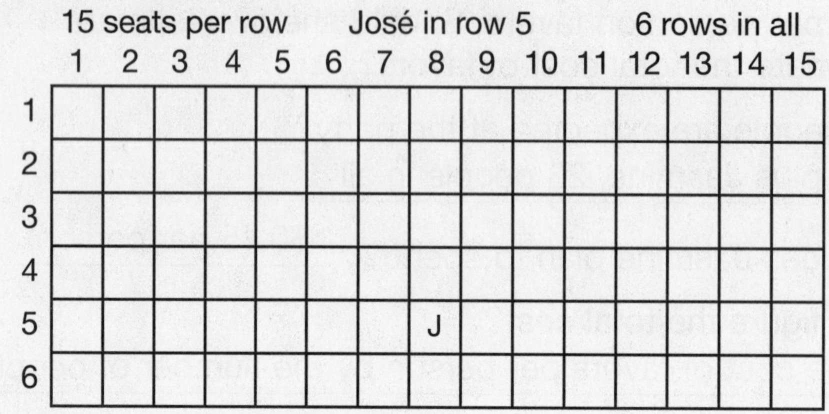

Use the picture to solve the problem.

How many people are in front of José?

There are 4 rows in front of him.
15 seats per row
So, 4 × 15 = 60 people in front of José.

How many people in all?

6 rows in all
15 seats per row
So, 6 × 15 = 90 people in all

Check your answer.

Each ☐ = 1 person
Count the ☐ in the grid.
There are 90 ☐ in all.

---

1. How many people are behind José? ______

2. Ahmed is 3 rows in front of José. How many people are behind Ahmed? ______

Name ___________________________

Exploring Division Patterns

In your book you used basic facts and place-value patterns to divide numbers. Here is another way to divide using place-value.

280 ÷ 7 = ?

Divide 28 tens into 7 equal groups.

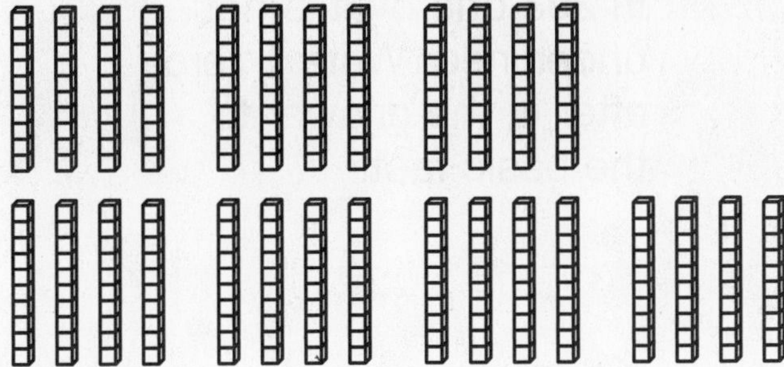

28 tens ÷ 7 = 4 tens

280 ÷ 7 = 40

Divide. Use the place-value blocks to help.

1. 160 ÷ 8

a. 1 hundred and 6 tens is the same as ________ tens.

b. ________ tens ÷ 8 = 2 tens

c. 160 ÷ 8 = ________

2. 2,000 ÷ 5

a. 2 thousands is the same as ________ hundreds.

b. ________ hundreds ÷ 5 = ________ hundreds.

c. 2,000 ÷ 5 = ________

Find each quotient.

3. 120 ÷ 3 = ________

4. 600 ÷ 3 = ________

5. 2,400 ÷ 8 = ________

6. 3,600 ÷ 9 = ________

7. 3,000 ÷ 6 = ________

8. 120 ÷ 2 = ________

Use with pages 292–293.

Name ________________________________

Another Look
7-2

Estimating Quotients

Estimate 293 ÷ 7.

Step 1 Underline the first two digits of the number to be divided.

29 3 (29 underlined)

Step 2 Find a basic fact with 7 and a number close to the underlined number.

29 is close to 28.
28 ÷ 7 = 4

Step 3 For each digit not underlined in the number to be divided (293), write a 0 after the answer to the basic fact.

In 293 one digit is not underlined. Write 1 zero after 4, the answer to the basic fact.

So, 293 ÷ 7 is about 40.

---

1. Estimate 332 ÷ 6.

a. 33 is close to ______.

b. 30 ÷ 6 = _____.

c. 332 ÷ 6 is about _______.

2. Estimate 284 ÷ 9.

a. 28 is close to ______.

b. 27 ÷ 9 = _____.

c. 284 ÷ 9 is about _______.

Estimate each quotient.

3. 132 ÷ 6 _______

4. 767 ÷ 9 _______

5. 316 ÷ 4 _______

6. 541 ÷ 6 _______

Use with pages 294–295.

Name ___________________________

Another Look
7-3

Exploring Division with Remainders

In your book, you used counters to explore division with remainders. Here is another way to divide.

Find $7\overline{)52}$.

Using grid paper, draw a box around 52 squares. Circle groups of 7 squares.

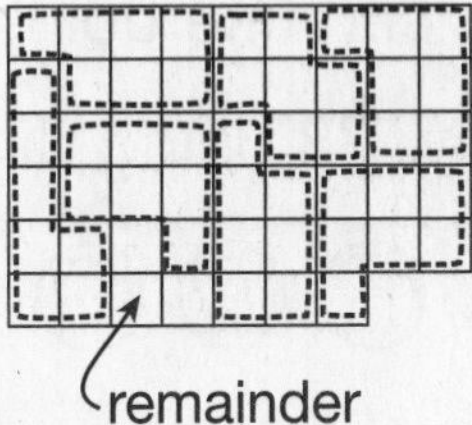

Find the quotient by counting the groups of 7.

There are __7__ groups of 7.

Find the remainder by counting the squares not in any group.

There are __3__ squares left over.

The answer is: __7 R3__

Find each quotient. Use grid paper.

1. Find $5\overline{)14}$. Circle 14 squares. Circle groups of 5 squares.

a. Find the quotient by counting the groups of 5. __________

b. Find the remainder by counting the left-over squares. __________

c. The answer is __________ .

2. Find $6\overline{)20}$.

a. The quotient is __________ .

b. The remainder is __________ .

c. The answer is __________ .

3. Find $9\overline{)47}$.

a. The quotient is __________ .

b. The remainder is __________ .

c. The answer is __________ .

Name ________________________________

Exploring Division

In your book you used place-value blocks to explore division. Here is another way to divide.

Find 73 ÷ 3.

You can use coins to show division.

Show 73 using dimes and pennies.

Divide the money into 3 equal groups. Start by dividing the dimes.

Exchange the remaining dimes for pennies.

Divide the pennies into 3 equal groups.

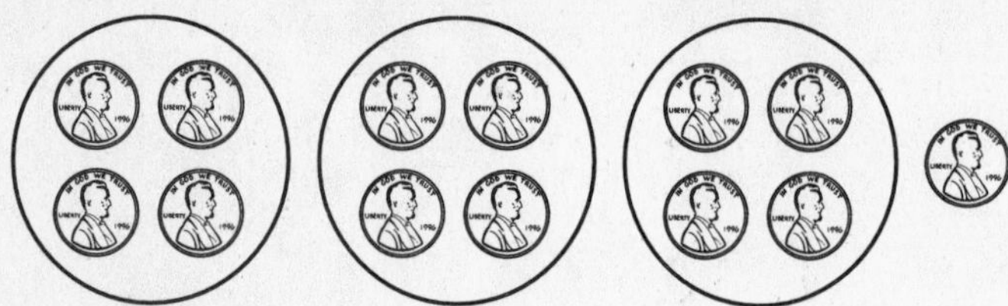

Count the number of cents in one group of dimes and 1 group of pennies.. This is the quotient. The number of cents left out of the groups is the remainder.

73 ÷ 3 = 24 R1

Find each quotient. Use coins to help.

1. 56 ÷ 4 = ________

2. 82 ÷ 3 = ________ **3.** 47 ÷ 2 = ________

4. 79 ÷ 6 = ________ **5.** 93 ÷ 5 = ________

Name ______________________________

Another Look 7-5

Dividing 2-Digit Dividends

Find 94 ÷ 4.

Step 1 Divide the tens. Think: 9 tens ÷ 4. Write the quotient above the 9.

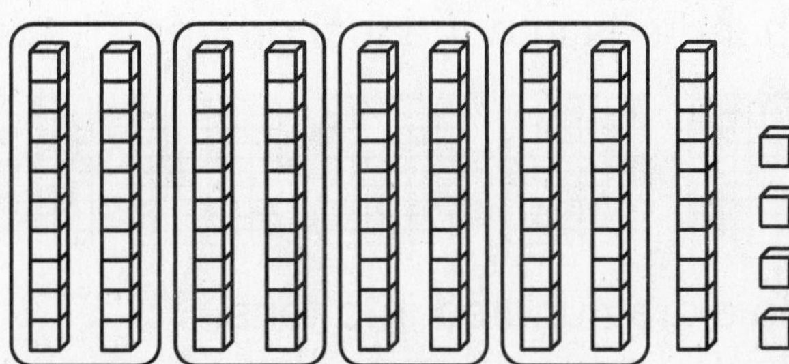

$$4\overline{)94}\;\text{quotient } 2$$

Step 2 You used 8 tens. There is 1 ten left over. Regroup 1 tens as ten ones.

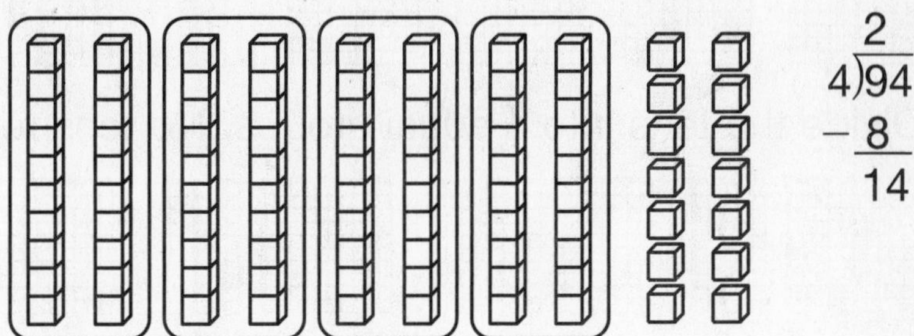

$$\begin{array}{r} 2 \\ 4\overline{)94} \\ -\underline{8} \\ 14 \end{array}$$

Step 3 Divide the ones. Think 14 ÷ 4. Write the quotient above the 4.

$$\begin{array}{r} 23 \\ 4\overline{)94} \\ -\underline{8} \\ 14 \\ -\underline{12} \\ 2 \end{array}$$

Step 4 You used 12 ones. There are 2 ones left over. Write 2 as the remainder.

94 ÷ 4 = 23 R2

Find each quotient. Follow the steps outlined above.

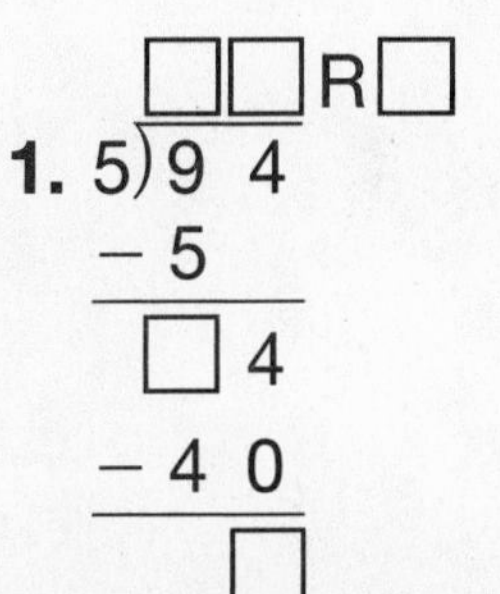

1. $\begin{array}{r} \square\square \text{ R}\square \\ 5\overline{)9\;4} \\ -\underline{5} \\ \square\;4 \\ -\underline{4\;0} \\ \square \end{array}$

2. $\begin{array}{r} \square\square \text{ R}\square \\ 3\overline{)8\;4} \\ -\underline{\square} \\ 2\square \\ -\underline{\square\square} \\ 0 \end{array}$

Name ________________________

Another Look
7-6

Finding 3-Digit Quotients

Use place-value blocks to divide 525 by 4.

Divide the hundreds into 4 equal groups. There is one extra hundred.

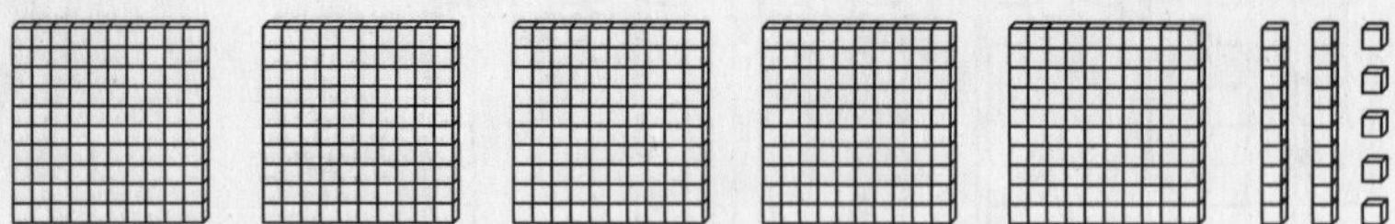

Regroup the extra hundred into tens.

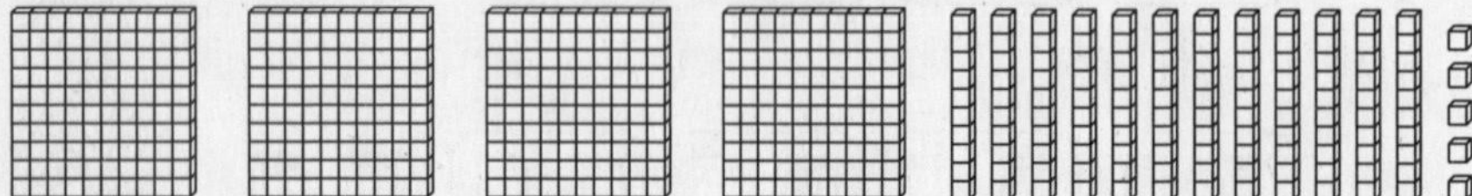

Divide the tens into 4 equal groups. No tens remain.

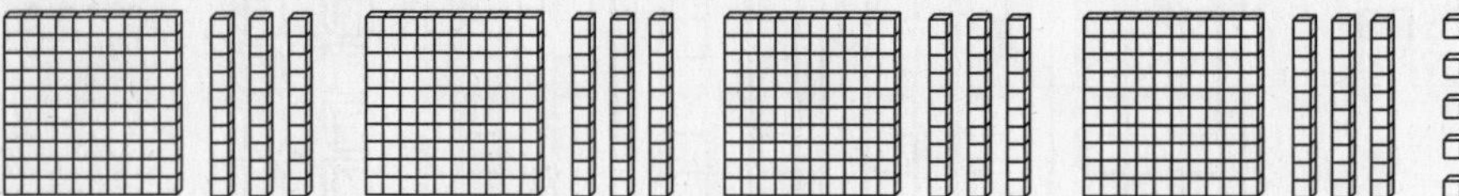

Divide the ones into 4 equal groups. 1 one remains.

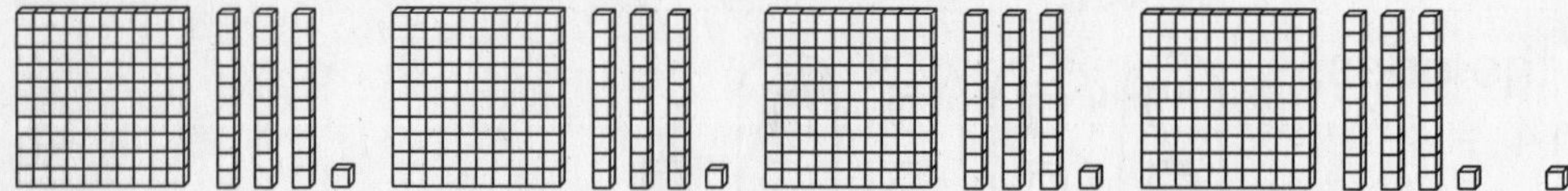

The quotient is the number of blocks in 1 of the 4 groups.

525 ÷ 4 = 131 R1

Use place-value blocks to find each quotient.

1. $8\overline{)968}$

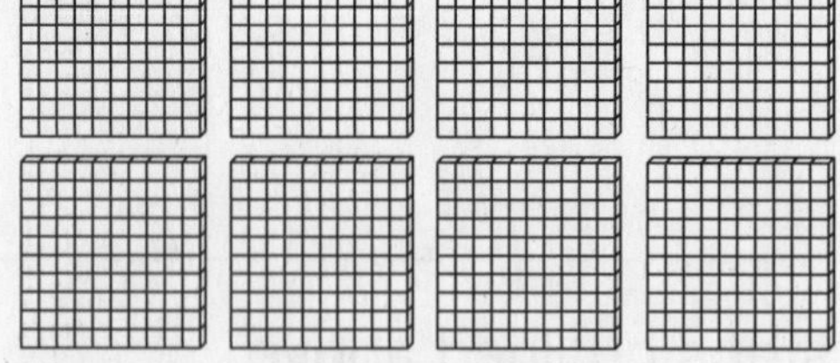

2. $6\overline{)795}$

Name ______________________________

Another Look 7-7

2- or 3-Digit Quotients

Divide 113 by 3.

Step 1

Compare 3 to the number in the hundreds place. Since 3 > 1, the quotient starts in the tens place.

$$3\overline{)113}$$

Step 2

Divide the tens into 3 equal groups.

$$\begin{array}{r} 3 \\ 3\overline{)113} \\ -9 \\ \hline 2 \end{array}$$

Think: 11 divided by 3 is **3** with **2** remaining.

Step 3

Bring down the ones and divide.

$$\begin{array}{r} 37 \\ 3\overline{)113} \\ -9 \\ \hline 23 \\ 21 \\ \hline 2 \end{array}$$

Think: 23 divided by 3 is **7** with **2** remaining.

113 ÷ 3 = 37 R2

Find each quotient.

1. $7\overline{)392}$

2. $8\overline{)206}$

3. $3\overline{)518}$

4. $5\overline{)677}$

Name ______________________________

Another Look
7-8

Zeros in the Quotient

Find 914 ÷ 3 = 3

3)914

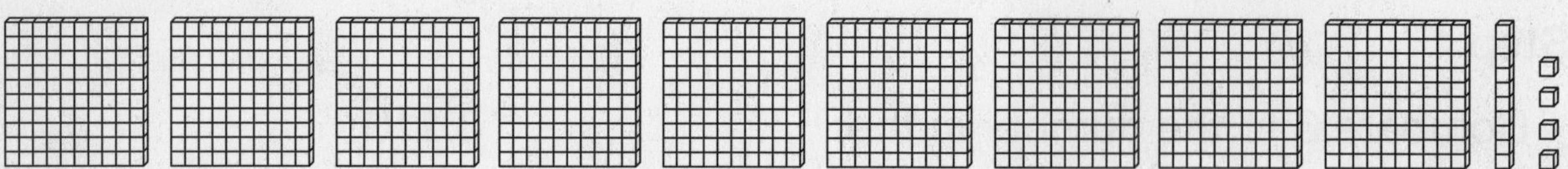

Divide the hundreds into 3 equal groups. No hundreds remain.

```
   3
3)914
 - 9
   0
```

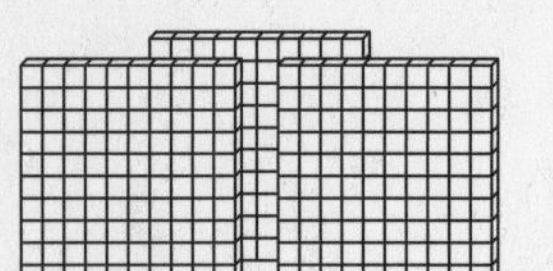
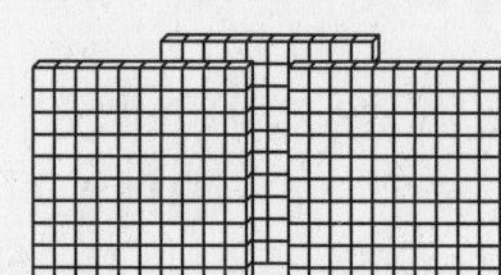
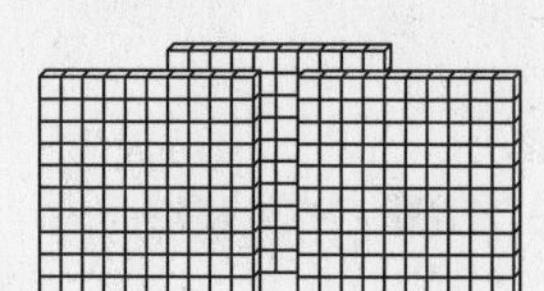

1 ten cannot be divided into 3 equal groups.

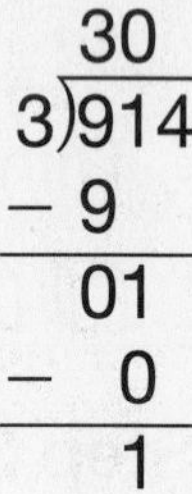

Regroup 1 ten as 10 ones.

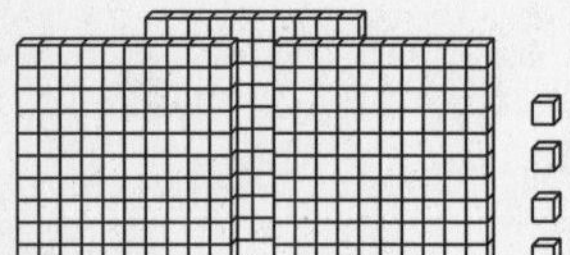
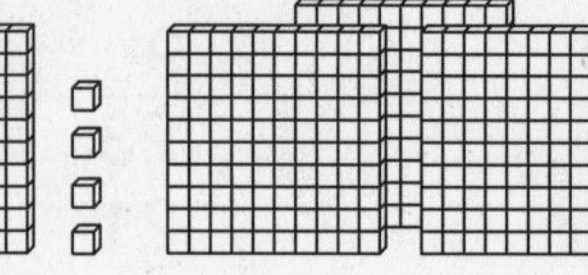
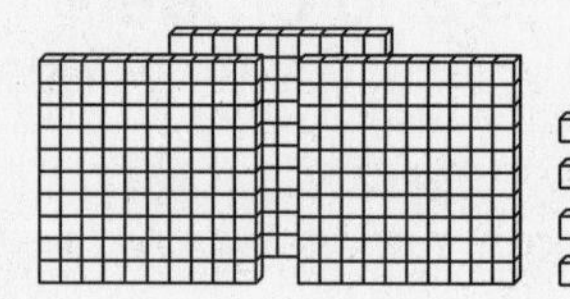

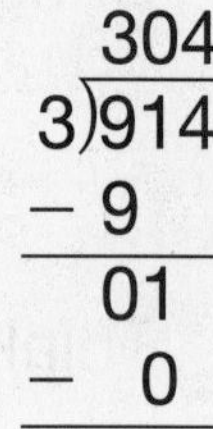

Divide the 14 ones into 3 equal groups.

914 ÷ 3 = 304 R2

Use place-value blocks to find each quotient.

1. 3)615

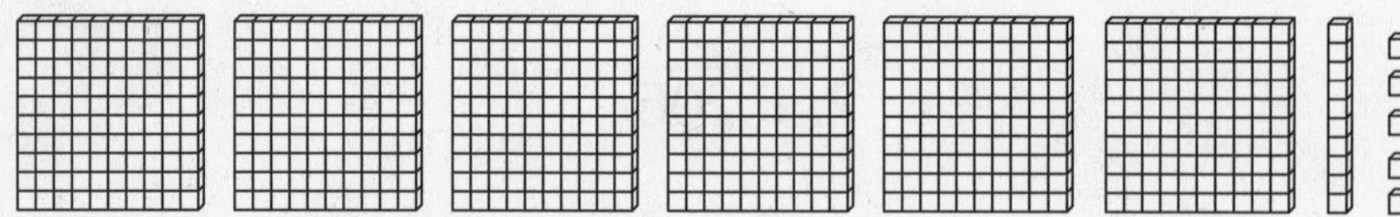

2. 4)436

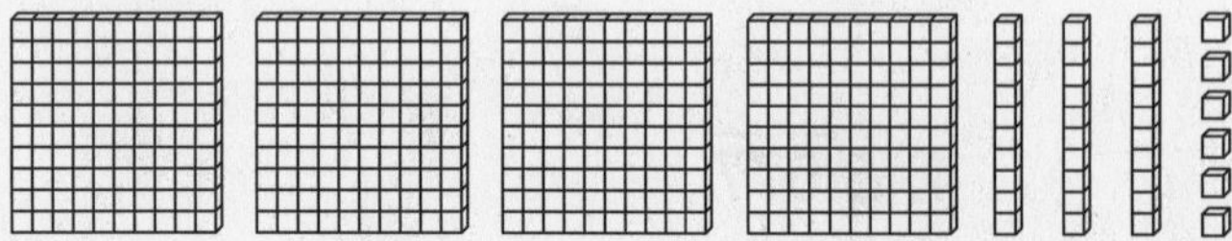

Name ______________________

Analyze Word Problems: Interpreting Remainders

Marci is making punch for a party. The recipe makes 27 cups of punch. If each guest drinks 2 cups of punch, how many guests will the recipe serve?

Write a division sentence for this problem. 27 ÷ 2 = 13 R1

13 guests can each have 2 cups. There is 1 cup of punch left over.

The Rotary Club is holding its annual fashion show. A total of 435 people will be attending. Each table at the fashion show seats 8 people. How many tables should be set up for the show?

1. How many people will be attending the fashion show?

____

2. How many people can sit at one table?

____

3. Write a division sentence for this problem.

____

4. How many full groups of 8 will be seated?

____

5. What does the remainder represent?

____

6. How many tables should be set up for the show?

____

Name ______________________________

Exploring Division with Money

In your book you used money to show division with money.
Here is another way to divide with money.

Find $2.65 ÷ 5.

Step 1 Show the first two digits as dimes. Show the rest as pennies.
26 dimes and 5 pennies = $2.65

Step 2 Draw circles around groups of 5 dimes. Write the number of groups after a decimal point. $0.5

Step 3 Regroup the left over dime as 10 pennies

Step 4 Draw circles around groups of 5 pennies. Write the number of groups of pennies as the second digit after the decimal point. $0.53

$2.65 ÷ 5 = $0.53

Find each quotient. Draw rings around groups of money to help.

1. $2.25 ÷ 3 = __________

2. $1.88 ÷ 4 = __________

Name ______________________________

Another Look 7-11

Dividing Money Amounts

Find \$4.52 ÷ 4.

Divide the way you would with whole numbers. Change $4\overline{)\$4.52}$ to $4\overline{)452}$.

Divide hundreds.

$$\begin{array}{r} 1 \\ 4\overline{)452} \\ -\,4 \\ \hline 0 \end{array}$$

Divide. 4 ÷ 4 = 1
Multiply. 1 × 4 = 4
Subtract. 4 − 4 = 0
Compare. 0 < 4

Bring down the tens and divide.

$$\begin{array}{r} 11 \\ 4\overline{)452} \\ -\,4 \\ \hline 05 \\ -\,4 \\ \hline 1 \end{array}$$

Divide. 5 ÷ 4 = 1
Multiply. 1 × 4 = 4
Subtract. 5 − 4 = 1
Compare. 1 < 4

Bring down the ones and divide.

$$\begin{array}{r} 113 \\ 4\overline{)452} \\ -\,4 \\ \hline 05 \\ -\,4 \\ \hline 12 \\ -\,12 \\ \hline 0 \end{array}$$

Divide. 12 ÷ 4 = 3
Multiply. 3 × 4 = 12
Subtract. 12 − 12 = 0
Compare. 0 < 4

So: 452 ÷ 4 = 113

Now show dollars and cents in the quotient. \$4.52 ÷ 4 = \$1.13

Divide.

1. \$5.34 ÷ 3

a. First change $3\overline{)\$5.34}$ to $3\overline{)}$

b. 534 ÷ 3 = __________

c. \$5.34 ÷ 3 = __________

2. \$6.50 ÷ 5 = __________

3. \$4.72 ÷ 2 = __________

4. \$3.24 ÷ 4 = __________

5. \$7.23 ÷ 3 = __________

6. \$6.15 ÷ 5 = __________

7. \$7.56 ÷ 6 = __________

Name ________________

Another Look 7-12

Exploring Mean

In your book you found the mean using paper strips. Here is another way to find the mean.

Find the mean of 12, 5, 9, and 10.

Use counters to help you find the mean. Place the 4 groups of counters on your desk.

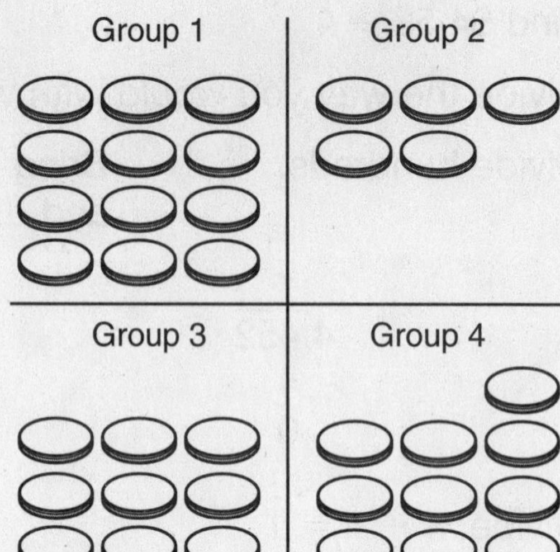

How many counters all together do you have? 36

Mix up the counters and place them into 4 equal groups.

How many counters are in each group now? 9

The mean of 12, 5, 9, and 10 is 9.

Use counters to find the mean for each set of data.

1. 3, 4, 10, and 7.

a. How many counters in all will you put on your desk? ________

b. How many groups of counters will you have? ________

c. Place the counters into equal groups. How many are in each group? ________

d. What is the mean of 3, 4, 10, and 7? ________

2. 11, 13, and 6.

a. How many counters in all will you put on your desk? ________

b. How many groups of counters will you have? ________

c. Place the counters into equal groups. How many are in each group? ________

d. What is the mean of 11, 13, and 6? ________

3. What is the mean of 11, 7, 5, 10, and 12? ________

Name ______________________________

Another Look
7-13

Exploring Divisibility

In your book you checked divisibility using a calculator. Here is another way to check for divisibility.

A number is **divisible** by another number if there is no remainder.

You can use counters to help you explore divisibility.

Is the number 12 divisible by 6? Can you put 12 counters in 6 equal groups?

So, 12 is divisible by 6.

Is the number 5 divisible by 3? Can you put 5 counters in 3 equal groups?

So, 5 is not divisible by 3.

1.

a. Can you put 18 counters in 3 equal groups? ________

b. Is 18 divisible by 3? ________

2.

a. Can you put 23 counters in 2 equal groups? ________

b. Is 23 divisible by 2? ________

3. Is 75 divisible by 3? ________

4. Is 120 divisible by 6? ________

5. Is 33 divisible by 2? ________

Name ___________________________

Analyze Strategies: Work Backward

Laurie made a sandwich with 2 slices of bread that each weighed 1 oz and some turkey. She weighed the sandwich and found it weighed 7 ounces. How much turkey did she use?

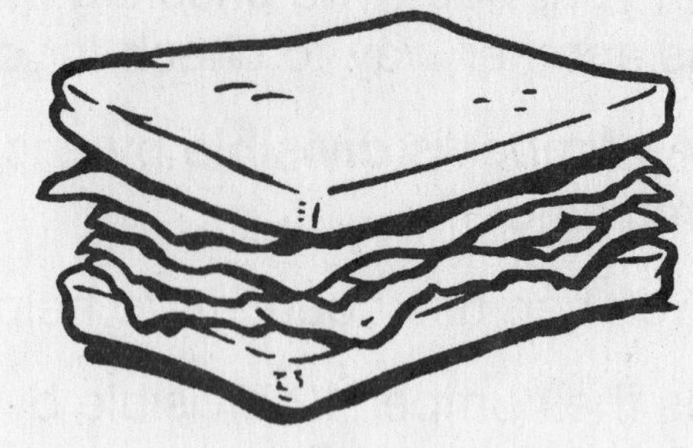

Try working backward. Find the total weight of the bread.

2×1 oz $= 2$ oz

Now you can find the weight of the turkey in the sandwich.

Weight of sandwich	−	Weight of bread	=	Weight of turkey

7 oz − 2 oz = 5 oz

There are 5 ounces of turkey in Laurie's sandwich.

Check your answer.

2 slices of bread × 1 oz bread = 2 oz bread

5 oz turkey + 2 oz bread = 7 oz sandwich

---

1. Harold made a juice drink with 16 ounces of orange juice and some cranberry juice. He divided the drink into three 7-ounce glasses with none left over. How much cranberry juice did he use?

a. What is the total amount of juice drink Harold made? __________

b. How much cranberry juice did he use? __________

2. Kim mixed 22 ounces of tomato sauce with some olive oil. She spread 4 oz of the mixture on each of 3 pizzas.

a. What is the total amount of mixture Kim used on the pizzas?

____

b. How much of the mixture did she have left over? __________

 Use with pages 332–333.

Name ________________________________

Exploring Solids

In your book you found solids by looking around your classroom. Here is another way to explore solids.

Look outside your window. Think about things you see outside.

Here are 6 different types of solids.

Cylinder

Sphere

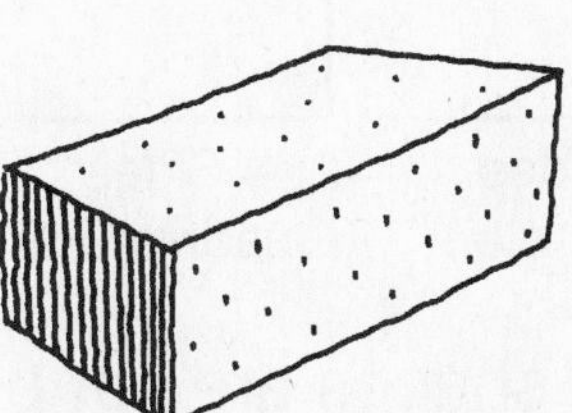
Rectangular Prism

Cone

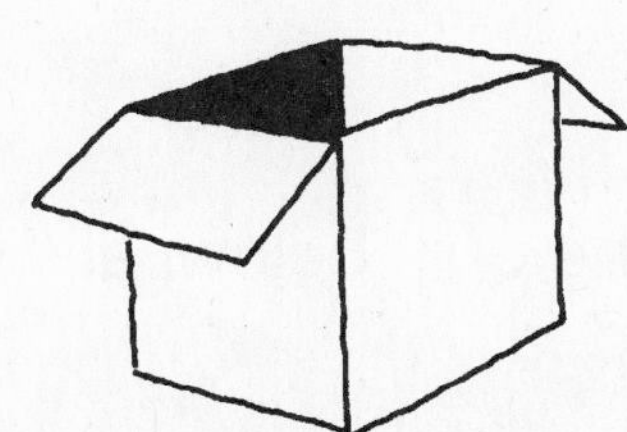
Cube

Pyramid

Match each object with the solid that it looks like. Use the solids and objects above to help you.

A.

B.

C.

1. cone ______

2. sphere ______

3. cylinder ______

Name ______________________________

Exploring Polygons

In your book you explored polygons by finding them in a photograph. Here is another way to explore polygons.

Polygons are closed shapes with straight edges. You have learned about 5 different polygons. Here is an example of each.

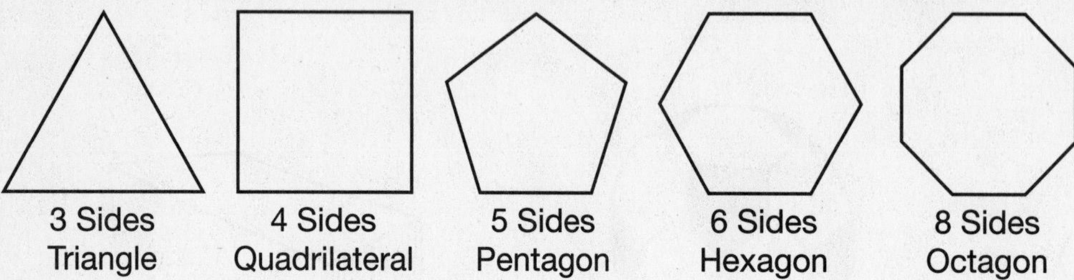

These shapes are not polygons.

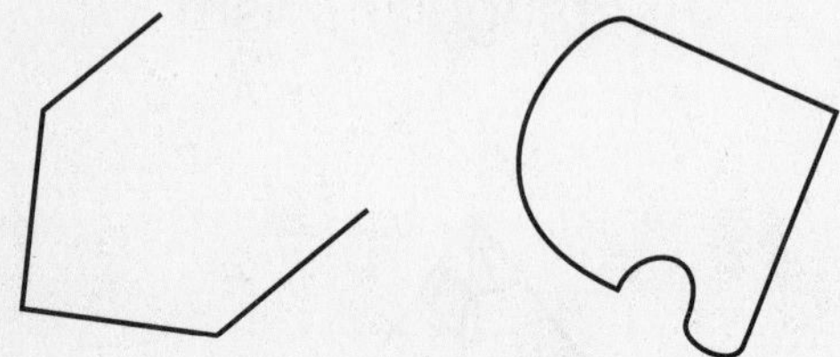

Quilts are made of polygons. In the quilt below, all the triangles (3-sided figures) are striped.

Use colored pencils or crayons to shade each polygon.

triangles - yellow   pentagons - orange   octagons - green
quadrilaterals - red   hexagons - blue

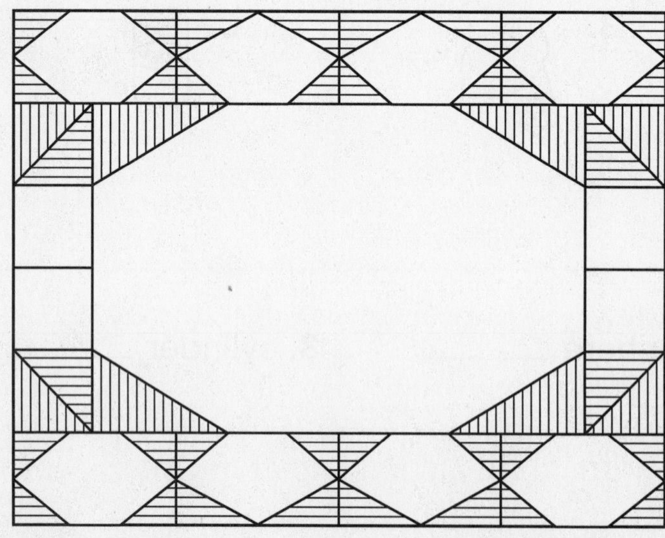

 Use with pages 346–347.

Name ______________________________

Another Look 8-3

Exploring Triangles

In your book you made polygons using different triangles. Here is a way to understand how triangles can look different but still have the same name.

Name	Length of sides	Examples
Equilateral triangle	3 sides are the same length	2 cm, 2 cm, 2 cm; 1 in., 1 in., 1 in.
Isosceles triangle	2 sides are the same length	3 cm, 3 cm, 2 cm; 19 in., 12 in., 12 in
Scalene triangle	No sides are the same length	4 cm, 3 cm, 2 cm; 1 in., 2 in., 1.5 in.

Label the equilateral triangles E, the scalene triangles S and the isosceles triangles I.

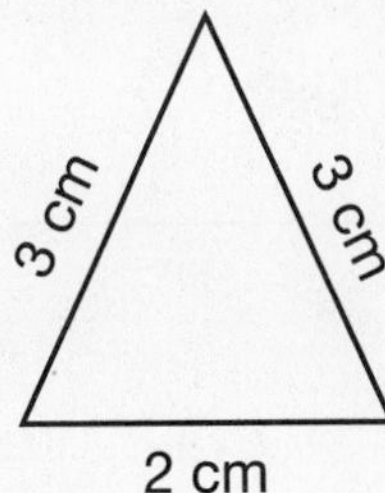

1 cm
2.5 cm
2 cm

1 in.
1 in.
1 in.

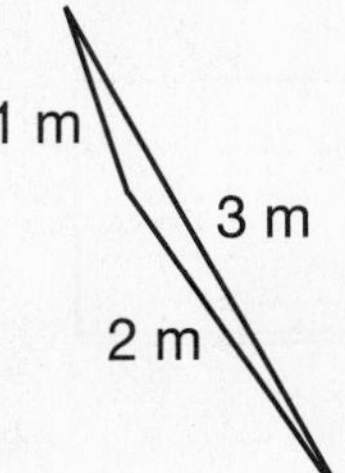

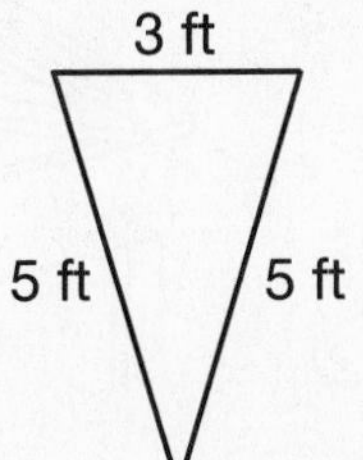

2 m
2 m
2 m

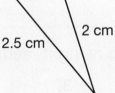

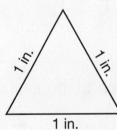

Name ______________________________

Another Look
8-4

Triangles and Angles

There are four different types of angles.

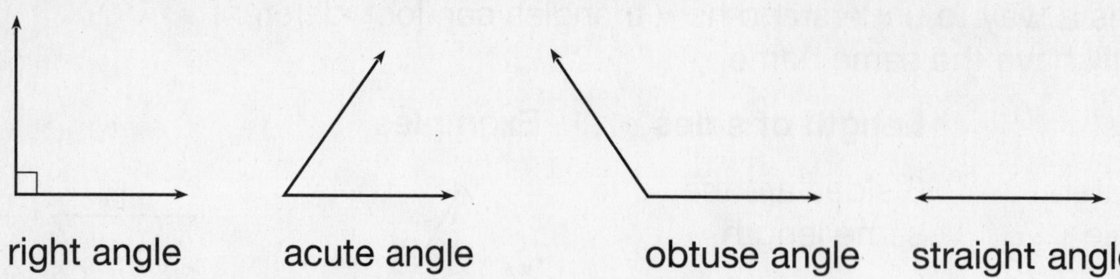

right angle   acute angle   obtuse angle   straight angle

Triangles are made up of these angles. Compare these triangles with the angles above.

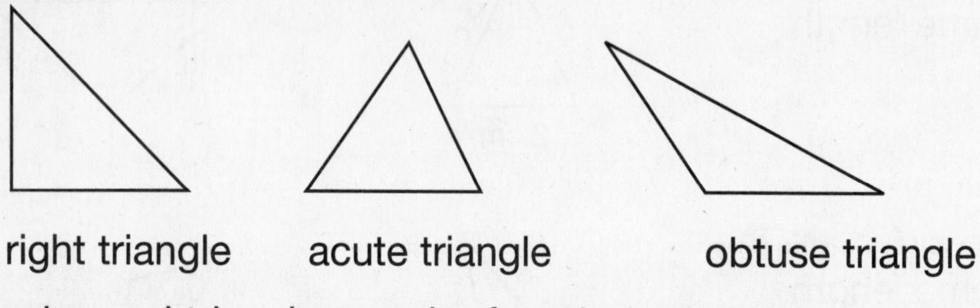

right triangle   acute triangle   obtuse triangle

Angles and triangles can be found everywhere.

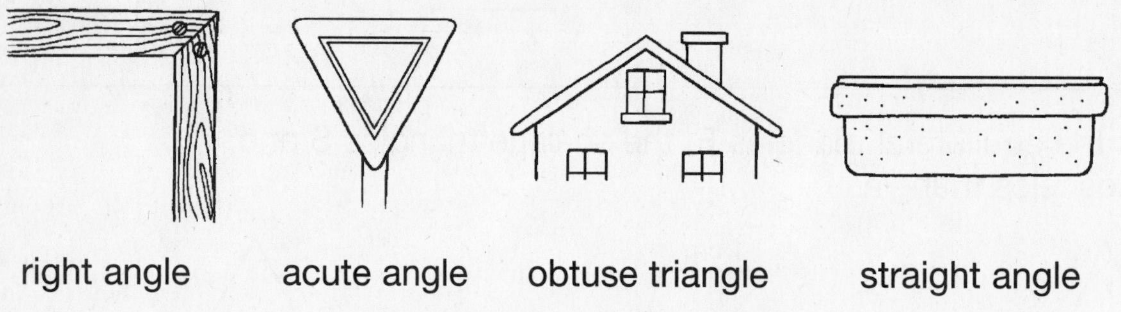

right angle   acute angle   obtuse triangle   straight angle

Name each triangle or angle shown as right, acute, or obtuse.

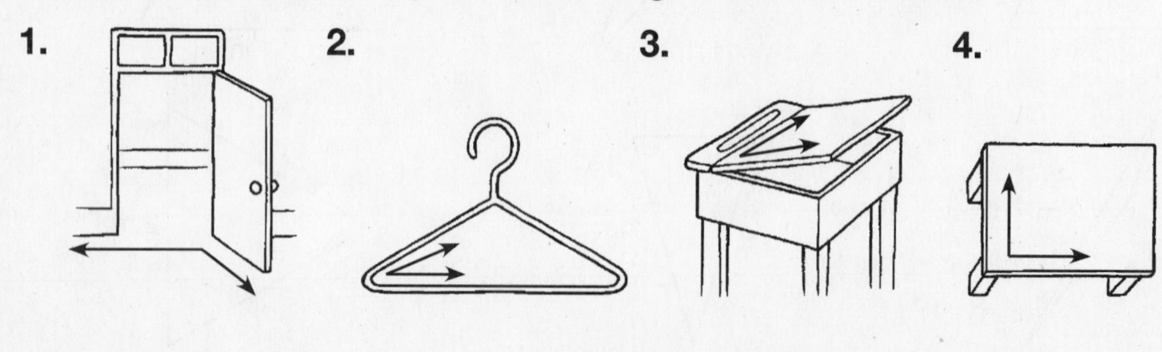

1. ____________
2. ____________
3. ____________
4. ____________

Name ______________________________

Another Look
8-5

Exploring Congruent Figures and Motions

In your book you drew and traced figures to find congruent figures and show motions. Here is another way to explore congruent figures and motions.

Congruent figures are figures that have the same size and shape.

Here is a triangle that has been flipped.

The two triangles are congruent.

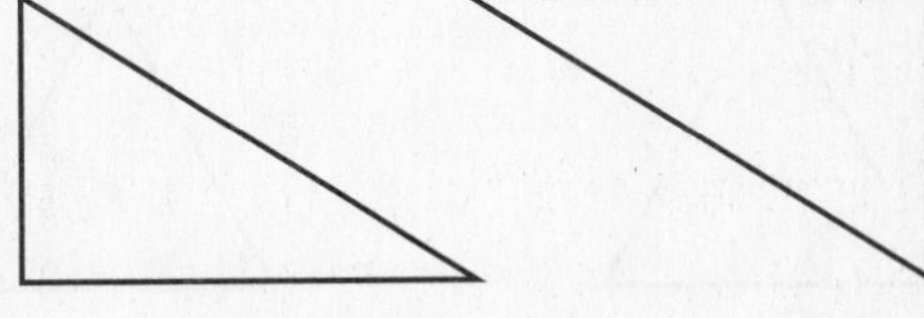

Here is a rectangle that has been turned.

The two rectangles are congruent.

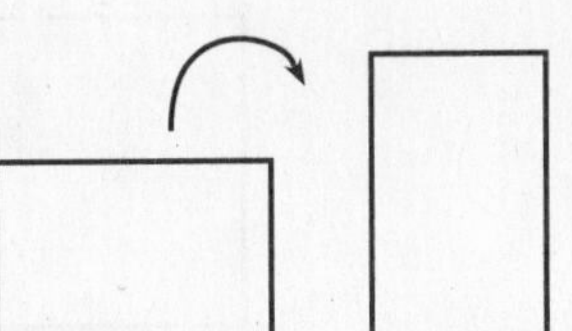

Here is a square that has been slid on top of a rectangle.

The square and the rectangle are not congruent.

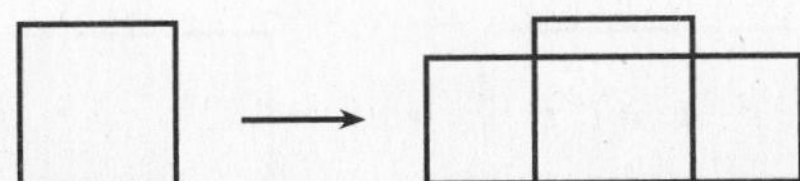

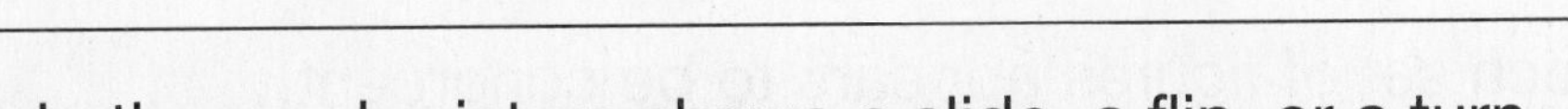

Write whether each picture shows a slide, a flip, or a turn.

1.

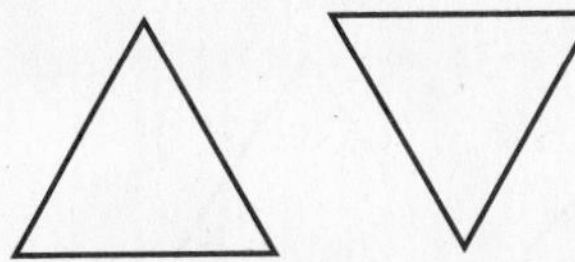

____

2.

____

3.

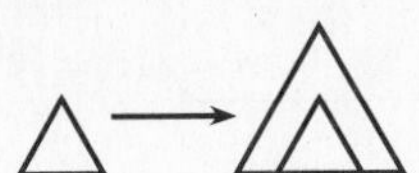

____

4.

____

Name ______________________________

Another Look
8-6

Exploring Similar Figures

In your book you made similar shapes, using geoboards. Here is another way to explore what makes shapes congruent, similar, or neither. Similar figures have the same shape but not necessarily the same size.

Polygon **Congruent** **Similar** **Neither**

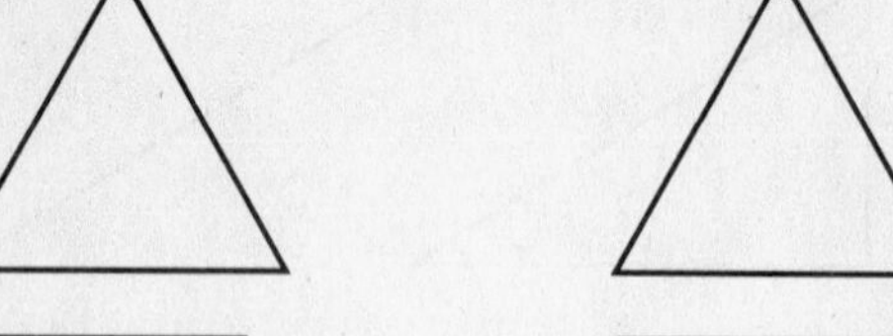

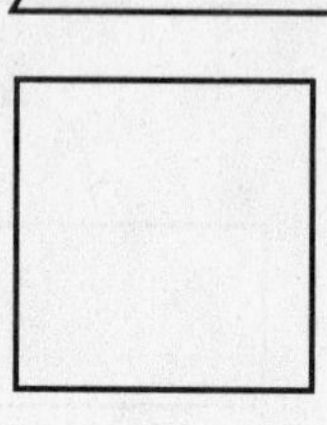

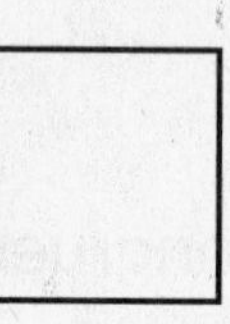
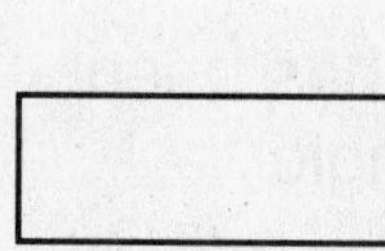
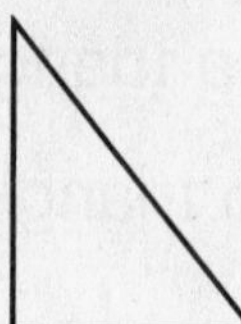

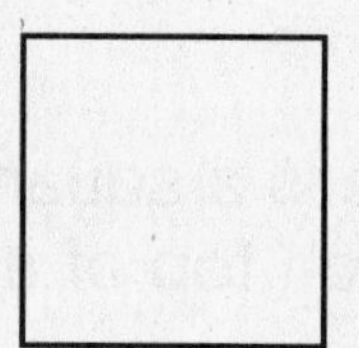

Write whether each set of figures appears to be congruent, similar or neither.

1.

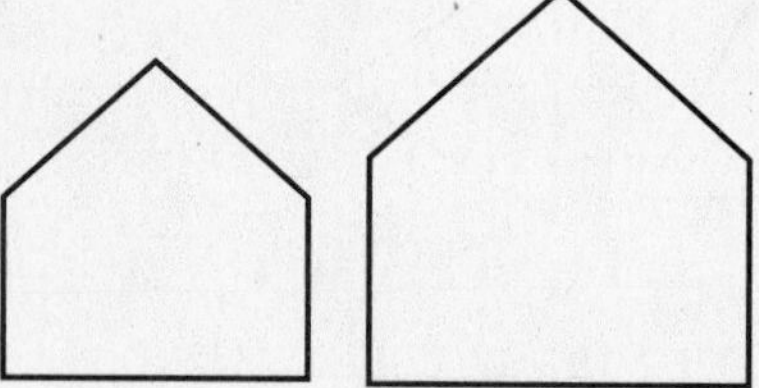

____

2.

____

3.

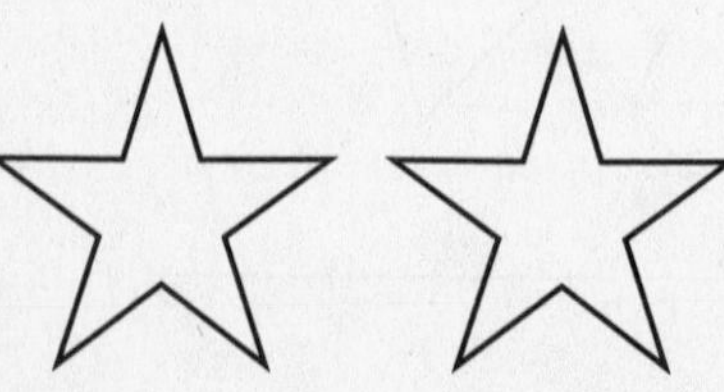

____

4.

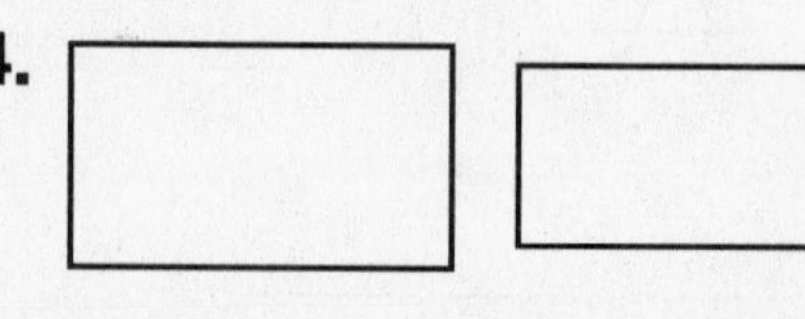

____

Name ____________________

Lines and Line Segments

The letters K and H are made up of line segments.

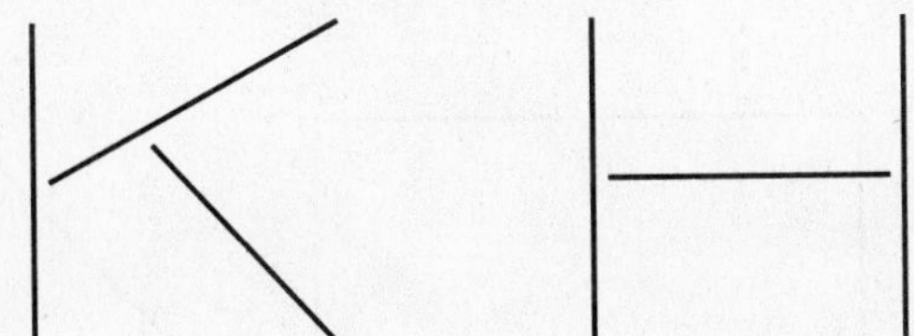

Intersecting lines or line segments meet at a **point.**

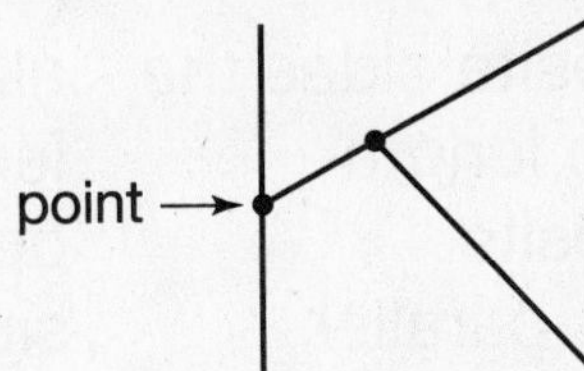

The two sides of the H are **parallel.** They never intersect.
The bar of the H is **perpendicular** to the two sides.
Perpendicular lines form right angles.

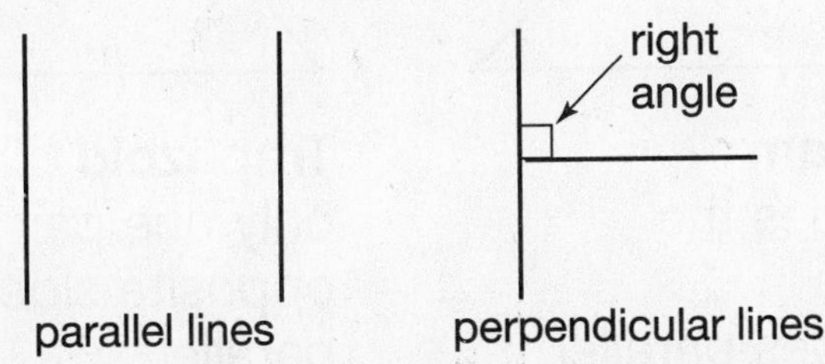

Write *parallel* or *perpendicular* for each.

1.

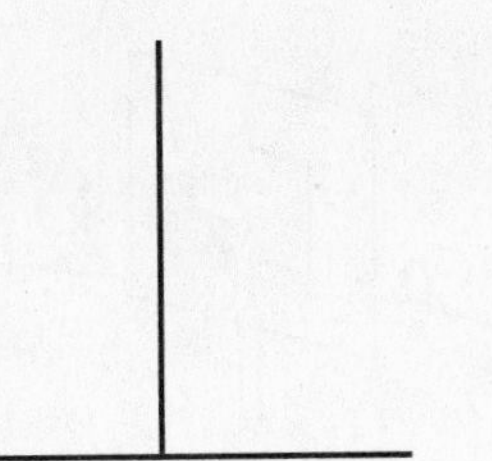

____

2.

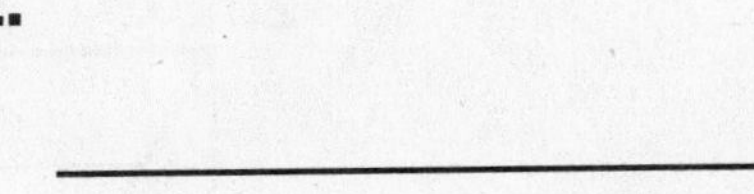

____

3.

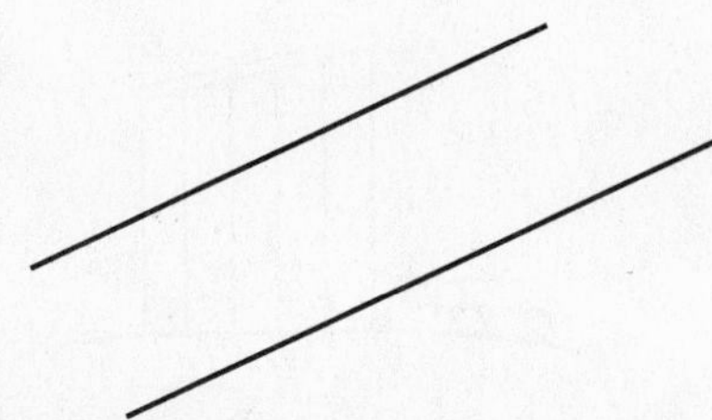

____

4.

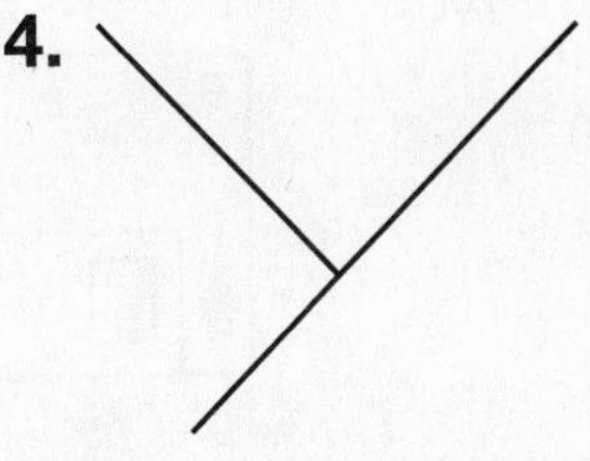

____

Name ________________________________

Another Look
8-8

Quadrilaterals

Quadrilaterals are shapes that have 4 sides and 4 angles. Here are 5 different kinds of quadrilaterals:

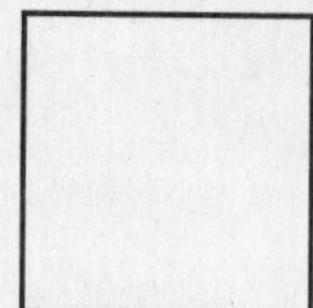  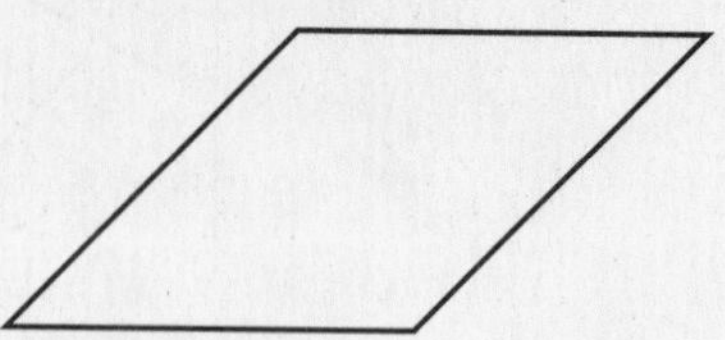

Quadrilateral	Square	Rectangle	Rhombus
Sides	all the same length opposite sides parallel	opposite sides the same length opposite sides parallel	all the same length opposite sides parallel
Angles	4 right angles	4 right angles	

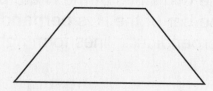

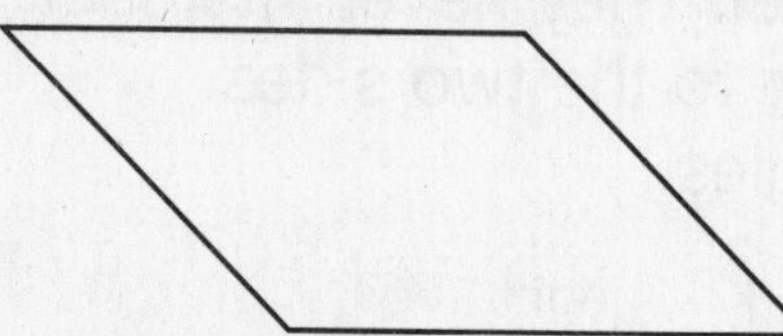

Quadrilateral	Parallelogram	Trapezoid
Sides	opposite sides the same length opposite sides parallel	only one pair of opposite sides parallel

Write the name of each quadrilateral. Use the examples above to help.

1. 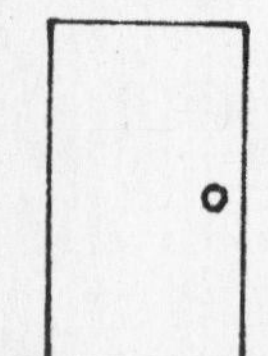
____

2. 

____

3. 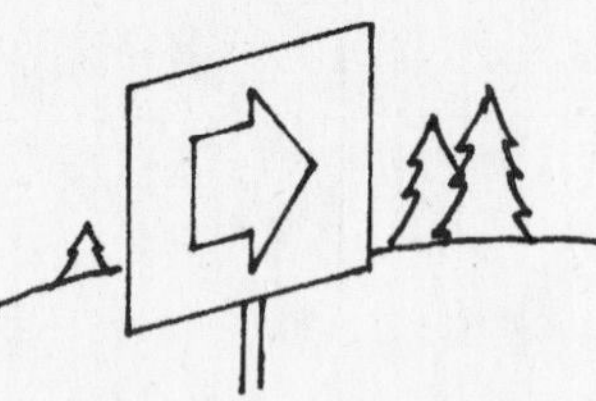
____

4. 
____

5. 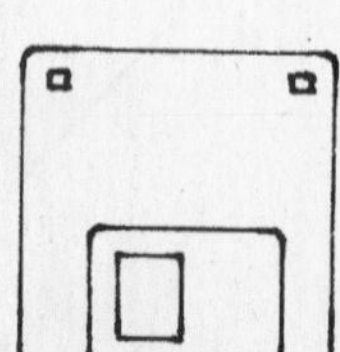
____

6. 
____

Name ______________________

Another Look 8-9

Exploring Line Symmetry

In your book you learned to test a figure for symmetry by using folded pieces of paper. Here is another way to find out if two halves of a figure are congruent. Figures that have symmetry have opposite halves that match.

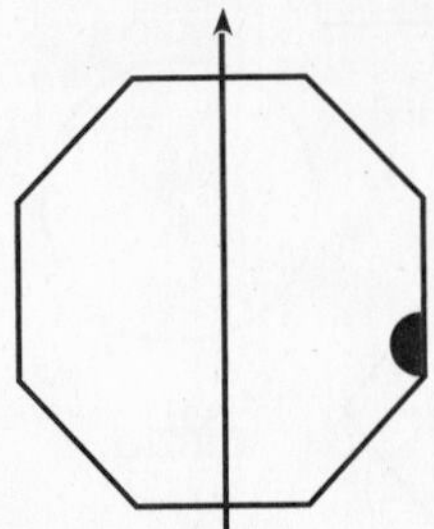

This figure does not have a line of symmetry. The two halves do not match. There is a spot on one side, but not on the other.

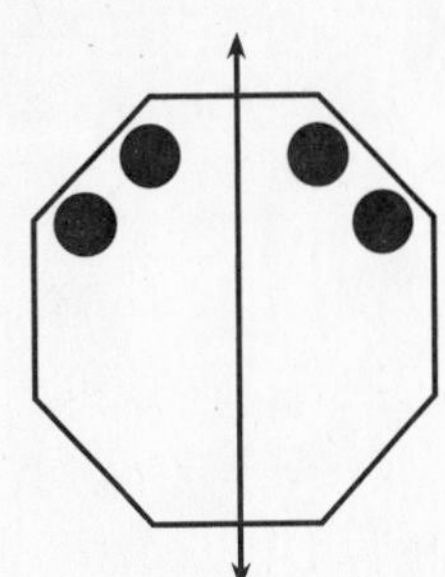

This figure has one line of symmetry. Both sides match. The spots on one half match the spots on the other half.

Each figure below is divided into 2 pieces. Write *yes* if the 2 pieces match. Write *no* if the pieces do not match.

1.

____

2.

____

3.

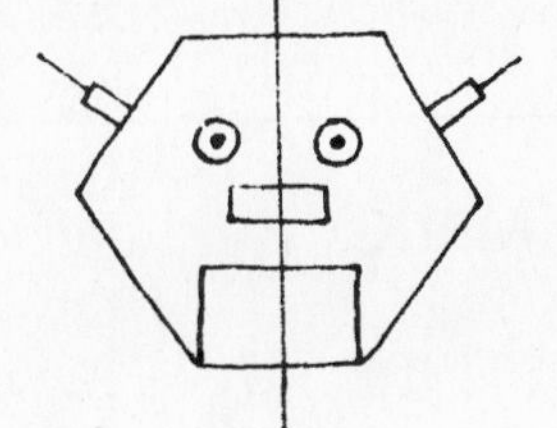

____

4.

____

Write *yes* if the face has a line of symmetry. Write *no* if the face does not.

5.

____

6.

____

Name ______________________________

Analyze Strategies: Use Objects/ Act It Out

In what order are the polygons? The circle is behind the triangle, but in front of the square. The square is behind the circle but in front of the diamond.

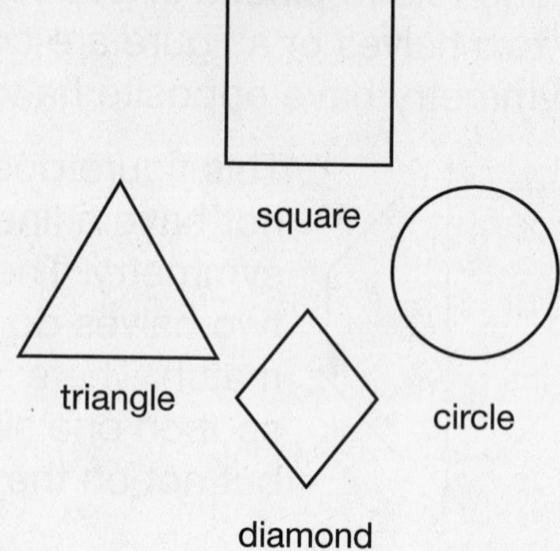

- Start with the objects you need to help you.

- As you read each clue, put down an object.

The **circle** is behind the triangle but in front of the square

Front Back

- The second clue will help you place the last object.

The **square** is behind the circle but in front of the diamond.

Now you know the order!

Sarah finished the race before Tim but after Mary Lou. Mark finished ahead of Sarah but after Mary Lou.

Use the clues to draw the shapes in the correct order.

1. What is the order of people in the first clue? ______________
2. Did anyone finish ahead of Mark? ______________
3. Who finished last? ______________

Name ______________________

Another Look 8-11

Exploring Perimeter

The perimeter of a polygon is the distance around it. In your book you used geoboards to find the perimeter. Here is another way to find the perimeter of a polygon using dot paper.

To find the perimeter of this rectangle, count the units along each side. Then add.

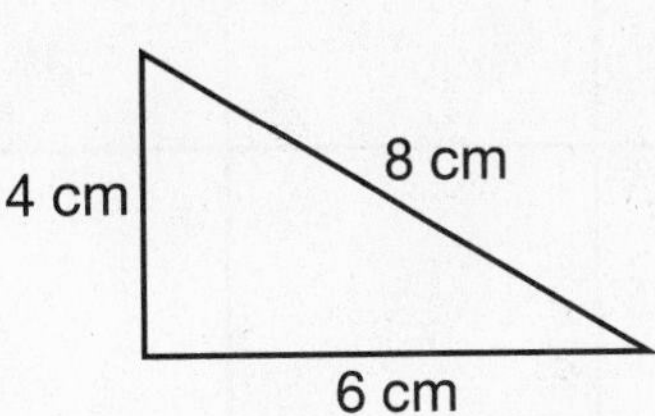

2 units + 4 units + 2 units + 4 units = 12 units

The perimeter is 12 units.

If the length of each side is given, just find the sum of the lengths.

4 cm + 6 cm + 8 cm = 18 cm

4 cm
8 cm
6 cm

The perimeter of the triangle is 18 cm.

Find the perimeter of each polygon.

1. ______________________

2. ______________________

3. 5 yd
2 yd
____

4. 1 m
2 m
3 m
2 m
1 m
3 m
____

Name ______________________

Another Look
8-12

Exploring Areas of Rectangles

In your book you found area using grid paper.
Here is another way to find area.

This square is equal to 1 square inch.

The area is the amount of space that a figure covers.

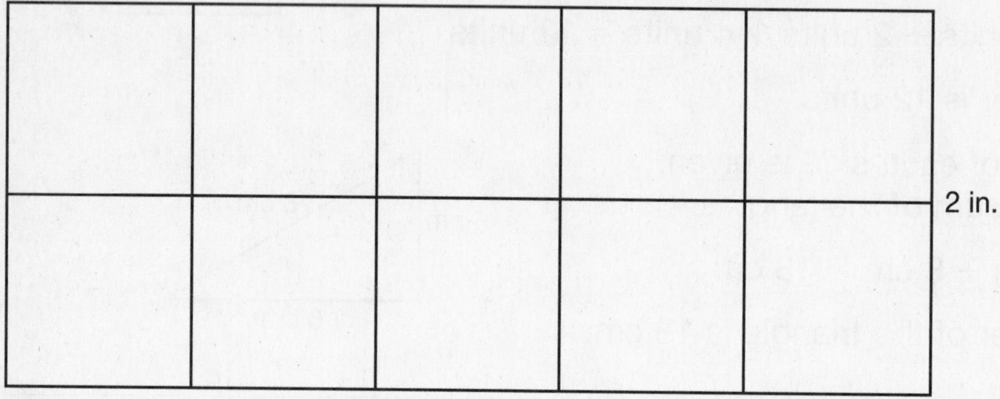

Count the number of square inches to find the area of the rectangle. 10 square inches

You can also multiply the number of square inches along the width and length of the rectangle.

Count the number of square inches along the width.
5 square inches

Count the number of square inches along the length.
2 square inches

Find the product of these two numbers to find the area of the rectangle. $5 \times 2 = 10$ square inches

---

Find the area of each rectangle.

1.
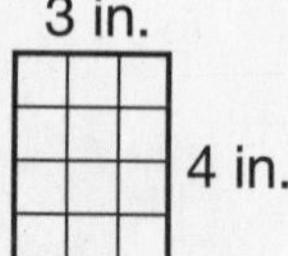

____

2.
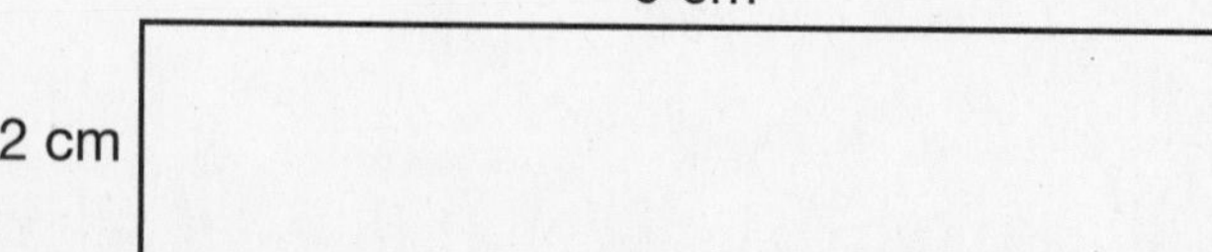

____

Name ___

Exploring Volume

In your book you counted cubes to find volume. Here is another way to find volume. Volume is the number of cubic units that a three-dimensional figure contains.

One cubic centimeter is a cube that measures 1 centimeter on each edge. This cube represents 1 cubic centimeter.

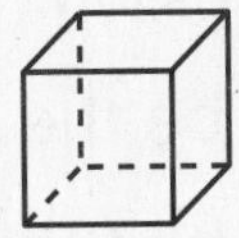

You can find volume by counting cubic units such as cubic inches, cubic centimeters, cubic feet, or cubic meters.

This small box is 3 cm long, 4 cm wide, and 2 cm high. How many 1-cubic-centimeter cubes will fit in the box?

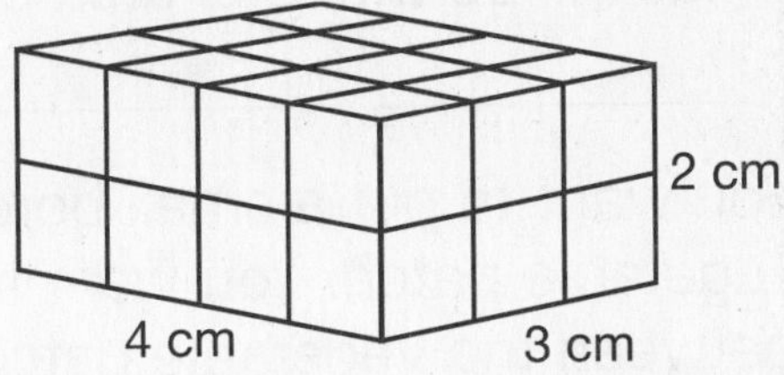

How many cubes long is the box? 4

How many cubes wide? 3

How many cubes high? 2

To find the total number of cubic centimeters in the box, multiply the length, width, and height.

$3 \times 4 \times 2 =$ 24

The volume is 24 cubic centimeters.

Find the volume of each rectangular prism.

1. 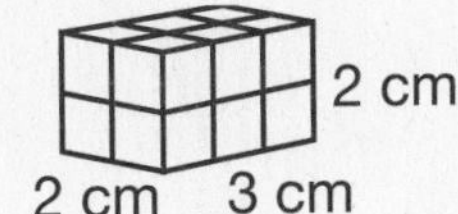

___

2. 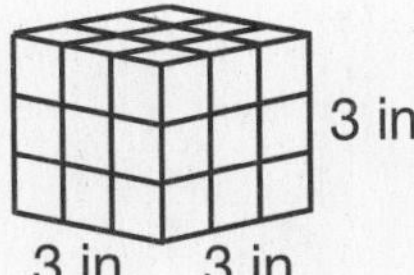

___

3. 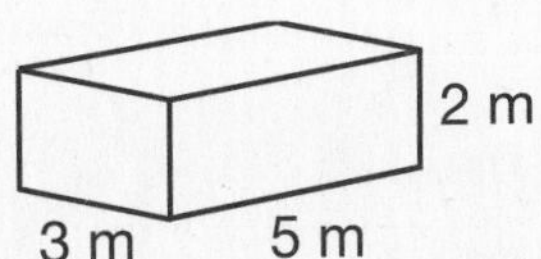

___

4. 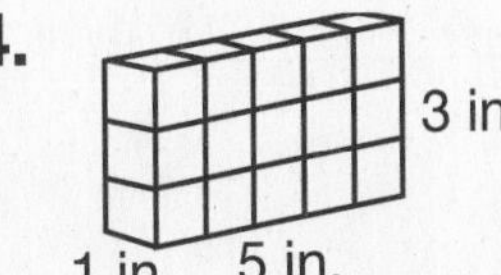

___

Name ______________________________

Another Look
8-14

Decision Making

You are making a vegetable plot in your garden. You want to have 4 rows of carrots, 6 rows of potatoes and 3 rows of radishes. Each row of vegetables needs to be 1 foot wide and 5 feet long.

What will be the area containing carrots? 20 square feet

What will be the area containing potatoes? 30 square feet

What will be the area containing radishes? 15 square feet

What will be the total area of the vegetable patch? 65 square feet

---

You want to put a small border of rocks around your vegetable patch. You want to leave a path 1 foot wide between the vegetable patch and the rock border.

1. Draw a picture to show what your vegetable garden will look like. Remember to label all the measurements.

2. What is the perimeter of your vegetable patch including the path?

____

Name ______________________

Exploring Fractions

In your book you used geoboards to show fractions. Here is another way to explore fractions.

To show $\frac{1}{4}$, divide a square into 4 equal parts.

Shade 1 part. Here are four different ways to divide it into 4 equal parts.

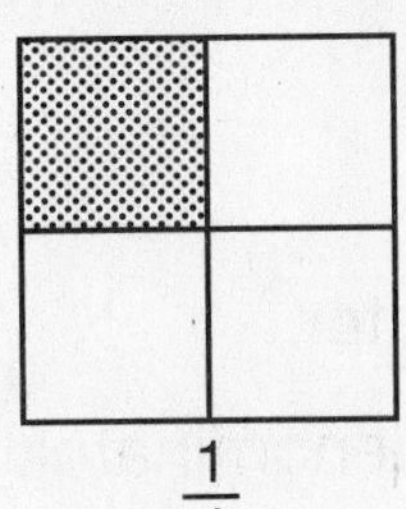

$\frac{1}{4}$

or

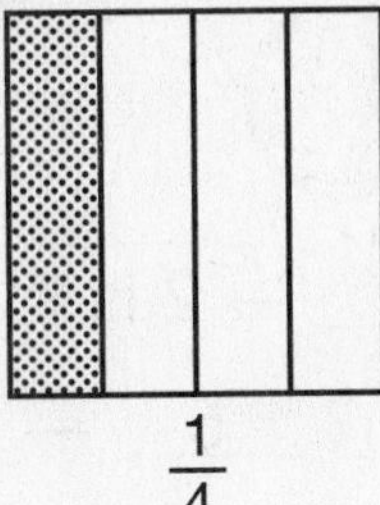

$\frac{1}{4}$

or

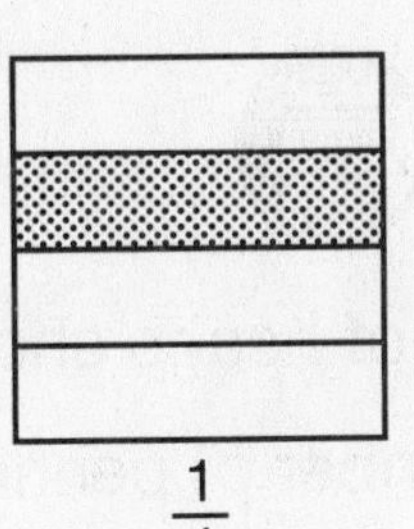

$\frac{1}{4}$

or

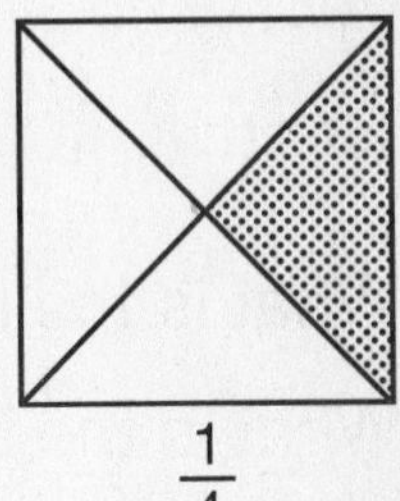

$\frac{1}{4}$

For each square, there are 4 equal parts.

For each square, the fraction for the shaded part is $\frac{1}{4}$.

Write a fraction for each shaded part.

1.

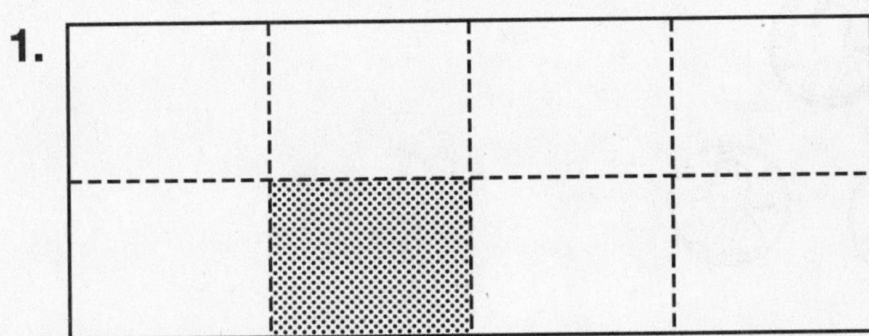

a. This rectangle is divided into ______ equal parts.

b. The fraction for the shaded part is ______.

2.

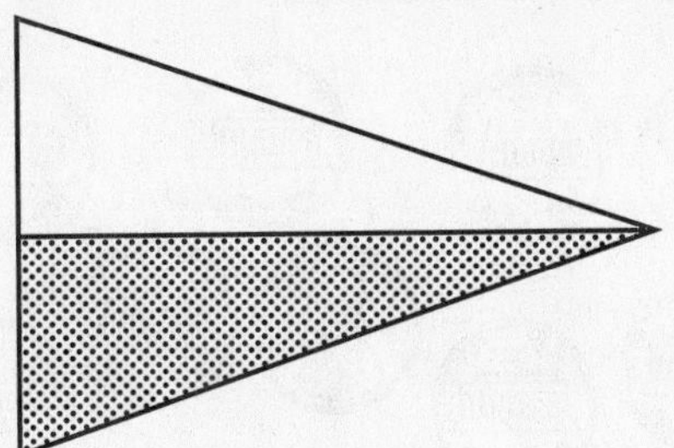

______

3.

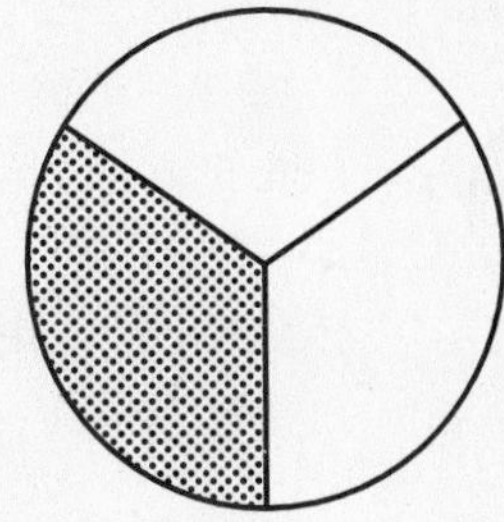

______

Name ___________________________

Another Look 9-2

Naming and Writing Fractions

You can use pennies to help you name and write fractions.

Example What fraction of the pennies show heads?

What is the number of heads shown? __2__ → 2 is the numerator.

What is the total number of pennies shown? __5__ → 5 is the denominator.

So, $\frac{2}{5}$ is the fraction of pennies showing heads.

Write a fraction that tells what part of each group of pennies is showing heads.

1.

a. What is the number of heads shown? ________

b. What is the total number of pennies shown? ________

c. What fraction of the pennies shows heads? ________

2.

What fraction shows heads? ________

3.

What fraction shows heads? ________

Name ______________________________

Estimating Fractional Amounts

You can use certain **benchmark** fractions to estimate fractional amounts.

The benchmark fractions you can use for estimating are $\frac{1}{4}$, $\frac{1}{3}$, $\frac{1}{2}$, $\frac{2}{3}$, and $\frac{3}{4}$.

How full is each glass of water? Use benchmarks to estimate.

Write a fraction that shows about how full each container is. Use benchmark fractions to estimate.

1. 

about ________ full

2. 

about ________ full

3. 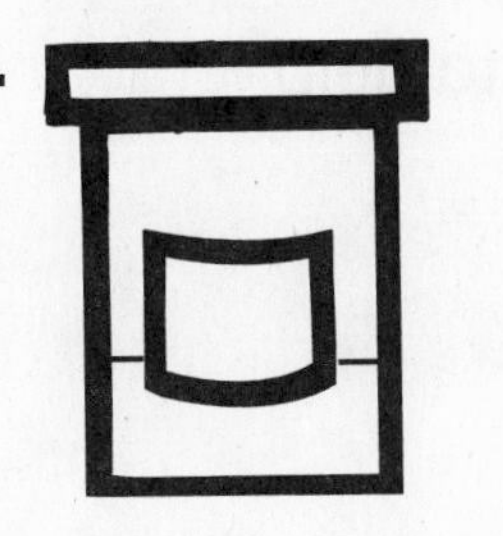

about ________ full

4. 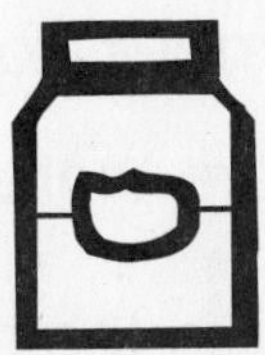

about ________ full

Name ______________________

Another Look 9-4

Exploring Mixed Numbers

In your book you used fraction strips to explore mixed numbers and improper fractions. Here is another way to find mixed numbers.

You can use drawings.
The rectangles below are each divided into 4 equal parts.
Each whole rectangle represents one whole.

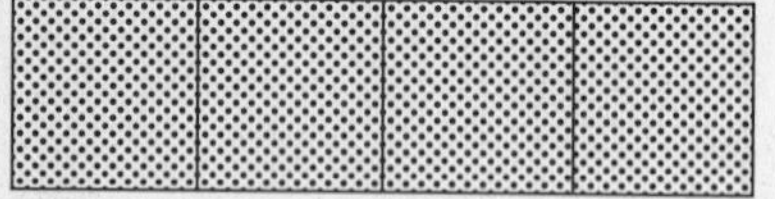 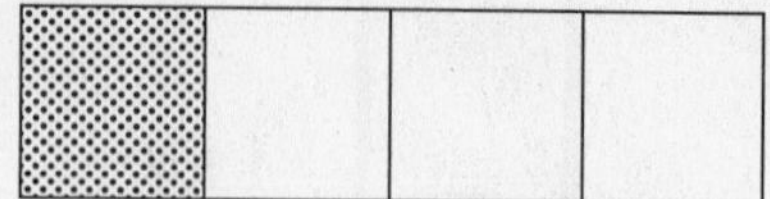

What is the improper fraction that shows the shaded parts of the rectangles above? Count the number of shaded fourths.

Write that number over 4. $\frac{5}{4}$

What is the mixed number? Count the number of shaded wholes.

Then count the number of fourths in incomplete wholes. $1\frac{1}{4}$

Show $1\frac{2}{3}$ with rectangle drawings.

 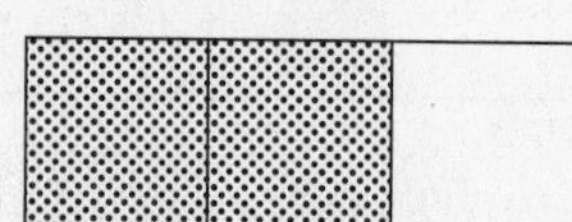

What improper fraction shows the shaded amount above? 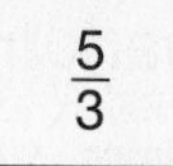

---

1. a. Draw a picture in the space below to show $1\frac{1}{2}$.

b. What improper fraction is the same as $1\frac{1}{2}$? ______

2. Write $\frac{4}{3}$ as a mixed number. You may draw a picture to help.

a. How many wholes are there? ______

b. What mixed number is the same as $\frac{4}{3}$? ______

3. Write $1\frac{3}{4}$ as an improper fraction. ______

4. Write $\frac{6}{5}$ as a mixed number. ______

Name ______________________________

Decision Making

Akbar wants to plant a vegetable garden. In his area, he can plant the vegetables at the time shown:

Beets: February through August
Carrots: January 1 through the middle of September
Parsnips: March 15 through August 31
Rhubarb: January through March
Peas: August 1 through November 15
Shallots: November and December

Make a table to help Akbar plan his garden. Since beets can be planted February through August, on the row next to beets, shade in the boxes under the months from February through August.

	Jan	Feb	Mar	Apr	May	June	July	Aug	Sept	Oct	Nov	Dec
Beets		▒	▒	▒	▒	▒	▒	▒				
Carrots												
Parsnips												
Rhubarb												
Peas												
Shallots												

____

1. Complete the table above with the data given.
2. Akbar has some free time on March 21. What can he plant on that day?

____

____

3. On November 1, Akbar is at the garden store. What should he buy for immediate planting?

____

4. What vegetables can Akbar plant at the very beginning of the year?

____

Name ____________________

Exploring Equivalent Fractions

In your book you used fraction strips to find equivalent fractions. Here is another way to explore equivalent fractions.

You can use drawings to find equivalent fractions.

Draw a rectangle and divide it into 2 equal sections. Shade $\frac{1}{2}$.

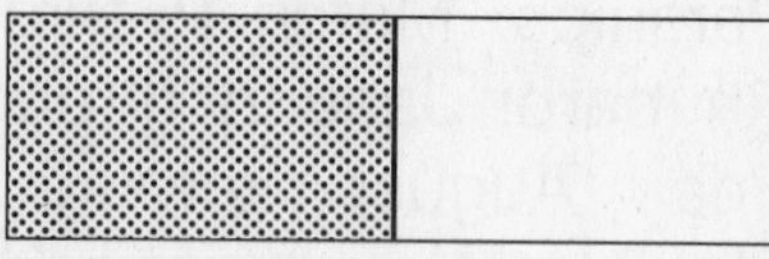

Now draw a rectangle of the same size and divide it into 3 equal sections.

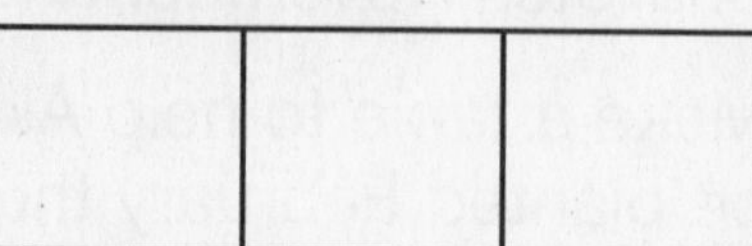

Can you shade whole sections of the second rectangle so it looks like the first rectangle? No

Draw a rectangle of the same size and divide it into 4 equal sections.

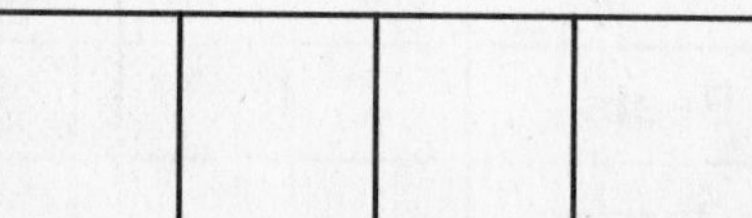

Can you shade whole sections of this rectangle so it looks like the first rectangle? Yes

How many fourths did you shade? 2

So, $\frac{2}{4}$ and $\frac{1}{2}$ are equivalent fractions.

Decide if each pair of fractions is equivalent. Use drawings to help.

1. $\frac{2}{3}$ and $\frac{4}{6}$

a. Draw a rectangle, divided into thirds, with $\frac{2}{3}$ shaded.

Then draw a rectangle, divided into sixths, with $\frac{4}{6}$ shaded.

b. Are the two fractions equivalent? ________

2. $\frac{2}{5}$ and $\frac{1}{8}$ ________

3. $\frac{3}{4}$ and $\frac{6}{8}$ ________

4. $\frac{3}{6}$ and $\frac{1}{2}$ ________

5. $\frac{5}{6}$ and $\frac{2}{8}$ ________

Name ______________________________

Another Look
9-7

Naming and Writing Equivalent Fractions

You can use drawings to name and write equivalent fractions.

Find an equivalent fraction for $\frac{1}{2}$.

Here is a rectangle divided into 2 equal parts with $\frac{1}{2}$ shaded.

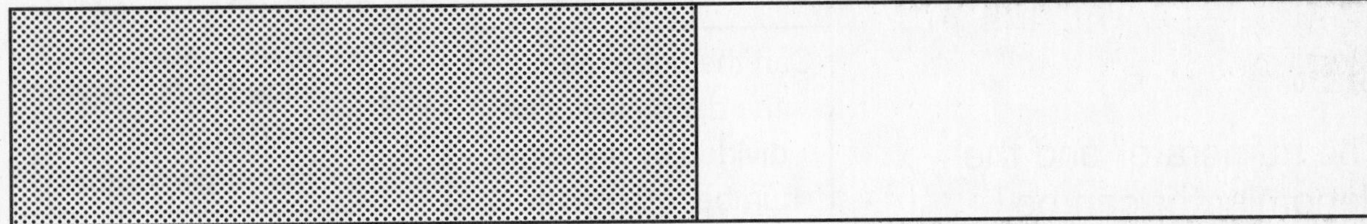

Divide the rectangle into different equal parts.

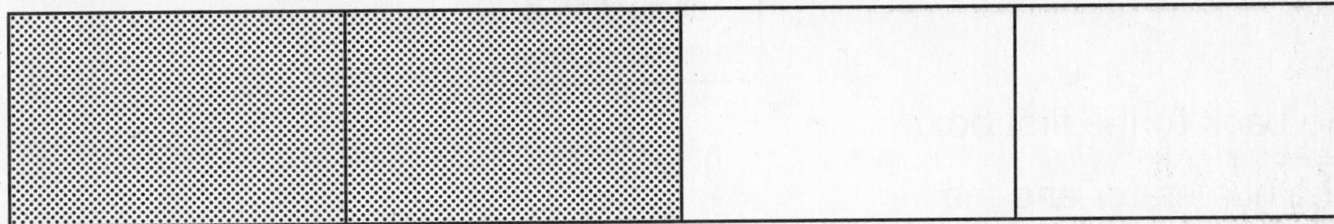

You can divide the rectangle into 4 equal parts with $\frac{2}{4}$ shaded.

$\frac{2}{4}$ is equivalent to $\frac{1}{2}$.

Find equivalent fractions. Use drawings to help.

1. $\frac{1}{3}$

a. Draw a rectangle. Divide it into thirds and shade $\frac{1}{3}$.

b. Draw three more lines in your rectangle to divide it into sixths.

c. Write an equivalent fraction for $\frac{1}{3}$. 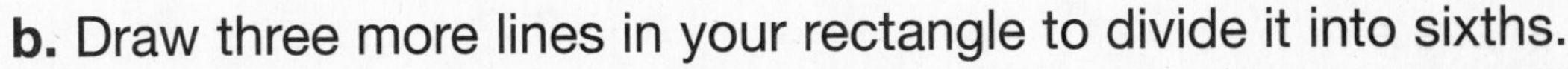

2. $\frac{3}{4}$ = ______________

3. $\frac{3}{6}$ = ______________

4. $\frac{2}{8}$ = ______________

5. $\frac{2}{3}$ = ______________

Name ______________________________

Another Look
9-8

Simplest Form Fractions

How do you know if a fraction is in its simplest form? Follow the steps in this flowchart to find out.

Example

Is $\frac{8}{32}$ in its simplest form?

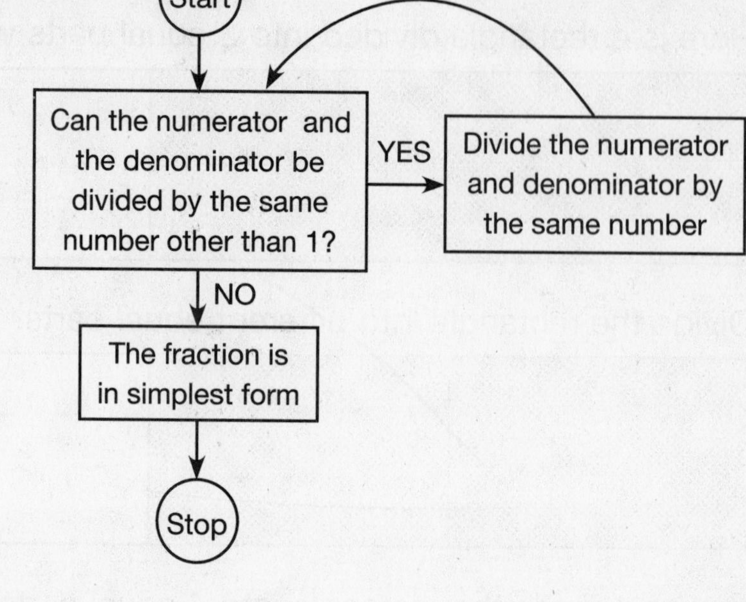

Start

The numerator and the denominator can be divided by 2, so follow the Yes arrow.

$\frac{8 \div 2}{32 \div 2} = \frac{4}{16}$

Go back to the first box.

The numerator and the denominator can be divided by 4, so follow the Yes arrow.

$\frac{4}{16} \div \frac{4}{4} = \frac{1}{4}$

Go back to the first box.

One is the only number that will divide both 1 and 4, so follow the No arrow.

$\frac{1}{4}$ is the simplest form fraction for $\frac{8}{32}$.

Is each fraction in simplest form? If it is, write *yes*. If not, write it in simplest form. Follow the steps in the flowchart.

1. $\frac{10}{12}$ ________ **2.** $\frac{18}{24}$ ________ **3.** $\frac{4}{5}$ ________

4. $\frac{9}{15}$ ________ **5.** $\frac{7}{12}$ ________ **6.** $\frac{5}{30}$ ________

7. $\frac{6}{36}$ ________ **8.** $\frac{20}{50}$ ________ **9.** $\frac{12}{48}$ ________

10. $\frac{5}{13}$ ________ **11.** $\frac{18}{21}$ ________ **12.** $\frac{19}{20}$ ________

Name ______________________________

Another Look 9-9

Comparing and Ordering Fractions

You can compare fractions using drawings.

Which is greater, $\frac{5}{8}$ or $\frac{1}{3}$?

Draw two rectangles of equal size.

Divide the first rectangle into 8 equal parts.
Divide the second into 3 equal parts.

Shade $\frac{5}{8}$ of the first rectangle and $\frac{1}{3}$ of the second rectangle.

Compare the shaded areas. Are they the same size? If so, the fractions are equivalent. If not, the rectangle with the greater amount of shading is the greater fraction.

$\frac{5}{8}$ is greater than $\frac{1}{3}$.

Are the fractions equivalent? If so, write *yes*. If not, circle the greater fraction. Use drawings to help.

1. $\frac{3}{4}$ $\frac{5}{6}$ __________

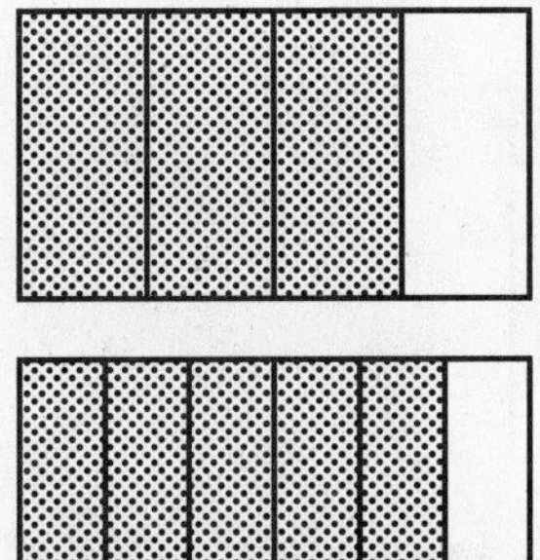

2. $\frac{4}{8}$ $\frac{1}{2}$ __________

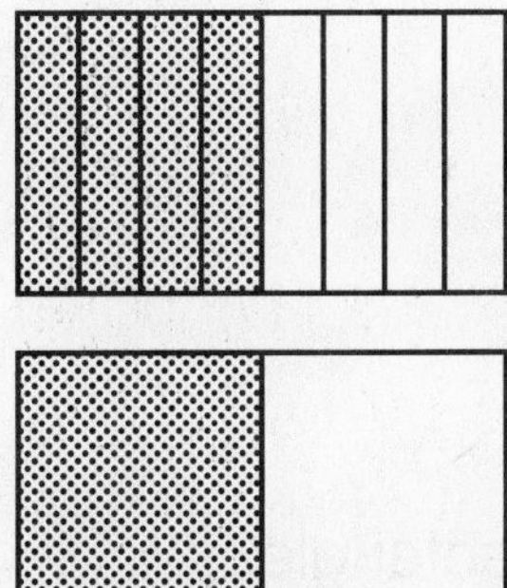

3. $\frac{2}{3}$ $\frac{3}{8}$ __________

4. $\frac{1}{3}$ $\frac{1}{2}$ __________

5. $\frac{1}{8}$ $\frac{1}{3}$ __________

6. $\frac{2}{3}$ $\frac{4}{6}$ __________

Name ____________________

Another Look
9-10

Exploring a Fraction of a Set

In your book you learned to find a fraction of a set by using counters. Here is another way you can find a fraction of a set. Use grid paper and some colored pencils.

Find $\frac{4}{7}$ of 21.

Draw a rectangle around 21 squares.
Divide the rectangle into 7 equal sections.
There are 3 squares in each section.
$21 \div 7 = 3$

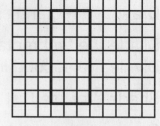

Shade 4 sections.

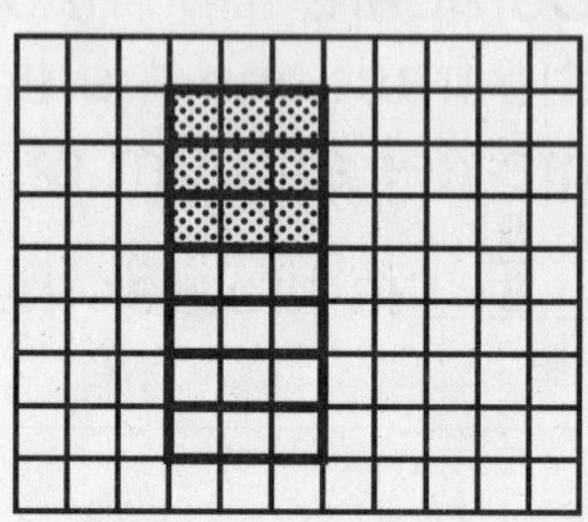

There are 12 squares total in the 4 sections.

$4 \times 3 = 12$

$\frac{4}{7}$ of 21 = 12

Find the number for each fraction of a set. You may use grid paper to help.

1. $\frac{5}{6}$ of 12

a. Draw a rectangle around 12 squares.

b. Divide the rectangle into 6 equal pieces.

c. Shade $\frac{5}{6}$ of the rectangle.

d. $\frac{5}{6}$ of 12 = ________

2. $\frac{3}{4}$ of 16

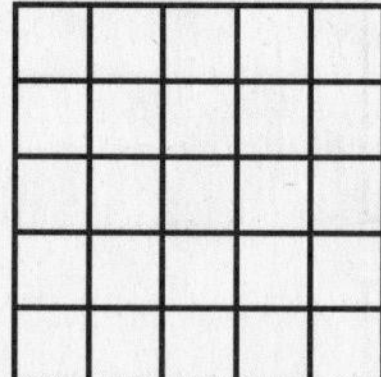

a. Draw a rectangle around 16 squares.

b. Divide the rectangle into 4 equal pieces.

c. Shade $\frac{3}{4}$ of the rectangle.

d. $\frac{3}{4}$ of 16 = ________

3. $\frac{5}{6}$ of 18 ________

4. $\frac{3}{8}$ of 32 ________

5. $\frac{5}{7}$ of 49 ________

6. $\frac{3}{5}$ of 60 ________

7. $\frac{5}{8}$ of 24 ________

8. $\frac{3}{5}$ of 25 ________

 Use with pages 408–409.

Name ______________________________

Exploring Units of Length

In your book you estimated and measured lengths of classroom objects. Here is another way to explore units of length.

Use the rulers to measure the length of the pen below.

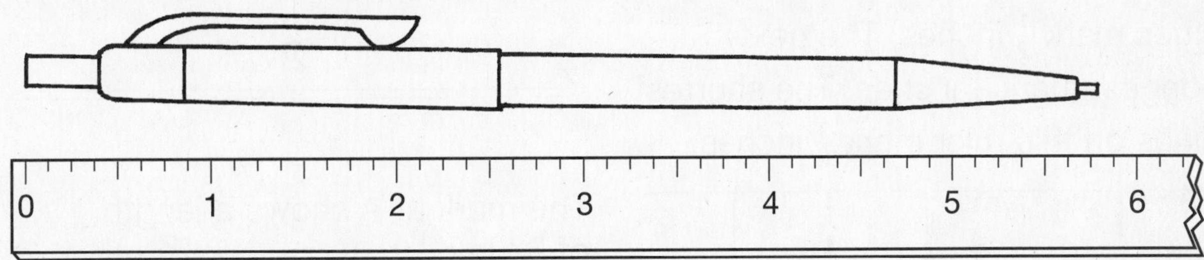

The length of the ball point pen is between 5 and 6 inches. It is more than halfway between the 5 and 6 inch marks. The length of the pen measured to the nearest inch is 6 inches.

What is the length of this arrowhead measured to the nearest inch?

The tip of the arrowhead is just past the 2 in. mark. It is less than halfway to the 3 in. mark. The arrowhead is 2 in. long measured to the nearest inch.

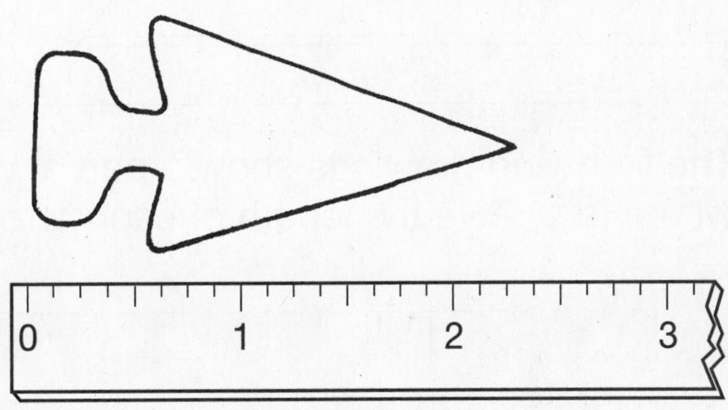

Use a ruler to measure these common objects. Give their lengths to the nearest inch.

1. 

____

2. 

____

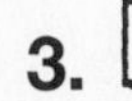

3. 

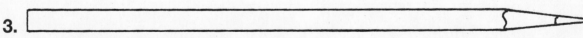

____

4. 

____

Name ______________________

Another Look 9-12

Measuring Fractional Parts of an Inch

This is an enlarged view of the scale on a ruler. Notice that it is divided into 8 sections. The longest lines are inch marks and are labeled with whole numbers. The next longest lines mark $\frac{1}{2}$ inches. The next longest mark $\frac{1}{4}$ inches. The shortest lines on this ruler mark $\frac{1}{8}$ inches.

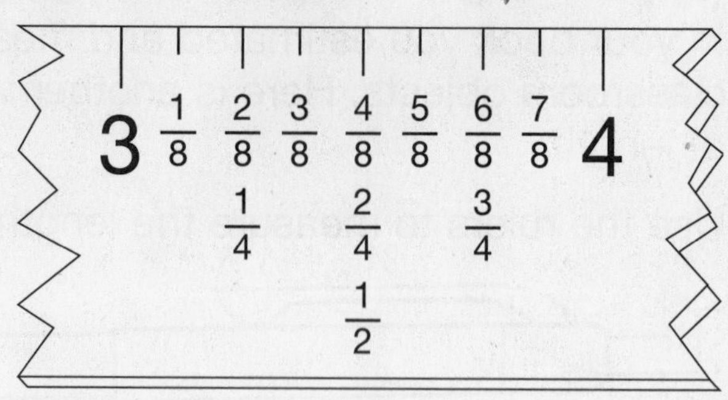

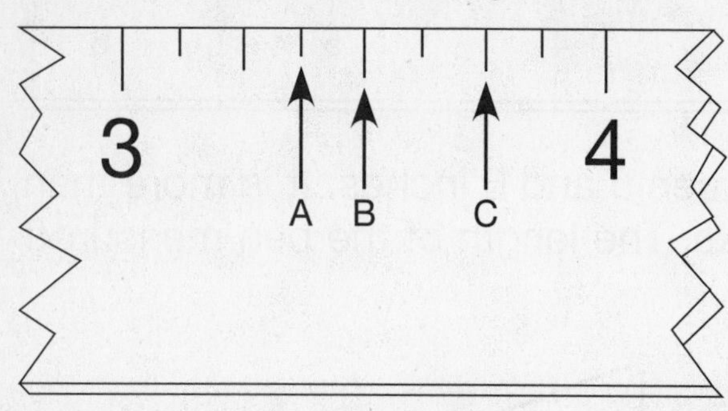

The mark at A shows a length of $3\frac{3}{8}$ in.

The mark at B shows a length of $3\frac{1}{2}$ in.

The mark at C shows a length of $3\frac{3}{4}$ in.

The following drawings show a partial view of arrows being measured with rulers. Give the length of each arrow to the nearest:

1. $\frac{1}{8}$ in.

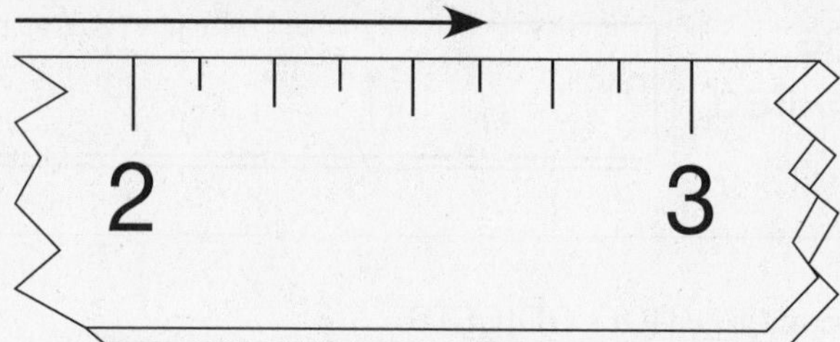

____

2. $\frac{1}{4}$ in.

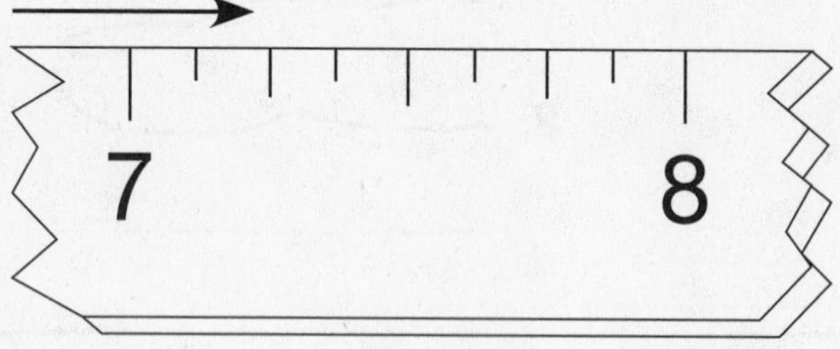

____

3. $\frac{1}{2}$ in.

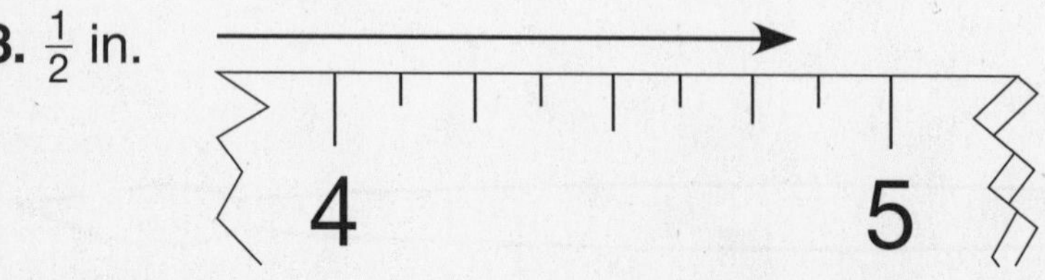

____

Name ______________________________

Another Look 9-13

Exploring Feet, Yards, and Miles

In your book you used a calculator to explore distances. Here is another way to understand feet, yards, and miles.

1 mile = 5,280 feet   1 mile = 1,760 yards

The track at Merrimack Middle School is 500 yards. If Marianne runs 2 laps, has she run more or less than 1 mile?

1 lap is 500 yards.
So, 2 laps is 500 + 500 = 1,000 yards
1,000 is less than 1,760.
So, 2 laps is __less than__ 1 mile.

Solve. Use the picture to help.

1. How many yards would you have to drive or walk to reach the top of the mountain?

   ____

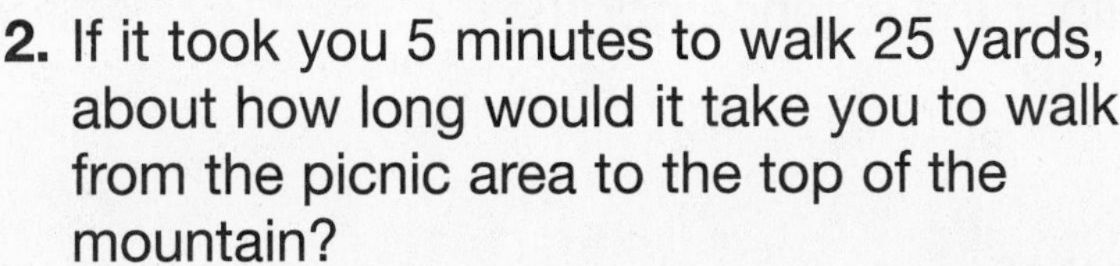

2. If it took you 5 minutes to walk 25 yards, about how long would it take you to walk from the picnic area to the top of the mountain?

   ____

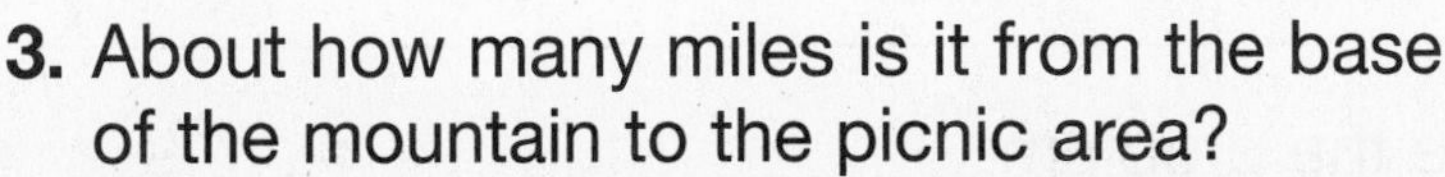

3. About how many miles is it from the base of the mountain to the picnic area?

   ____

4. About how many miles long is the mountain road from the base of the mountain to the very top?

   ____

5. A car is limited to driving 25 miles per hour (or about 730 yards per minute) on the mountain road. About how long will it take for a car to drive all the way up the mountain road?

   ____

Name ______________________________

Another Look
9-14

Analyze Strategies: Use Logical Reasoning

There are 90 students in the sixth grade at Meadow Pond Middle School. Use the table to find out how many students are in neither the science nor the computer club.

Club	Number of Students
Science	25
Computer	36
Both	18
Neither	?

First find out how many students in the 6th grade are only in the science club and only in the computer club, by subtracting the number of students who participate in both clubs.

25 − 18 = 7, so 7 students are only in the science club.
35 − 18 = 17, so 17 students are only in the computer club.

How many students are in clubs?

7 students just in science club + 17 students just in computer club + 18 students in both clubs = 42 students total

How many students are in neither the science nor the computer club?

90 − 42 = 48

__48__ students are in neither the science nor the computer club.

Use logical reasoning to solve the problem.

There are 33 students in Mr. Walker's class at Stone Elementary. 13 students collect trading cards, 17 students collect action figures, and 9 students collect both cards and figures.

1. How many students collect just action figures? ________

2. How many students collect just trading cards? ________

3. How many do not collect cards or figures? ________

Name ______________________

Exploring Adding Fractions with Like Denominators

In your book you used fraction strips to add fractions with like denominators. Here is another way to add fractions.

Use the denominator as the number of equal sections to divide a rectangle. Use the numerators to shade in sections. Then count the number of shaded sections you have.

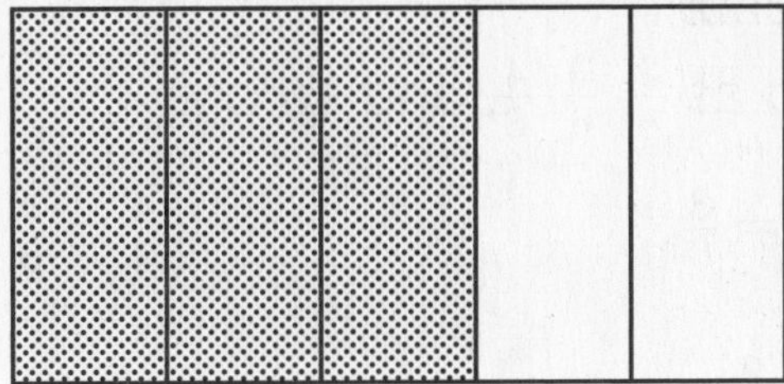

Find $\frac{1}{5} + \frac{2}{5}$.

Divide the rectangle into 5 equal sections.

Shade $\frac{1}{5}$. Then shade $\frac{2}{5}$.

What is the total amount shaded?

$\frac{3}{5}$ are shaded, so $\frac{1}{5} + \frac{2}{5} =$ $\underline{\frac{3}{5}}$

Use the rectangles to help find each sum.

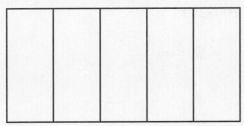

1. $\frac{2}{5} + \frac{2}{5} =$ ______

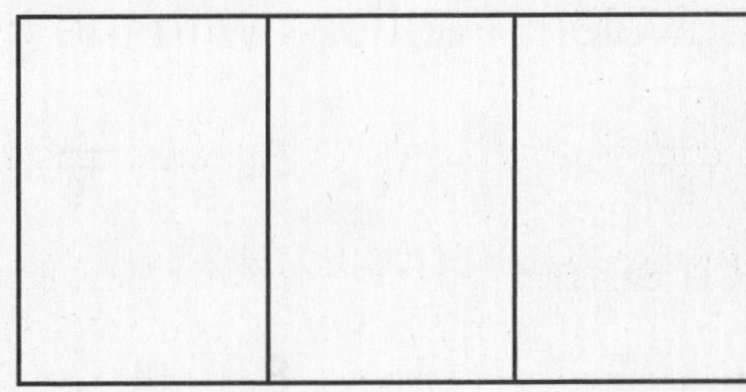

2. $\frac{1}{3} + \frac{1}{3} =$ ______

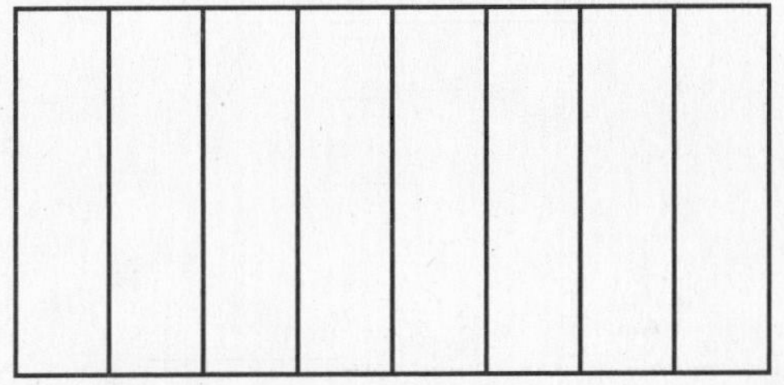

3. $\frac{1}{8} + \frac{3}{8} =$ ______

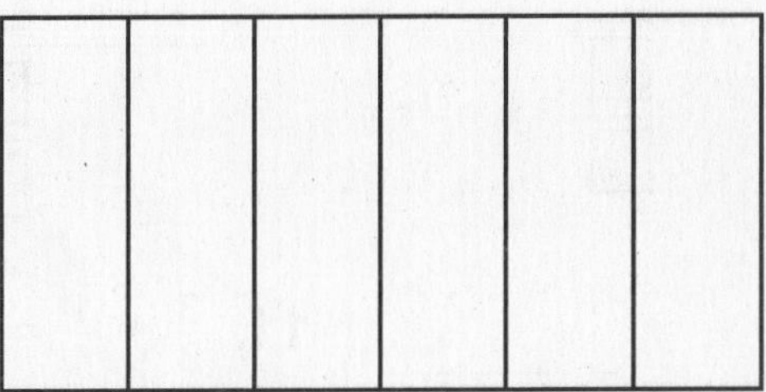

4. $\frac{1}{6} + \frac{5}{6} =$ ______

Name ______________________________

Exploring Adding Fractions with Unlike Denominators

In your book you added two fractions with unlike denominators by renaming a fraction. Here is a closer look at renaming fractions.

How do you rename a fraction?
Multiply the numerator and denominator by the same number to make a new, equivalent fraction.

The fraction $\frac{1}{2}$ can be renamed as $\frac{2}{4}$, $\frac{3}{6}$, $\frac{4}{8}$, and so on.

$\frac{1 \times 2}{2 \times 2} = \frac{2}{4}$ $\qquad$ $\frac{1 \times 3}{2 \times 3} = \frac{3}{6}$ $\qquad$ $\frac{1 \times 4}{2 \times 4} = \frac{4}{8}$

Add $\frac{1}{3}$ and $\frac{1}{6}$.

$$\begin{array}{rcl} \frac{1 \times 2}{3 \times 2} & = & \frac{2}{6} \\ + \frac{1}{6} & = & \frac{1}{6} \\ \hline & & \frac{3}{6} \end{array}$$

Simplify. $\frac{3 \div 3}{6 \div 3} = \frac{1}{2}$

Complete.

1. $\frac{3 \times 2}{5 \times 2} = \frac{6}{\square}$ $\qquad$ **2.** $\frac{1 \times 3}{8 \times 3} = \frac{\square}{\square}$ $\qquad$ **3.** $\frac{2 \times \square}{9 \times 2} = \frac{\square}{18}$

Write equivalent fractions with the given denominator.

4. $\frac{1}{4} = \frac{\square}{8}$ $\qquad$ **5.** $\frac{2}{3} = \frac{\square}{9}$ $\qquad$ **6.** $\frac{5}{6} = \frac{\square}{12}$

Find each sum.

7.
$$\begin{array}{rcl} \frac{1}{8} & = & \frac{1}{8} \\ + \frac{1}{2} & = & \frac{\square}{8} \\ \hline & & \frac{\square}{\square} \end{array}$$

8.
$$\begin{array}{rcl} \frac{2}{9} & = & \frac{2}{9} \\ + \frac{1}{3} & = & \frac{\square}{\square} \\ \hline & & \frac{\square}{\square} \end{array}$$

9.
$$\begin{array}{rcl} \frac{3}{5} & = & \frac{\square}{\square} \\ + \frac{3}{10} & = & \frac{\square}{10} \\ \hline & & \frac{\square}{\square} \end{array}$$

10. $\frac{1}{3} + \frac{1}{9} =$ ________ $\qquad$ **11.** $\frac{3}{8} + \frac{1}{4} =$ ________ $\qquad$ **12.** $\frac{1}{2} + \frac{1}{6} =$ ________

13. $\frac{4}{5} + \frac{1}{10} =$ ________ $\qquad$ **14.** $\frac{2}{5} + \frac{1}{10} =$ ________ $\qquad$ **15.** $\frac{1}{6} + \frac{2}{3} =$ ________

Name ______________________

Adding Fractions

Only fractions with like denominators can be added. Before adding fractions with unlike denominators, you must rename the fractions so their denominators "match."

Decide whether or not to rename a fraction. Then solve the problem.

Example: $\frac{1}{5} + \frac{2}{5} = ?$

a. Do you need to rename a fraction? If so, which one? Explain.

No. Both fractions already have the same denominator.

b. Solve the problem. $\frac{1}{5} + \frac{2}{5} = \frac{3}{5}$

Example: $\frac{1}{5} + \frac{1}{10} = ?$

a. Do you need to rename a fraction? If so, which one? Explain.

Yes. Rename $\frac{1}{5}$ as $\frac{2}{10}$ so it can be added to $\frac{1}{10}$.

b. Solve the problem. $\frac{2}{10} + \frac{1}{10} = \frac{3}{10}$

---

1. $\frac{1}{6} + \frac{5}{6} = ?$

a. Do you need to rename a fraction? If so, which one? Explain.

____

b. Solve the problem: ______________

2. $\frac{1}{6} + \frac{5}{18} = ?$

a. Do you need to rename a fraction? If so, which one? Explain.

____

b. Solve the problem: ______________

Find each sum. Simplify.

3. $\frac{1}{8} + \frac{3}{8} =$ ____________

4. $\frac{2}{3} + \frac{2}{9} =$ ____________

Name ______________________________

Another Look
10-4

Decision Making

Your class wants to paint a design on the courtyard wall. The principal will let you use left-over paint from the supply closet. Here is what you have available:

Yellow	$\frac{1}{2}$ can	White	$\frac{1}{2}$ can
Red	$\frac{1}{2}$ can	Black	1 can
Blue	1 can	Green	$\frac{1}{2}$ can
Each can holds a gallon of paint. One gallon will cover about 100 square feet.			

If the wall measures 100 square feet, is there enough yellow and red paint to cover it?

$\frac{1}{2}$ can yellow + $\frac{1}{2}$ can red = 1.

Since 1 whole can will cover 100 square feet, there is enough paint.

1. If the wall measures 200 square feet, is there enough yellow, red, white, and green paint to cover it? Explain.

____

____

____

____

2. If the wall measures 200 square feet, is there enough black and white paint to cover it? Explain.

____

____

____

 Use with pages 440–441.

Name ______________________________

Another Look
10-5

Exploring Subtracting Fractions

In your book you subtracted fractions with like and unlike denominators using fraction strips. Here is a closer look at how to subtract fractions. For fractions with like denominators, follow these steps:

Find $\frac{7}{8} - \frac{3}{8}$.

Step 1 Use fraction strips that match the denominators. $\boxed{\frac{1}{8}}$

Step 2 Model the larger fraction.

$\boxed{\frac{1}{8}}\ \boxed{\frac{1}{8}}\ \boxed{\frac{1}{8}}\ \boxed{\frac{1}{8}}\ \boxed{\frac{1}{8}}\ \boxed{\frac{1}{8}}\ \boxed{\frac{1}{8}}$

Step 3 Model the smaller fraction.

$\boxed{\frac{1}{8}}\ \boxed{\frac{1}{8}}\ \boxed{\frac{1}{8}}$

Step 4 Line the strips up. Take away pairs of fractions. Count the remaining fraction strips.

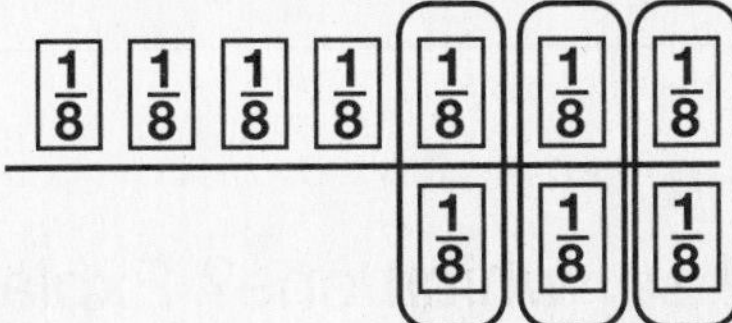

$\frac{7}{8} - \frac{3}{8} = \frac{4}{8}$ $\qquad\qquad$ $\frac{4 \div 4}{8 \div 4} = \frac{1}{2}$

Use fraction strips or draw a picture to solve each problem.

1. $\frac{8}{9} - \frac{2}{9} =$ ____________ **2.** $\frac{3}{4} - \frac{1}{4} =$ ____________

3. $\frac{5}{8} - \frac{1}{8} =$ ____________ **4.** $\frac{11}{12} - \frac{5}{12} =$ ____________

5. $\frac{4}{5} - \frac{2}{5} =$ ____________ **6.** $\frac{2}{3} - \frac{1}{3} =$ ____________

7. $\frac{5}{6} - \frac{1}{6} =$ ____________ **8.** $\frac{6}{7} - \frac{3}{7} =$ ____________

9. $\frac{7}{10} - \frac{3}{10} =$ ____________ **10.** $\frac{8}{9} - \frac{5}{9} =$ ____________

Name ______________________

Another Look
10-6

Subtracting Fractions

Only fractions with like denominators can be subtracted. Before subtracting fractions with unlike denominators, you must rename the fractions so their denominators "match."

Example: $\frac{2}{5} - \frac{1}{5} = ?$

a. Do you need to rename a fraction? If so, which one? Explain.
No. Both fractions already have the same denominator.

b. Solve the problem. $\frac{2}{5} - \frac{1}{5} = \frac{1}{5}$

Example: $\frac{1}{5} - \frac{1}{10} = ?$

a. Do you need to rename a fraction? If so, which one? Explain.
Yes. Rename $\frac{1}{5}$ as $\frac{2}{10}$ so you can subtract $\frac{1}{10}$.

b. Solve the problem. $\frac{2}{10} - \frac{1}{10} = \frac{1}{10}$

---

1. $\frac{5}{6} - \frac{1}{6} = ?$

a. Do you need to rename a fraction? If so, which one? Explain.

____

b. Solve the problem. ______________

2. $\frac{1}{6} - \frac{1}{18}$

a. Do you need to rename a fraction? If so, which one? Explain.

____

b. Solve the problem ______________

Find each difference.

3. $\frac{1}{2} - \frac{1}{4} =$ ________ **4.** $\frac{5}{8} - \frac{1}{8} =$ ________ **5.** $\frac{2}{3} - \frac{1}{9} =$ ________

Name ______________________________

Analyze Word Problems: Choose an Operation

Len has a collection of baseball cards. Pitchers make up $\frac{1}{12}$ of his collection while outfielders make up $\frac{2}{3}$ of his collection. What fractional part of his collection are pitchers and outfielders?

Since you want to combine the fractional parts of pitchers and outfielders, you have to add $\frac{1}{12}$ and $\frac{2}{3}$.

The denominators are unlike.

Rename $\frac{2}{3}$. $\frac{2}{3} = \frac{8}{12}$

×4

$\frac{2}{3} = \frac{8}{12}$

×4

Find the sum and simplify.

$\frac{1}{12} + \frac{8}{12} = \frac{9}{12} = \frac{3}{4}$

$\frac{3}{4}$ of Len's baseball cards are pitchers and outfielders.

Solve.

1. Maria has a coin collection. Nickels make up $\frac{3}{8}$ of her collection. Pennies make up $\frac{1}{4}$ of her collection. What fractional part of her collection are pennies and nickels? ________

2. Patsy has $\frac{7}{8}$ yd of red ribbon and $\frac{3}{4}$ yd of yellow ribbon.
   a. How much more red ribbon does she have than yellow ribbon? ________
   b. If Patsy uses $\frac{1}{2}$ yd of each color ribbon, how much ribbon of each color will Patsy have left over?

   Red: ________

   Yellow: ________

3. Simon has $\frac{7}{8}$ of a bag of marbles. He gives $\frac{1}{4}$ of them to his friend. How much of the bag does he have left? ________

Name ____________________

Another Look
10-8

Exploring Weight

In your book you chose the better estimate for the weight of certain items. Another way is to match items that weigh about the same.

Look at each item. Imagine trying to pick up each item. Think, "Which items would require about the same amount of strength to pick up?"

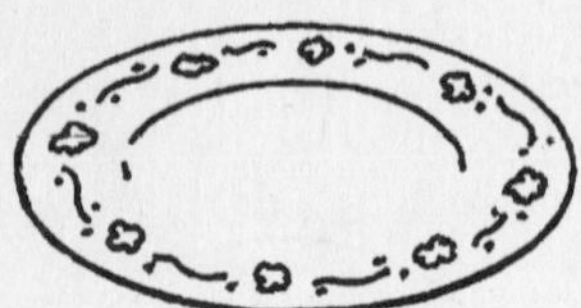

You could pick up a salad bowl and a dinner plate with one hand. You would need both hands or help from a friend to pick up the chair.

Circle the two items that weigh about the same.

1. 

2.   

3.  

4.   

5.   

Name ______________________________

Exploring Capacity

In your book you chose the better estimate for the capacity of certain items. Another way is to match items that have about the same capacity.

Look at each container. Imagine filling each container with water. Think, "Which containers would hold about the same amount of water?"

 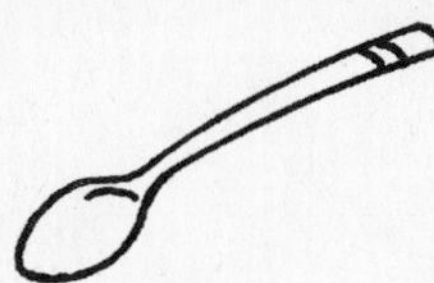 

A few drops would fill the teaspoon. The glass and the coffee cup hold about 1 cup each.

Circle the two items that have about the same capacity.

1. 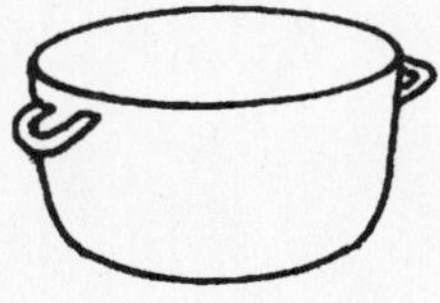  

2. 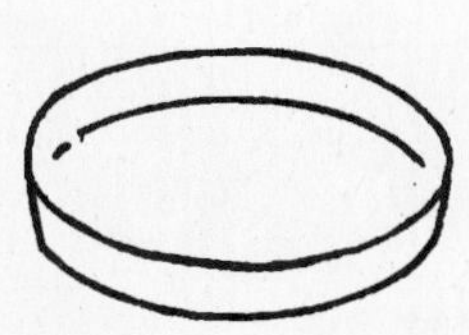  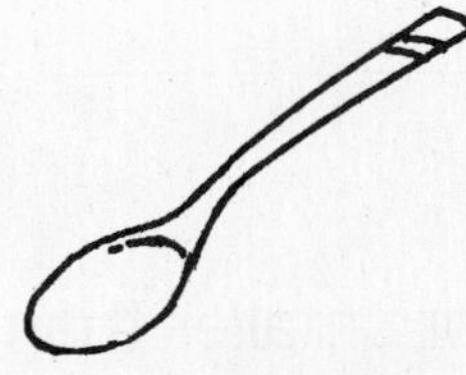

3. 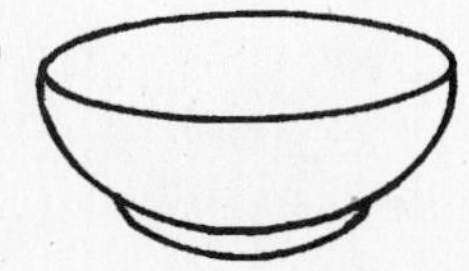  

4.   

5.   

Name ______________________________

Another Look
10-10

Changing Units: Length, Weight, and Capacity

12 qt = ☐ gal

A quart is smaller than a gallon.

When you change from smaller units to larger units, you divide.

4 qt = 1 gal

12 qt ÷ 4 = 3 gal

12 qt = 3 gal

6 lb = ☐ oz

A pound weighs more than an ounce.

When you change from larger units to smaller units, you multiply.

1 lb = 16 oz

6 lb × 16 = 96 oz

6 lb = __96__ oz

---

1. 5 qt = ☐ pt

a. Is a quart larger or smaller than a pint? __________

b. Should you multiply or divide? __________

c. 1 qt = ________ pt

d. 5 qt = ________ pt

2. 80 oz = ☐ lb

a. Is an ounce larger or smaller than a pound? __________

b. Should you multiply or divide? __________

c. 1 lb = ________ oz

d. 80 oz = ________ lb

3. 14 c = ________ pt **4.** 6 yd = ________ ft **5.** 7 ft = ________ in.

Name ______________________________

Another Look 10-11

Compare Strategies: Draw a Picture/Make a Table

Make a table and draw a picture to solve the problem. Decide which strategy you prefer.

For every 12 cans of food donated to the food drive, Belmont Market donates 3 pounds of apples. By the end of the week, 84 cans of food had been donated. How many pounds of apples will Belmont Market donate?

You can solve this problem by making a table. Find a pattern to complete the table.

Number of cans	12	24	36	48	60	72	84
Pounds of apples	3	6	9	12	15	18	21

Add 12 more cans and 3 more pounds of apples for each column in the table. Continue until you find the answer.

Another way to solve this problem is to draw a picture. Use squares for cans and circles for pounds of apples. Count the number of pounds of apples in your drawing.

[12] [12] [12] [12] [12] [12] [12]

(3) (3) (3) (3) (3) (3) (3)

$3 \times 7 =$ __21__, so Belmont Market will donate 21 pounds of apples.

Use any strategy to solve each problem.

1. Belmont Market has also decided to donate 5 lb of fresh fruit for every 15 lb of canned goods donated. How many pounds of fresh fruit will Belmont Market donate if 90 lb of canned goods are donated? ______________

2. Jenny likes to swim laps. After every 12 laps, she takes 4 dives. On Saturday, she swam 48 laps. How many dives did she take? ______________

3. For every 2 miles Russell walks, he takes a rest. How many rests does he take on a 12-mile walk? ______________

Name ______________________________________

Exploring Algebra: Using a Balance Scale Model

In your book you used a balance scale model to help find an unknown value in an equation. Here is another way to find the unknown value.

Find the value of *n*.

$6 + \boxed{n} = 11$

Suppose a closed envelope holds the unknown number. You can find the unknown value.

$6 + n = 11$

Ask yourself, "What must be in the envelope to make the equation true?"

Count up from 6 to 11 to find the answer.

7, 8, 9, 10, 11

You counted up 5 numbers. So, $n = 5$

Find the value of each $\boxed{n}$.

1. $9 + \boxed{n} = 17$ ________
2. $8 + \boxed{n} = 21$ ________
3. $11 + \boxed{n} = 12$ ________
4. $6 + \boxed{n} = 14$ ________
5. $\boxed{n} + 12 = 18$ ________
6. $\boxed{n} + 3 = 7$ ________
7. $\boxed{n} + 4 = 11$ ________
8. $\boxed{n} + 16 = 21$ ________
9. $10 + 7 = \boxed{n}$ ________
10. $3 + 4 = \boxed{n}$ ________
11. $8 + 11 = \boxed{n}$ ________
12. $12 + 11 = \boxed{n}$ ________

Name ______________________

Another Look
11-1

Reading and Writing Decimals

You see decimals every day. Money amounts are often written as decimals.

$2.43 is read "2 dollars and 43 cents."

To read the same decimal as a non-money amount, drop "dollars" and change "cents" to "hundredths."

2.43 is read as "2 and 43 hundredths."

If there is only one number after the decimal point, use "tenths" instead of "hundredths."

2.4 is read as "2 and 4 tenths."

---

1. $4.57 is read as "4 ______________ and 57 ______________."
2. 4.57 is read as "4 ______________ 57 ______________."
3. 4.5 is read as "4 ______________ 5 ______________."

Write the word name for each decimal.

4. 3.65 ______________________
5. 4.39 ______________________
6. 17.1 ______________________
7. 21.35 ______________________
8. 142.6 ______________________
9. 67.35 ______________________

Write the decimal for each word name.

10. 4 and 6 tenths __________
11. 3 and 44 hundredths __________
12. 42 and 1 tenth __________
13. 6 and 52 hundredths __________
14. 7 and 9 tenths __________
15. 4 and 98 hundredths __________

Name ______________________________

Another Look
11-2

Exploring Decimal Place-Value Relationships

In your book you used grids to show decimals.
Here is another way to explore decimal place-value relationships.

Use simple fractions to look at decimals.

0.1 = one tenth = $\frac{1}{10}$

0.10 = ten hundredths = $\frac{10}{100}$

Can you reduce $\frac{10}{100}$? __Yes__.

Divide the numerator and denominator by 10. $\frac{10 \div 10}{100 \div 10} = \frac{1}{10}$

So, $\frac{1}{10} = \frac{10}{100}$, one tenth equals ten hundredths, and 0.1 = 0.10.

Write 0.5 in hundredths. 0.5 = 5 tenths = $\frac{5}{10}$

Multiply the numerator and the denominator by 10 to change tenths to hundredths. $\frac{5 \times 10}{10 \times 10} = \frac{50}{100}$ $\frac{50}{100}$ = fifty hundredths = 0.50.

So 0.5 written in hundredths is __0.50__.

---

1. Write 0.2 in hundredths.

a. Write the fraction for 0.2. ________

b. Multiply the numerator and denominator by 10.
Write the new fraction. ________

c. Write the new fraction as a decimal in hundredths. ________

2. Write 0.70 in tenths.

a. Write the fraction for 0.70. ________

b. Divide the numerator and denominator by 10.
Write the new fraction. ________

c. Write the new fraction as a decimal in tenths. ________

Write each decimal in hundredths.

3. 0.4 ________ **4.** 0.7 ________ **5.** 0.9 ________

Write each decimal in tenths.

6. 0.60 ________ **7.** 0.80 ________ **8.** 0.30 ________

Name ______________________________

Another Look 11-3

Compare Strategies: Make an Organized List/Use Objects

Suppose you have 18 coins, all dimes and pennies, that total $1.26. How many of each coin do you have?

You can make an organized list to solve this problem. Then check your answer using objects.

Value	Dimes	Pennies	Number of Coins
$1.26	10	26	36
$1.26	11	16	27
$1.26	12	6	18

There are 12 dimes and 6 pennies.

12 dimes = $1.20 and 6 pennies = $0.06.
$1.20 + $0.06 = $1.26.
12 dimes and 6 pennies are 18 coins.
The answer is correct.

$1.20
$0.06

Suppose you have the same number of pennies and nickels. The coins total $0.18. How many of each coin do you have?

1. What do you know? ______________________________

____

2. Make an organized list or draw a picture of the objects you can use to solve the problem.

3. How many of each coin do you have? ______________________________

Name ______________________________

Another Look 11-4

Comparing and Ordering Decimals

Order the following decimals from least to greatest: 9.43, 9.24, 9.40. Use a number line to help.

All of the decimals start with the whole number 9. Draw a number line from 9.0 to 10.0.

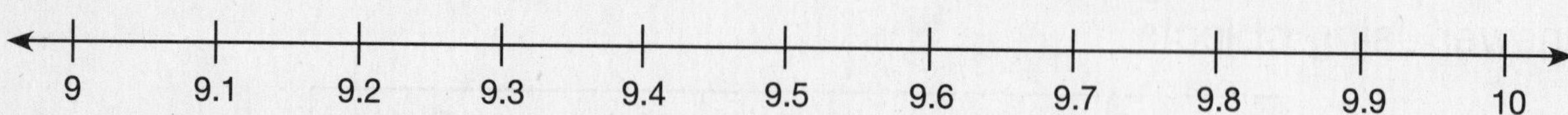

Look at the number in the tenths place in each decimal to help you find the order.
$2 < 3 < 4$, so 9.**2**4 is less than 9.**4**3 and 9.**4**0.

Now look at the number in the hundredths place in 9.43 and 9.40.
$0 < 3$, so 9.4**0** is less than 9.4**3**.

Write the decimals in order on the number line.

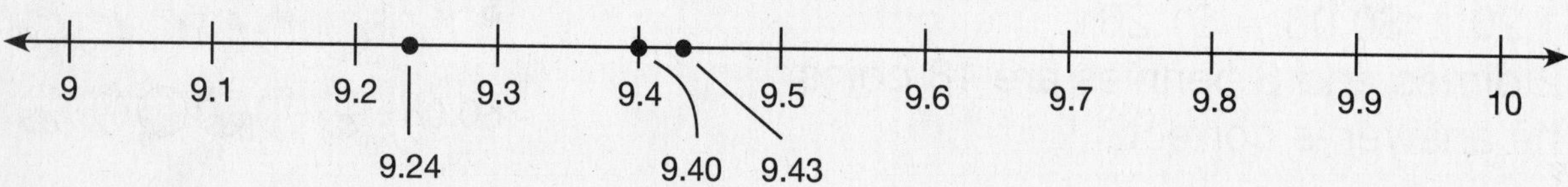

So, the order of the decimals from least to greatest is 9.24, 9.40, 9.43.

Order the decimals from least to greatest. Draw a number line to help.

1. 1.23, 1.01, 1.19

a. Draw a number line from 1.0 to 2.0.

b. Look at the number in the tenths place for each decimal to help find the order. Then look at the number in the hundredths place. Write the numbers on your number line above.

c. Write the order of the decimals from least to greatest. ______________________

2. 5.34, 5.21, 5.64, 5.61, ______________________

Name ______________________

Another Look
11-5

Rounding Decimals

You can round decimals to the nearest whole number by using a simple rule.

Rule: If the digit in the tenths place is less than 5, don't change the digit in the ones place. If it is 5 or greater, add 1 to the digit in the ones place.

Example 1 Round 24.28 to the nearest whole number.

Step 1 Look at the digit in the tenths place. Ignore all other digits!

$2 < 5$, so don't change the ones digit.

Step 2 Drop the decimal part and write the new whole number.

24.28 rounded to the nearest whole number is 24.

Example 2 Round 26.72 to the nearest whole number.

Step 1 Look at the digit in the tenths place.

$7 > 5$, so add 1 to the digit in the ones place.

Step 2 Drop the decimal part and write the new whole number.

26.72 rounded to the nearest whole number is 27.

Round each decimal to the nearest whole number.

1. 2.47

a. What is the digit in the tenths place? ______

b. Do you add 1 to the digit in the ones place or keep it as it is? ______

c. What is 2.47 rounded to the nearest whole number? ______

2. 11.51

a. What is the digit in the tenths place? ______

b. Do you add 1 to the digit in the ones place or keep it as it is? ______

c. What is 11.51 rounded to the nearest whole number? ______

Name ______________________________

Another Look 11-6

Exploring Fractions as Decimals

In your book you used grids to show fractions as decimals. Here is another way to explore fractions as decimals.

Decimals and fractions both show parts of a whole. You can change a fraction to an equivalent fraction in tenths or hundredths. Then write the decimal.

Example 1 Find a decimal for $\frac{1}{2}$.

$2 \times 5 = 10$, so multiply the numerator and denominator by 5 to find an equivalent fraction in tenths.

$\frac{1 \times 5}{2 \times 5} = \frac{5}{10}$ So, $\frac{1}{2} = \frac{5}{10}$ = five tenths = 0.5.

Example 2 Find a decimal for $\frac{1}{4}$.

$4 \times 25 = 100$, so multiply the numerator and denominator by 25 to find an equivalent fraction in hundredths.

$\frac{1 \times 25}{4 \times 25} = \frac{25}{100}$ So, $\frac{1}{4} = \frac{25}{100}$ = twenty-five hundredths = 0.25

Find the decimal for each fraction. Use equivalent fractions to help.

1. $\frac{2}{5}$

a. $\frac{2 \times 2}{5 \times 2} = \frac{\square}{10}$

b. What is the decimal for $\frac{2}{5}$?

____

2. $\frac{9}{20}$

a. $\frac{9}{20} \times \frac{\square}{\square} = \frac{\square}{100}$

b. What is the decimal for $\frac{9}{20}$?

____

3. $\frac{3}{4}$

a. $4 \times \square = 100$

b. What is the decimal for $\frac{3}{4}$?

____

4. $\frac{1}{25}$

a. $25 \times \square = 100$

b. What is the decimal for $\frac{1}{25}$?

____

Name ______________________________

Another Look 11-7

Estimating Sums and Differences

When estimating sums and differences with decimals, round each decimal to the nearest whole number. Then add or subtract.

> Tip: Do not change the whole number part if the decimal part is 0.49 or less. Add 1 to the whole number part if the decimal part is 0.50 or greater.

Estimate the sum of 29.49 and 31.50.

Step 1 Round 29.49 to the nearest whole number.

Round 29.**49** to 29.

Step 2 Round 31.50 to the nearest whole number.

Round 31.**50** to 32.

Step 3 Add the rounded numbers.
29 + 32 = 61

29.49 + 31.50 is about 61.

Round to the nearest whole number.

1. 4.1 ________ **2.** 8.29 ________ **3.** 35.62 ________

4. 16.5 ________ **5.** 17.99 ________ **6.** 24.09 ________

Estimate each sum or difference. Round to the nearest whole number.

7. 1.7 + 2.9
↓ ↓
☐ + ☐ = ________

8. 10.12 − 7.30
↓ ↓
☐ − ☐ = ________

9. 21.49 + 8.50 = ________

10. 2.05 − 0.03 = ________

11. 5.2 + 3.5 = ________

12. 8.79 + 31.4 = ________

13. 12.17 − 4.20 = ________

14. 6.8 − 2.7 = ________

Name ______________________________

Another Look
11-8

Exploring Adding and Subtracting Decimals

In your book you used grids to add and subtract decimals. Here is another way.

Find the sum of 0.46 and 0.70.

Step 1 Write the numbers in a column, lining up the decimal points.

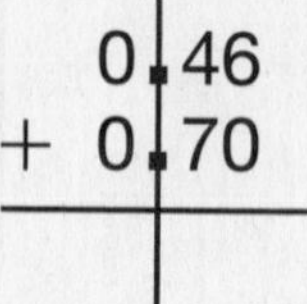

Step 2 Add as if you were adding whole numbers.

Step 3 Place a decimal point in the answer directly below where it occurs in the problem.

```
  0.46
+ 0.70
------
  1.16
```

The sum of 0.46 and 0.70 is 1.16.

Find each sum or difference.

1. 0.90 + 0.36

a. Write the numbers in a column.

b. Add and then place the decimal point.

c. 0.90 + 0.36 = __________

2. 0.40 − 0.14

a. Write the numbers in a column.

b. Subtract. Regroup as needed. Then place the decimal point.

c. 0.40 − 0.14 = __________

3. 0.24 − 0.20

4. 0.48 + 0.15

5. 0.36 + 0.24

6. 0.43 − 0.20

7. 0.70 − 0.55

8. 0.98 − 0.76

9. 0.71 − 0.35

10. 0.69 + 0.35

11. 0.80 − 0.59

12. 0.85 + 0.35

Name ______________________________

Another Look
11-9

Adding and Subtracting Decimals

Adding and subtracting decimals can be easy. Just follow these steps.

6.71 + 32.02 + 8.4

A
Line up the decimal points.

```
  6.71
 32.02
+ 8.4
```

B
Write zeros as needed.

```
  6.71
 32.02
+ 8.40
```

C
Add. Regroup if necessary.

```
 1 1
  6.71
 32.02
+ 8.40
 47.13
```

28.7 − 17.92

A
Line up the decimal points.

```
  28.7
− 17.92
```

B
Write zeros as needed.

```
  28.70
− 17.92
```

C
Subtract. Regroup if necessary.

```
    16
   7 6 10
  28.70
− 17.92
  10.78
```

Find each sum or difference. Estimate to check your answer.

1. 7.3 + 3.45
2. 18.32 + 1.05
3. 44.27 + 32.78
4. 17.39 + 14.82
5. 15.03 + 16.7
6. 7.89 − 0.15
7. 10.42 − 3.03
8. 25.28 − 18.32
9. 55.47 − 15.49
10. 65.3 − 18.91

Name ______________________________

Exploring Centimeters, Decimeters, and Meters

In your book you explored metric measurement by finding the distance around balls of different sizes. Here is another way to explore centimeters, decimeters, and meters.

Here are benchmarks you can use to estimate centimeters, decimeters, and meters.

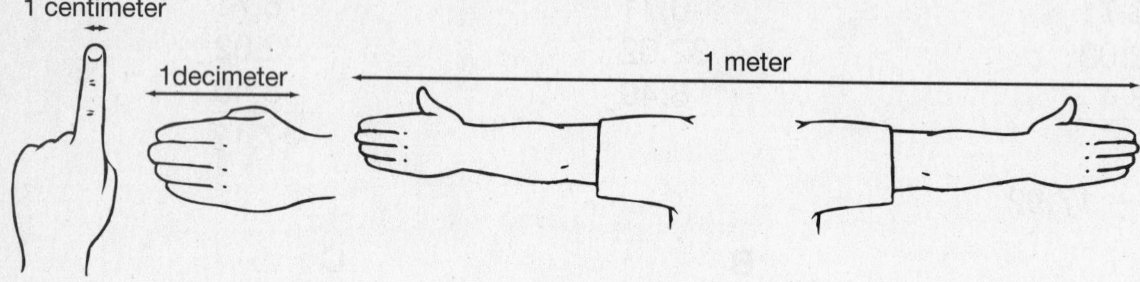

Which unit of measure would you use to measure the length of this page?

The page isn't as long as your outstretched arms, so meters would be too large.

You could measure this page with your finger, but that would take a lot of time. So, centimeters would be too small.

Decimeters is the best unit of measure.

Circle the better unit of measure for each object.

1. 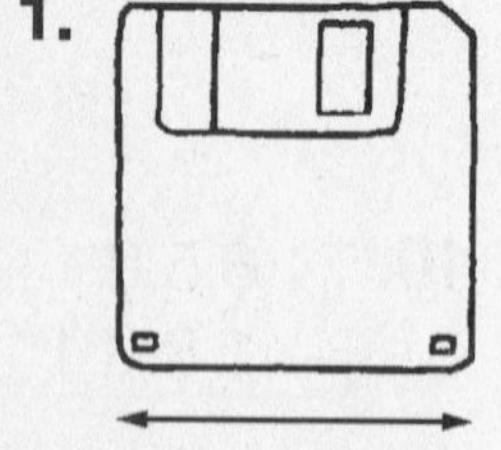

centimeters
or
meters

2. 

centimeters
or
meters

3. 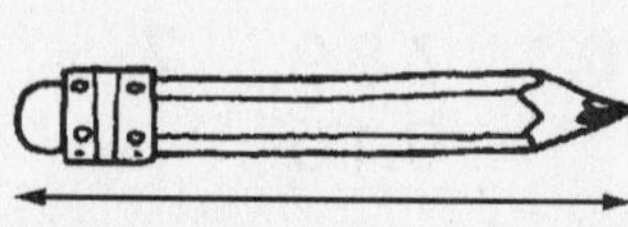

decimeters
or
meters

Name ______________________________________

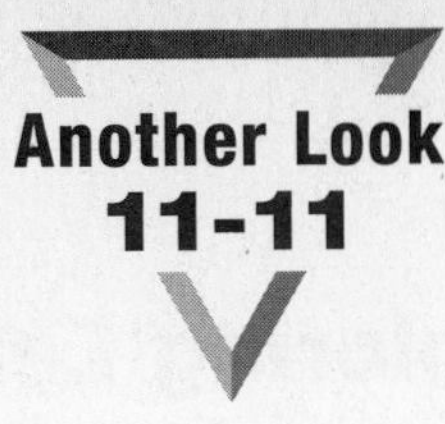

Meters and Kilometers

The meter (m) and kilometer (km) are units of length in the metric system. A kilometer measures longer distances.

1 km = 1,000 m

2 km = ▩ m

Meters are shorter than kilometers.

To change to a lesser unit, *multiply*.
Think: 1 km = 1,000 m
$2 \times 1{,}000 = 2{,}000$

2 km = 2,000 m

There are 2,000 meters in 2 kilometers.

7,000 m = ▩ km

Kilometers are longer than meters.

To change to a greater unit, *divide.*
Think: 1,000 m = 1 km
$7{,}000 \div 1{,}000 = 7$

7,000 m = 7 km

7 kilometers are the same as 7,000 meters.

Compare 2 km and 7,000 m.
2 km = 2,000 m
Since 2,000 m $<$ 7,000 m

2 km (<) 7,000 m

Complete the table.

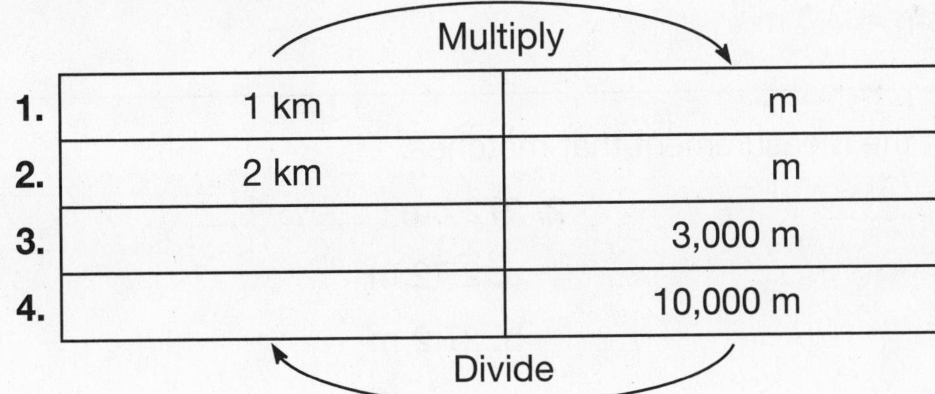

1.	1 km	m
2.	2 km	m
3.		3,000 m
4.		10,000 m

Complete. Write $>$, $<$, or $=$.

5. 7 km ◯ 7,000 m

6. 5 m ◯ 5 km

7. 140 m ◯ 14 km

8. 6 km ◯ 6,000 m

9. 1 km ◯ 100 m

10. 40 m ◯ 40 km

11. 300 km ◯ 3,000 m

12. 86 km ◯ 86,000 m

Name ______________________________

Another Look 11-12

Exploring Length and Decimals

In your book you measured your arm span and height in centimeters and meters. Here is another way to explore length and decimals.

Centimeters and meters are used to measure length.

To change meters to centimeters, multiply by 100.

To multiply by 100, *move the decimal point 2 places to the right.*

4.35 m = ▩ cm

4.35 m   4.35.   435 cm

move 2 places right

4.35 m = 435 cm

To change centimeters to meters, divide by 100.

To divide by 100, *move the decimal point 2 places to the left.*

330 cm = ▩ m

330 cm   3.30.   3.30 m

move 2 places left

330 cm = 3.3 m

Write the letter of the measurement that matches.

1. 2.36 m __________

a. 23.6 cm

b. 236 cm

2. 272 cm __________

a. 2.72 m

b. 27.2 m

Complete.

3. 32 cm = __________ m

4. 1.4 m = __________ cm

5. 45.7 cm = __________ m

6. 0.07 m = __________ cm

7. 33.8 m = __________ cm

8. 19 m = __________ cm

9. 2.1 cm = __________ m

10. 3.2 m = __________ cm

Name ____________________

Exploring Mass

In your book you used a balance scale to explore mass. Here is another way to explore mass.

Grams and kilograms are metric units used to measure mass.

A gram is used to measure light objects.

To change grams to kilograms, divide by 1,000.

IN GOD WE TRUST LIBERTY 1996

3 grams

3 g = ■ kg

Think: 3 ÷ 1,000 = 0.003 *Move the decimal 3 places to the left.*

3g = 0.003 kg

A kilogram is used to measure heavy objects.

To change from kilograms to grams, multiply by 1,000.

3 kilograms

3 kg = ■ g

Think: 3 × 1,000 = 3,000 *Move the decimal 3 places to the left.*

3 kg = 3,000 g

Choose a reasonable unit of mass for each. Ask yourself if the mass of each object is closer to the mass of a penny or the mass of a dog. Write g or kg.

1. a cookie ________ **2.** a truck ________

3. a turkey ________ **4.** an apple ________

5. a horse ________ **6.** a dime ________

7. a teaspoon ________ **8.** a bowling ball ________

Write the letter of the measurement that matches.

9. 5 kg ______________ g

a. 5,000 g **b.** 0.005 g

10. 30,000 g ______________ kg

a. 3 kg **b.** 30 kg

Complete.

11. 8 kg = ______________ g **12.** 2,300 g = ______________ kg

13. 0.3 kg = ______________ g **14.** 230 kg = ______________ kg

Name ______________________________

Another Look 11-14

Exploring Capacity

In your book you explored capacity by filling containers with water. Here is another way to explore capacity.

Liters and milliliters are metric units used to measure liquids. The amount of liquid a container holds is its capacity.

Milliliters are used to measure the liquid in small containers. Liters are used to measure the liquid in large containers.

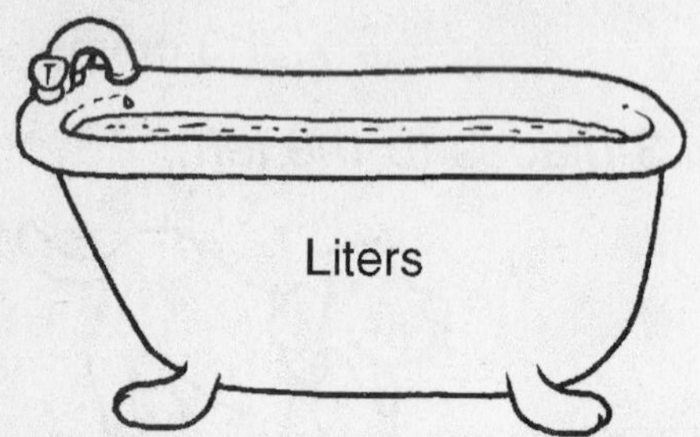

To change liters to milliliters, multiply by 1,000.

To multiply by 1,000, move the decimal point 3 places to the right.

7.2 L = ▩ mL

7.2 L   7.200.   7,200 mL

7.2 L = 7,200 mL

To change milliliters to liters, divide by 1,000.

To divide by 1,000, move the decimal point 3 places to the left.

4,500 mL = ▩ L

4,500 mL   4.500.   4.500 L or 4.5 L

4,500 mL = 4.5 L

Write the letter of the measurement that matches.

1. 3.2 L __________
a. 3,200 mL **b.** 32,000 mL

2. 650 mL __________
a. 6.5 L **b.** 0.65 L

Complete.

3. 5 L = ______________ mL

4. 62,000 mL = ______________ L

5. 8.2 L = ______________ mL

6. 510 mL = ______________ L

Name ____________________

Temperature

Follow these steps to read a thermometer.

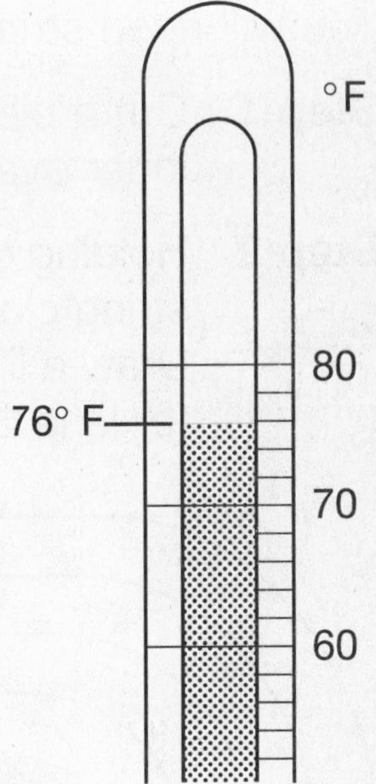

1. Find the top of the liquid in the thermometer.
2. Find the number on the thermometer that is closest to the top of the liquid.

   The closest number is 80.
3. The marks between the numbers indicate 2 degrees. So count those marks up or down by 2's to the top of the liquid.

   Point to each mark as you count down. Say, "80, 78, 76." Stop at the liquid. What is the temperature?

   The thermometer shows a temperature of 76°F.

Read each thermometer. Write the temperature on the line.

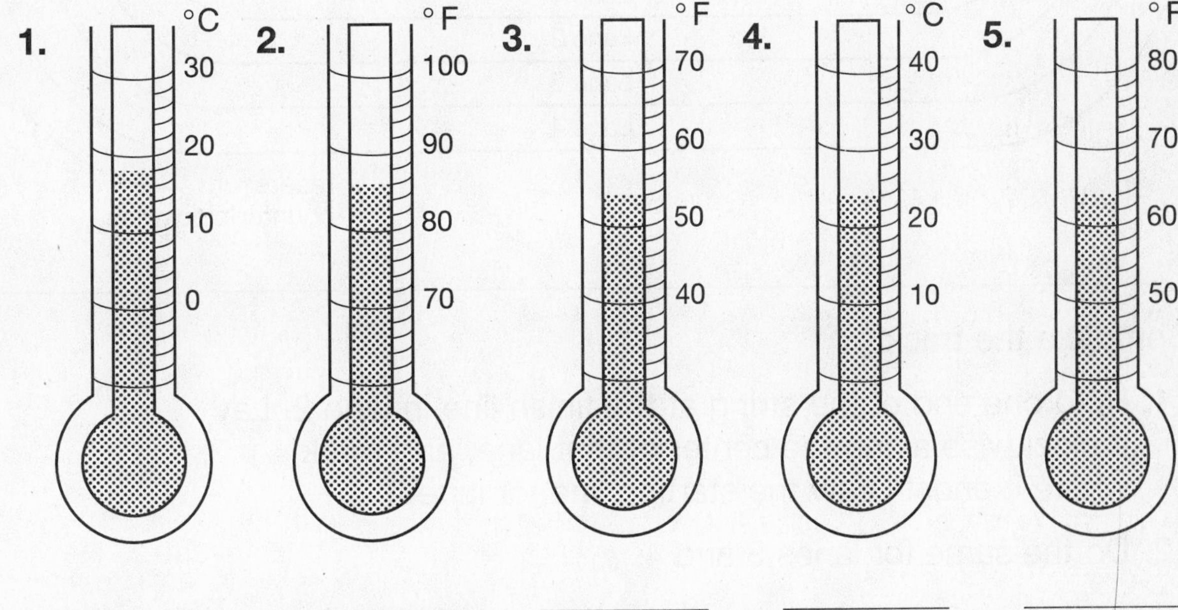

Name ______________________

Another Look 11-16

Decision Making

In your book you created your own track model. Here, you will complete a track model that has already been started. You will need string and scissors. Follow these steps:

Step 1 Cut a piece of string the same length as the perimeter of the inner oval.

Step 2 Holding one end of the string at the finish line in lane 1, lay the string clockwise along the center of the lane. Mark where it ends. Draw a line across the lane at the mark. This is the starting point for lane 1.

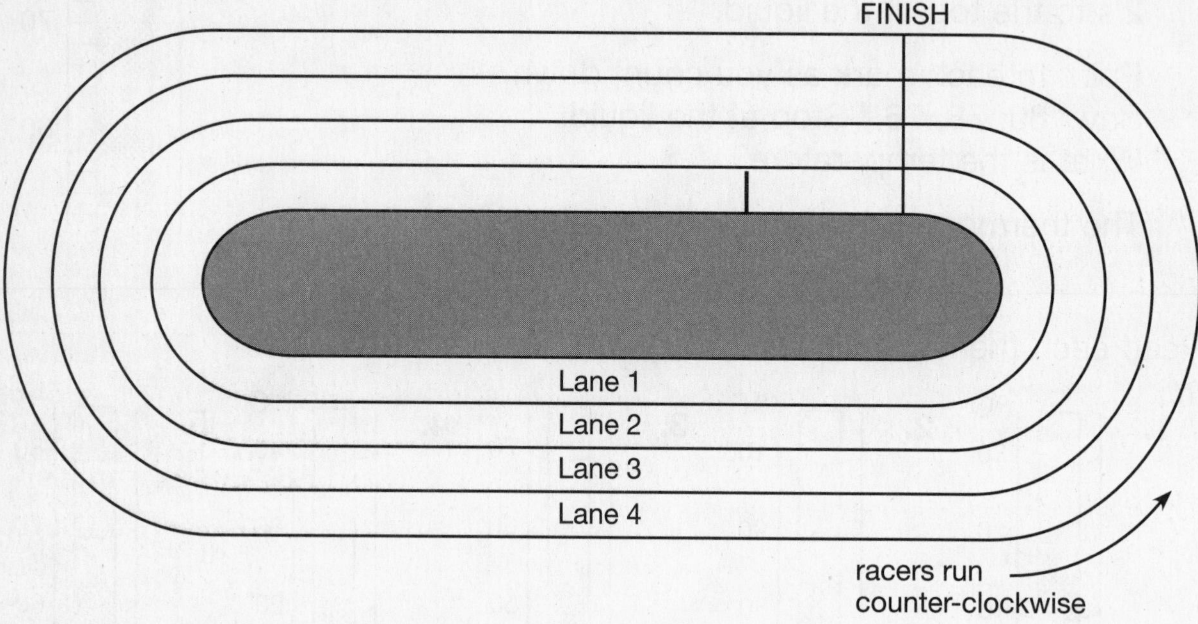

Complete the track.

1. Hold one end of the string at the finish line in lane 2. Lay it clockwise along the center of that lane, and mark where it ends. Draw the starting line for lane 2.
2. Do the same for lanes 3 and 4.

Name ______________________________

Another Look
12-1

Exploring Division Problems

In your book you used place-value patterns to help divide greater numbers. Here is another way.

Cross off an equal number of zeros in the divisor and the dividend, starting from the ones place and moving to the left. Then divide the smaller numbers.

For example, to divide 1,800 by 60, follow these steps:

Step 1 Cross off an equal number of zeros from both the divisor and the dividend.

1,80Ø ÷ 6Ø

Step 2 Rewrite the problem without the crossed out zeros.

180 ÷ 6

Step 3 Solve.

180 ÷ 6 = 30

Find each quotient by crossing off an equal number of zeros. Show the new problem. Then solve.

1. 3,500 ÷ 70 = ______________ = __________
2. 35,000 ÷ 70 = ______________ = __________
3. 4,800 ÷ 60 = ______________ = __________
4. 48,000 ÷ 60 = ______________ = __________
5. 8,100 ÷ 90 = ______________ = __________
6. 81,000 ÷ 90 = ______________ = __________
7. 2,400 ÷ 80 = ______________ = __________
8. 24,000 ÷ 80 = ______________ = __________
9. 4,800 ÷ 40 = ______________ = __________
10. 48,000 ÷ 40 = ______________ = __________
11. 3,000 ÷ 60 = ______________ = __________
12. 30,000 ÷ 60 = ______________ = __________

Name ______________________________

Another Look
12-2

Estimating Quotients with 2-Digit Divisors

Estimate 372 ÷ 72

Step 1 **37**2 ÷ 72 — Look at the two front digits of the dividend. What one-digit number divides 37 evenly? Only 1 and 37 divide 37 evenly.

Step 2 372 ÷ **7**2 — Look at the front digit of the divisor.

Step 3 **37**2 ÷ **7**2 — Compare 37 and 7. Is there a division fact that uses values close to these numbers? You know 36 ÷ 6 = 6

Step 4 Estimate the division by using fact.

36 ÷ 6 = 6, so 360 ÷ 60 = 60

372 ÷ 72 is about 60.

Estimate each quotient.

1. 492 ÷ 68

a. 49 can be divided evenly by ________.

b. Change the problem to 490 ÷ ________.

c. Estimate: ________

2. 814 ÷ 89

a. 81 can be divided evenly by ________.

b. Change the problem to 810 ÷ ________.

c. Estimate: ________

3. 238 ÷ 61

240 ÷ ________ = ________

4. 718 ÷ 91

720 ÷ ________ = ________

5. 561 ÷ 79

________ ÷ ________

= ________

6. 627 ÷ 87

________ ÷ ________

= ________

Name ____________________

Dividing by Tens

You can use place-value blocks to show division.

197 ÷ 30

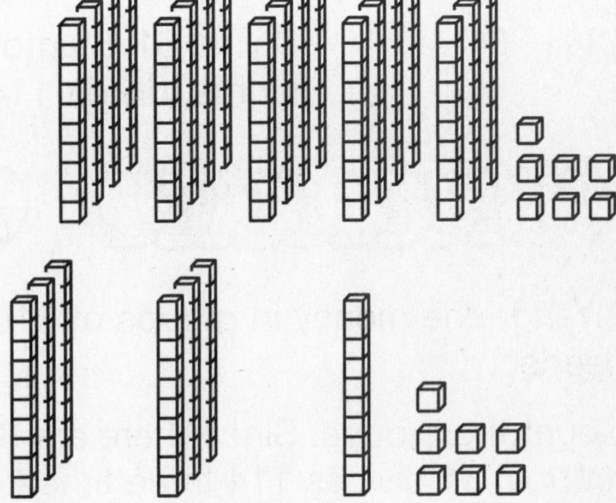

There are 6 groups of 30 with 17 left over.

197 ÷ 30 = 6 R17

Divide. You may use place value blocks to help.

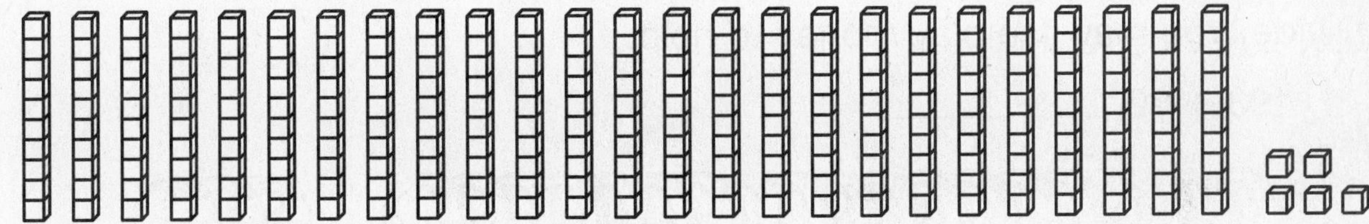

1. 255 ÷ 80

a. Circle groups of 80.

b. How many groups are there? ________

c. How many are not in a group? ________

d. 255 ÷ 80 = ________

2. 337 ÷ 40 = ________

3. 717 ÷ 90 = ________

4. 553 ÷ 70 = ________

5. 491 ÷ 50 = ________

6. 241 ÷ 30 = ________

7. 896 ÷ 60 = ________

Name ______________________

Another Look 12-4

Dividing with 2-Digit Divisors

You can use play money to help you divide.

114 ÷ 31 Divide $1.14 into groups of $0.31. In other words, divide 114¢ into groups of 31¢.

Arrange the money in groups of 31¢. Exchange dimes for pennies as needed.

Count the groups. Since there are 3 groups, 31 divides 114 three times. Since there is 21¢ left over, the remainder is 21.

114 ÷ 31 = 3 R21

Divide. You may use play money to help.

1. 193 ÷ 62 ________

2. 114 ÷ 83 ________

3. 337 ÷ 44 ________

4. 717 ÷ 96 ________

5. 553 ÷ 78 ________

6. 662 ÷ 84 ________

7. 439 ÷ 36 ________

8. 124 ÷ 41 ________

Name ______________________

Another Look
12-5

Decision Making

Write each time in minutes.

1. $1\frac{1}{4}$ hours ______
2. $\frac{3}{4}$ hour ______
3. $2\frac{3}{4}$ hours ______
4. $3\frac{1}{2}$ hours ______
5. $4\frac{1}{4}$ hours ______
6. $6\frac{3}{4}$ hours ______
7. $5\frac{1}{2}$ hours ______
8. $7\frac{1}{4}$ hours ______
9. $9\frac{1}{2}$ hours ______
10. $8\frac{3}{4}$ hours ______

Solve.

11. Joshua has 4 blank 90-minute videotapes. His favorite TV program is 30 minutes. How many programs can he tape? Explain how you found the answer.

____

____

12. For extra credit in a class, Sara wants to perform 6 hours of community service. She has 5 days in which to do it. If she does an equal amount each day, how many minutes per day will she work? Explain.

____

____

13. Sean worked on his math homework every weekday for 2 weeks. Each day, he spent $\frac{3}{4}$ hour on it. How many hours did he spend in all? Explain how you found the answer.

____

____

Name ______________________________

Another Look
12-6

Exploring Likely and Unlikely

In your book you explored likely and unlikely with miniature golf. Here is another way to understand likely and unlikely.

Sometimes you need to predict if an event can happen. You make predictions based on experiences you have had. Each statement shows the different ways you can think about an event.

You will eat. ⟶ certain
Think: You have to eat to live.

You have milk in your cereal. ⟶ likely
Think: Most people eat cereal with milk.

Your dinner will be served hot. ⟶ equally likely as unlikely
Think: You could have cold food instead.

Your dinner cost $100 to prepare. ⟶ unlikely
Think: Most meals do not cost this much.

You eat 100 pounds of beef for dinner. ⟶ impossible
Think: No one can eat this much.

Read each statement. Write whether the event is impossible, unlikely, equally likely as unlikely, likely, or certain.

1. Your school serves 1,000,000 lunches a day. ______________
2. The hamburgers cost $20.00 a pound. ______________
3. You eat a sandwich for lunch. ______________
4. You will have something new to eat this year. ______________
5. Cows produce milk. ______________
6. You eat a 2-pound steak for dinner. ______________
7. You have a drink with your lunch. ______________
8. You eat popcorn at the movies. ______________
9. Ice cream is made from hot dogs. ______________
10. The sun will rise in the east. ______________

 Use with pages 540–541.

Name ______________________________

Exploring Fairness

In your book you explored fairness using a number cube. Here is another way to explore fairness.

The **possible outcomes** of both spinner A and spinner B are 1, 2, 3, and 4.

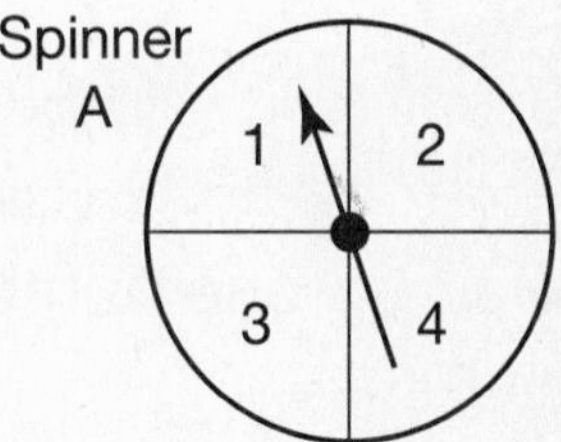

Example 1: Spinner A is divided into four equal parts. There is an **equally likely** chance of every possible outcome.

Spinner A is fair.

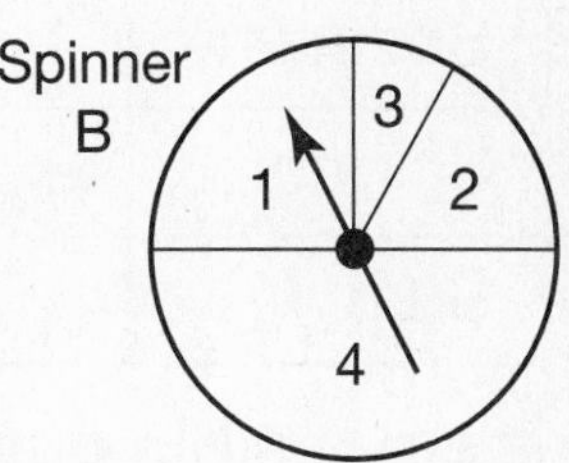

Example 2: Spinner B is divided into four parts but the parts are not equal. You have a greater chance of spinning 4 because that section is largest.

Spinner B is unfair.

Circle fair or unfair for each situation.

1. Spin the spinner.

fair or unfair

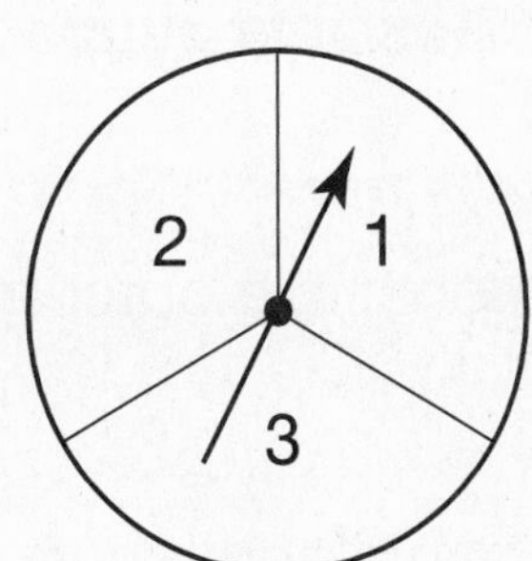

2. Spin the spinner.

fair or unfair

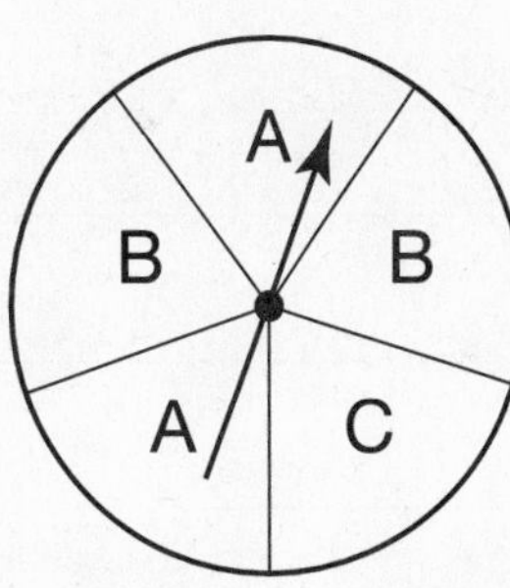

3. Pick a marble without looking.

fair or unfair

4. Toss a coin.

fair or unfair

Name ______________________

Another Look 12-8

Listing Possible Outcomes

Spin each spinner once. How many different sums are possible?
You can spin a 1 or a 2 on spinner A.
On spinner B you can spin either a 3, 4, 5, or 6.

Spinner A: 1, 2

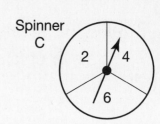

What are the possible combinations for both spinners together?

Pair up one number from each spinner and find the sums.

Spinner B: 3, 4, 5, 6

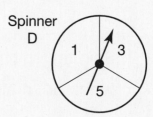

Spinner A	1	1	1	1	2	2	2	2
Spinner B	3	4	5	6	3	4	5	6
Sum	4	5	6	7	5	6	7	8

The **possible outcomes** (sums) are 4, 5, 6, 7, and 8.

A sum of 5, 6, or 7 is more likely than a sum of 4 or 8.

---

1. What are the possible outcomes for Spinner C?

Spinner C: 2, 4, 6

2. What are the possible outcomes for Spinner D?

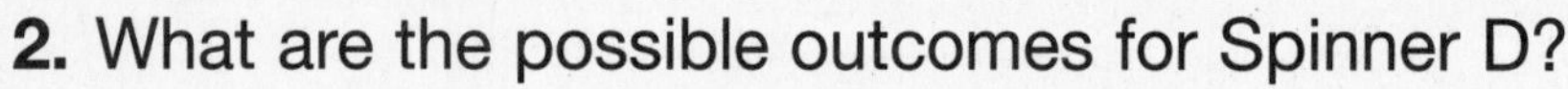

Spinner D: 1, 3, 5

3. Write the possible combinations for both spinners together.

4. How many different sums are possible? ________

5. List all the ways you can get a sum of 7.

____

Name ______________________________

Exploring Probability

In your book you used a number cube to explore probability. Here is another way to explore probability.

The spinner has 6 equal sections. So, the total number of different spins is 6.

You can spin an R, B, or G on this spinner.

What is the probability of spinning R?

There are 3 ways to spin R.
The probability of spinning R is $\frac{\text{number of ways to spin R}}{\text{total number of outcomes}} = \frac{3}{6}$

So, the probability is $\frac{3}{6} = \frac{1}{2}$.

Use the spinner above to answer **1–2.**

1. What is the probability of spinning B? ______

2. What is the probability of spinning G? ________

Use the spinner to find each probability.

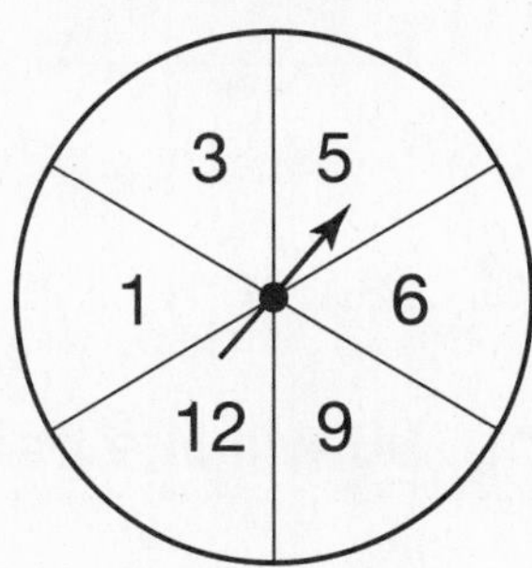

3. What is the probability of spinning a 3? ______

4. What is the probability of spinning an even number? ________

5. What is the probability of spinning a number less than 3? ______

Name ______________________

Exploring Predictions

In your book you played a guessing game to explore predictions. Here is another way to explore predictions.

In a survey, 20 students were asked their favorite breakfast food. The table shows the results.

Breakfast Food	
Cereal	10
Muffin	8
Bagel	2

Ten students like cereal.

The probability that someone likes cereal is 10 out of 20 or $\frac{10}{20}$.

Simplify: $\frac{10}{20} = \frac{1}{2}$.

The probability of an event can be used to predict future events.

You can use probability of $\frac{1}{2}$ to predict how many students out of 100 will like cereal.

Use equivalent fractions.

$$\frac{1}{2} \underset{\times 50}{\overset{\times 50}{=}} \frac{\square}{100}$$

You predict that 50 out of 100 students will like cereal.

Use the table.

1. What is the probability that a student likes bagels? $\frac{\square}{20} = \frac{\square}{\square}$

2. How many students out of 100 will like bagels?

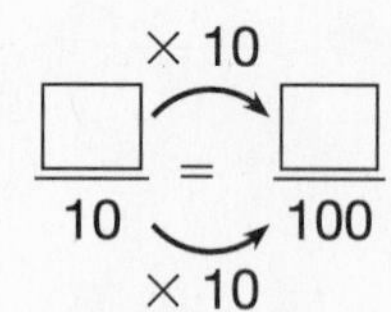

3. What is the probability that a student likes muffins? ______

4. Predict how many students out of 500 will like muffins.

______

5. Predict how many students out of 300 will like cereal.

______

Name ______________________________

Another Look
12-11

Analyze Strategies: Solve a Simpler Problem

Ellen has enough ribbon to wrap 12 gift boxes. How many cuts will she have to make to have 12 ribbons?

Think of a simpler problem to help find a solution.

Find the number of cuts needed to have 2 ribbons.

2 ribbons, 1 cut needed

Now try 3 ribbons.

3 ribbons, 2 cuts needed

Now try 4 ribbons.

4 ribbons, 3 cuts needed

Look for a pattern.

The number of cuts needed is always 1 less than the number of ribbons needed.

If 12 ribbons are needed, there must be 11 cuts.

Solve. Try finding a simpler problem.

1. Mrs. Wilson has enough ribbon to decorate 24 door wreaths. For 24 pieces of ribbon, how many cuts will she have to make? ________

2. Eight boys and 8 girls are in a tennis tournament. Each boy plays each girl once. How many games are played? ________

3. In a bag of mixed nuts, there is one Brazil nut for every 3 cashews. If there are 48 cashews, how many Brazil nuts will there be? ________

Name ____________________

Another Look 1-1

Pictographs and Bar Graphs

This **bar graph** shows the number of skyscrapers in some major cities. The **pictograph** shows the same data.

How many skyscrapers are there in Chicago, IL?

To find the data on the bar graph, follow the bar next to Chicago. It ends at 50, so there are __50__ skyscrapers in Chicago.

Cities with the Most Skyscrapers

New York, NY
Chicago, IL
Houston, TX
Los Angeles, CA
Hong Kong

0 10 20 30 40 50 60 70 80 90 100 110 120 130 140

Number of Skyscrapers

To find the data on the pictograph, find Chicago on the left. There are 5 symbols next to Chicago. Each symbol shows 10 skyscrapers. Count 1 ten for each symbol. 10. . . 20. . . 30. . . 40. . . 50. . . . Chicago has __50__ skyscrapers.

Cities with the Most Skyscrapers

New York, NY	13 symbols
Chicago, IL	5 symbols
Houston, TX	3 symbols
Los Angeles, CA	2 symbols
Hong Kong	2 symbols

(symbol) = 10 skyscrapers

Use the graphs to answer the questions.

1. Which city has about 30 skyscrapers? Houston, TX
2. Do Chicago, Houston, Los Angeles, and Hong Kong all together have more skyscrapers than New York? No
3. Which cities have fewer than 50 skyscrapers? Houston, Los Angeles, and Hong Kong
4. Suppose your town has 20 skyscrapers. How many symbols would you draw in the pictograph? 2

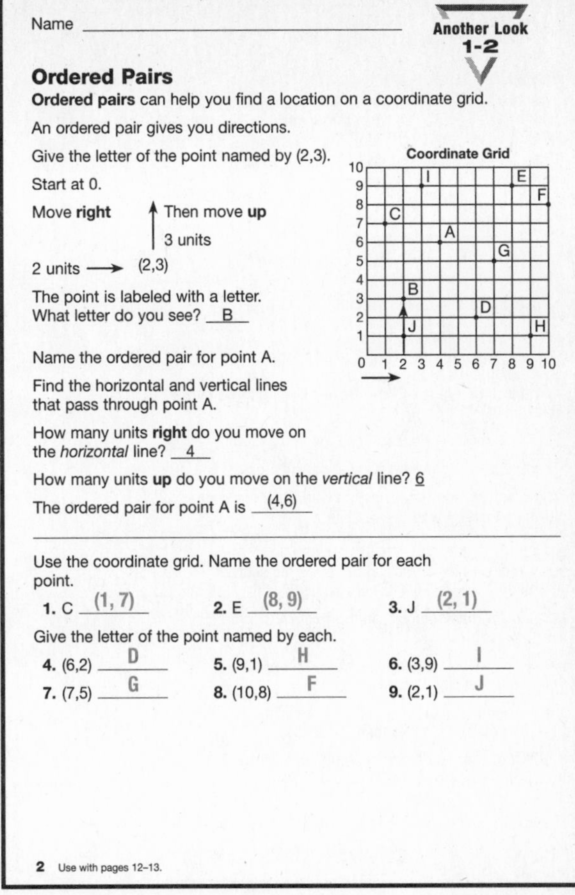

Name ____________________

Another Look 1-2

Ordered Pairs

Ordered pairs can help you find a location on a coordinate grid.

An ordered pair gives you directions.

Give the letter of the point named by (2,3).

Start at 0.

Move **right** 2 units → Then move **up** 3 units (2,3)

The point is labeled with a letter. What letter do you see? __B__

Name the ordered pair for point A.

Find the horizontal and vertical lines that pass through point A.

How many units **right** do you move on the *horizontal* line? __4__

How many units **up** do you move on the *vertical* line? __6__

The ordered pair for point A is __(4,6)__

Use the coordinate grid. Name the ordered pair for each point.

1. C __(1, 7)__ **2.** E __(8, 9)__ **3.** J __(2, 1)__

Give the letter of the point named by each.

4. (6,2) __D__ **5.** (9,1) __H__ **6.** (3,9) __I__
7. (7,5) __G__ **8.** (10,8) __F__ **9.** (2,1) __J__

Name ____________________

Another Look 1-3

Reading Line Graphs

You can read **line graphs** to get information. This line graph shows the number of students that were absent each month.

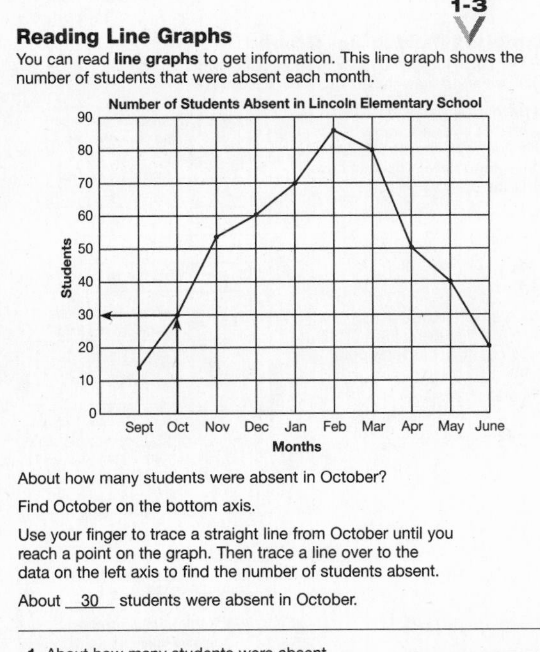

About how many students were absent in October?

Find October on the bottom axis.

Use your finger to trace a straight line from October until you reach a point on the graph. Then trace a line over to the data on the left axis to find the number of students absent.

About __30__ students were absent in October.

1. About how many students were absent in December? About 60 students
2. About how many students were absent in March? About 80 students
3. In which month were about 50 students absent? April
4. In which month were about 40 students absent? May

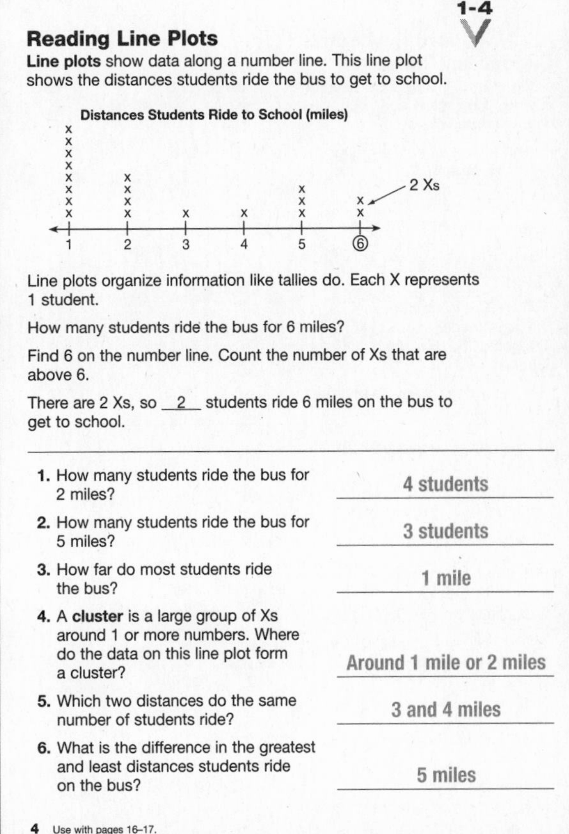

Name ____________________

Another Look 1-4

Reading Line Plots

Line plots show data along a number line. This line plot shows the distances students ride the bus to get to school.

Line plots organize information like tallies do. Each X represents 1 student.

How many students ride the bus for 6 miles?

Find 6 on the number line. Count the number of Xs that are above 6.

There are 2 Xs, so __2__ students ride 6 miles on the bus to get to school.

1. How many students ride the bus for 2 miles? 4 students
2. How many students ride the bus for 5 miles? 3 students
3. How far do most students ride the bus? 1 mile
4. A **cluster** is a large group of Xs around 1 or more numbers. Where do the data on this line plot form a cluster? Around 1 mile or 2 miles
5. Which two distances do the same number of students ride? 3 and 4 miles
6. What is the difference in the greatest and least distances students ride on the bus? 5 miles

Name ______________________

Another Look 1-5

Reading Stem-and-Leaf Plots

This stem-and-leaf plot shows the number of points scored by the Green Bay Packers in their games during the 1995 season.

The numbers in the stem are tens digits. The numbers in the leaf are ones digits.

Stem	Leaf
1	4 4 6 0
2	7 4 4 4 4 4
3	0 8 5 1 5 4

← Shows 14, 14, 16, and 10 points.

You can use the stem-and-leaf plot to find the greatest number of points the Green Bay Packers scored in one game in 1995.

First look for the greatest tens digit in the stem. 3

Then look for the greatest one digit in its leaf. 8

The greatest number of points scored by the Green Bay Packers in 1995 was 38 points.

1. What was the least number of points scored by the Green Bay Packers in 1995? 10 points
2. In how many games did the Packers score 14 points? 2 games
3. What would you say is a typical score for the Green Bay Packers? 24 points
4. In how many games did the Green Bay Packers score more than 25 points? 7 games
5. What was the difference in points between Green Bay's best and worst scores? 28 points

Name ______________________

Another Look 1-6

Analyze Word Problems: Introduction to Problem Solving Guide

This bar graph shows the lengths of the world's longest rivers.

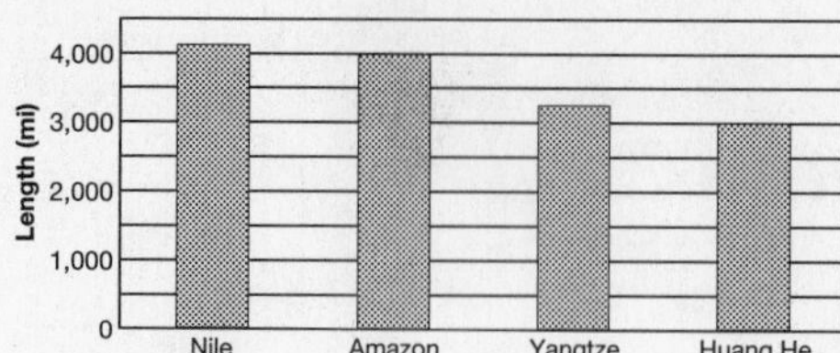

Find the difference in length between the longest and shortest rivers in the bar graph.

Step 1 Find the data in the bar graph.

The Nile is the longest river and is about 4,000 miles long. The Huang He is the shortest river and is about 3,000 miles long.

Step 2 Determine the operation to use.

Subtract the 2 lengths to find the difference.

Step 3 Find the answer.

4,000 miles − 3,000 miles = 1,000 miles

The Nile is 1,000 miles longer than the Huang He.

Find the total length of the Amazon and the Huang He rivers.

1. What is your first step? Find the lengths of the Amazon and Huang He rivers.
2. What operation will you use? Addition
3. Solve the problem. 4,000 miles + 3,000 miles = 7,000 miles

Name ______________________

Another Look 1-7

Analyze Word Problems: Choose an Operation

A dog breeder has 8 dogs. Then one of his dogs has 5 puppies. How many dogs does he have now? Decide what operation you will use.

Do you put together two groups (add) or compare two groups (subtract)?

The dog breeder wants to know how many animals he has all together. So, you are putting together the dogs and the puppies.

How many dogs does the breeder have now? 13 dogs

Which number sentence would you use to solve each of the following?

1. The dog breeder spends $7 a day on dog food. How much does she spend in 2 days? A

   A. $7 + $7 = ▩ **B.** $7 − $7 = ▩

2. Last year a dog license cost $10. This year it costs $14. How much more is a license this year? B

   A. $10 + $14 = ▩ **B.** $14 − $10 = ▩

3. The dog breeder has 12 puppies for sale. He sells 5 puppies one weekend. How many puppies are left? B

   A. 12 + 5 = ▩ **B.** 12 − 5 = ▩

4. One puppy sells for $25. Another sells for $40. How much do their sales total? B

   A. $40 − $25 = ▩ **B.** $40 + $25 = ▩

Name ______________________

Another Look 1-8

Exploring Making Bar Graphs

In your book you learned how to show data using a bar graph. Here is another way to draw the bars to show the data.

To draw a bar that shows the number of students who own Birds look at the scale for Students. You need to draw a bar that goes up to the line for 6.

Draw an arrow to the bar for birds.

Animal	Number of Students Who Own Animals
Bird	6
Cat	9
Dog	10
Pony	2
Gerbil	3

How can you draw a bar to show that 9 students own cats? The scale does not show odd numbers.

Since 9 is between 8 and 10, make the top of the bar halfway between 8 and 10.

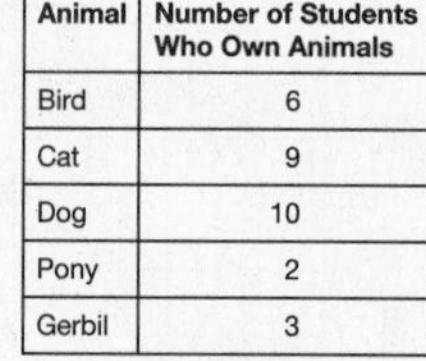

1. Complete the graph above.
   a. Draw the bar for the number of students who own dogs.
   b. Draw the bar for the number of students who own ponies.
   c. Draw the bar for the number of students who own gerbils.
2. Complete the bar graph to show the data in the table below.

Student	Hours Spent on Pet Care Weekly
Anika	9
Corine	14
Martin	16
Priscilla	4

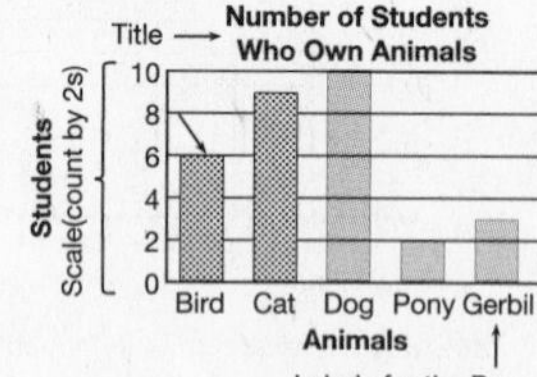

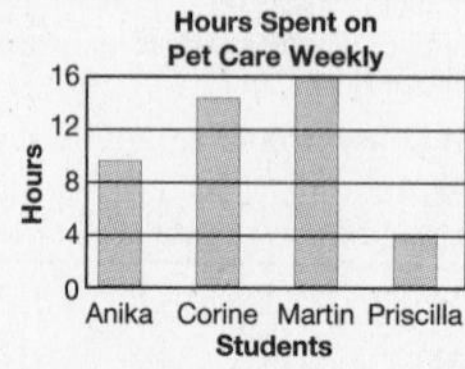

Name ______________________ **Another Look 1-9**

Exploring Making Line Plots

In your book, you showed data from a tally table on a line plot. You can show data from other tables on a line plot.

Look at the data in the table.

Miles Run	Days
2	2
3	4
4	5
5	3
6	2

To show on a line plot the number of days that Freda ran 4 miles, you need to make 5 Xs above the 4.

How can you show that Freda ran 2 miles on each of 2 days?

Since each X represents 1 day, make 2 Xs above the 2.

Complete the line plot.

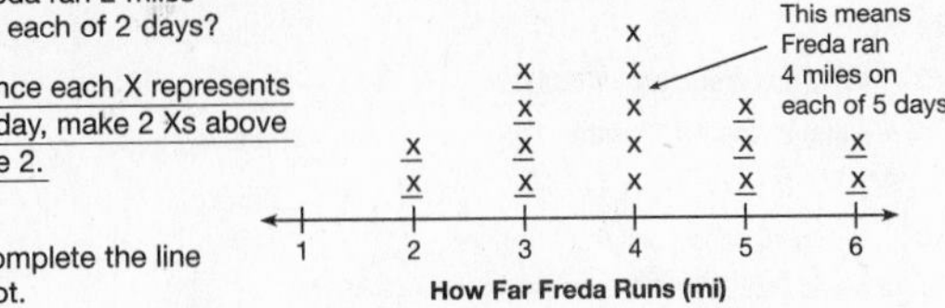

1. Complete the line plot to show the data in the table.

Weight (lb)	Number of Puppies
3	5
4	3
5	2
6	0
7	1

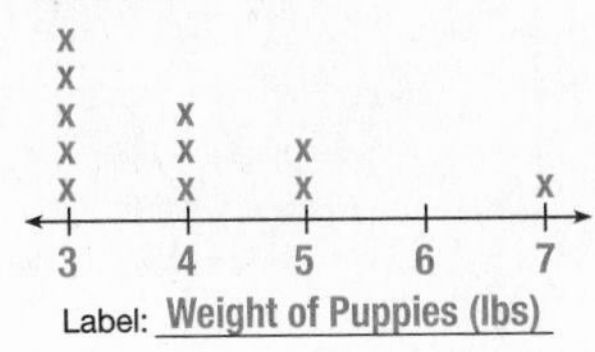

Label: Weight of Puppies (lbs)

Name ______________________ **Another Look 1-10**

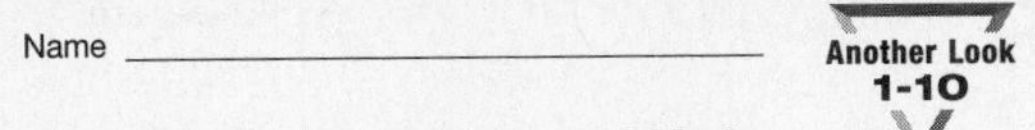

Exploring Range, Median, and Mode

In your book you explored range, median, and mode by arranging data cards. Here is another way to find range, median, and mode.

Suppose these are the weights (in pounds) of 9 cats.

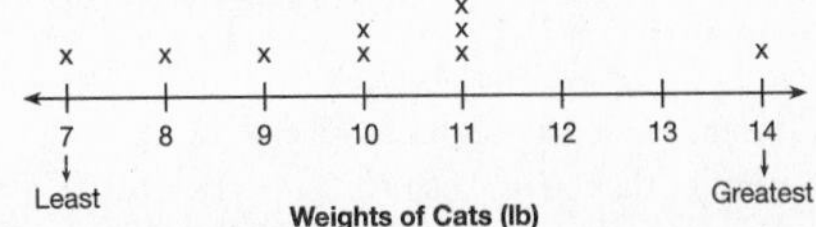

The **range** is the difference between the least and greatest weights.

14 lb − 7 lb = 7 lb

The **mode** is the number with the greatest number of X's. (If no number occurs more than once, there is no mode.) 11 lb

The **median** is the middle number. Circle pairs of X's—one from each side of the line plot. Stop when only one number remains.

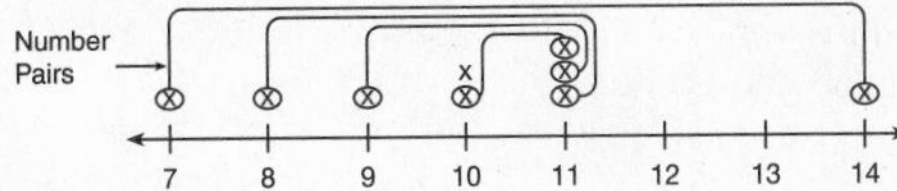

The median is 10 lb.

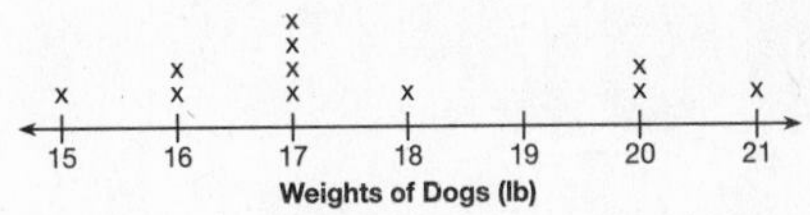

Use the line plot of dog weights (in pounds) for **1–3**.

1. Find the range of the weights. 21 − 15 = 6
2. Find the mode of the weights. 17 lb
3. Find the median weight. 17 lb

Name ______________________ **Another Look 1-11**

Exploring Algebra: What's the Rule?

In your book you explored finding a rule for number pairs by playing "Guess My Rule." Here is another way to find the rule for number pairs.

In	3	5	8	4
Out	7	9	12	

Step 1 Look at the first pair of numbers, 3 and 7. Think: What can you do to 3 to get 7?
You can add 4 to 3 to get 7.

Step 2 Check your rule with the next pairs of numbers.
Since 5 + 4 = 9 and 8 + 4 = 12, the rule checks.

Step 3 Write your rule in words. Write the operation and the number.
add 4
Write your rule with a variable. Use a letter in the place of the In number, then follow with the operation sign and the number.
$n + 4$

Step 4 Use your rule to complete the table. 4 + 4 = 8

Answer the questions, then complete the table.

In	8	10	11	6	9	14
Out	5	7	8	3	6	11

1. What can you do to 8 to get 5? Subtract 3.
2. What can you do to 10 to get 7? Subtract 3.
3. Write the rule in words. Subtract 3.
4. Write the rule using a variable. $n - 3$
5. Use the rule to complete the table.

Name ______________________ **Another Look 1-12**

Analyze Strategies: Guess and Check

Every morning, Rosie meets Tammi on their way to school. The girls walk a total of 11 blocks. They meet after Rosie walks 3 blocks. How far does each girl live from school?

Guesses		Sum	Difference
Rosie	Tammi	11	3
8	3	11	5
6	5	11	1
7	4	11	3

Rosie walks 3 blocks further than Tammi each day.

Guess: Find any two numbers whose sum is 11. 8 + 3 = 11

Write your guess in the table.

Check: What is the difference between the two numbers? 8 − 3 = 5

What should the difference be between the numbers? 3

Keep guessing until you find the pair that works.

How far does Rosie walk? 7 blocks Tammi Lee? 4 blocks

Use the table to record your guesses. Keep guessing until you find a pair that works.

1. Sam earned $8 in two days for helping his neighbor. On Friday he earned $2 more than on Saturday. How much did he earn each day?
   Friday $5
   Saturday $3

Guesses		Sum	Difference
Friday	Saturday	$8	$2

2. Millen swam a total of 30 yards in two tries. The second time she swam 10 yards farther than the first time. How far did she swim each time?
   1st time 10 yd
   2nd time 20 yd

Guesses		Sum	Difference
First Time	Second Time	30	10

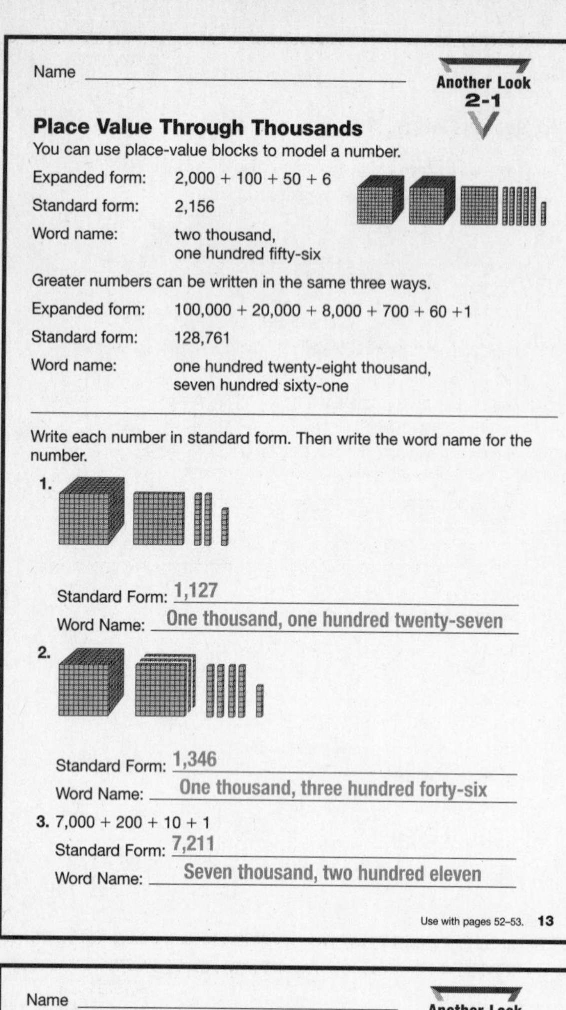

Name ______________________

Another Look 2-1

Place Value Through Thousands

You can use place-value blocks to model a number.

Expanded form: 2,000 + 100 + 50 + 6

Standard form: 2,156

Word name: two thousand, one hundred fifty-six

Greater numbers can be written in the same three ways.

Expanded form: 100,000 + 20,000 + 8,000 + 700 + 60 + 1

Standard form: 128,761

Word name: one hundred twenty-eight thousand, seven hundred sixty-one

Write each number in standard form. Then write the word name for the number.

1.

Standard Form: 1,127

Word Name: One thousand, one hundred twenty-seven

2.

Standard Form: 1,346

Word Name: One thousand, three hundred forty-six

3. 7,000 + 200 + 10 + 1

Standard Form: 7,211

Word Name: Seven thousand, two hundred eleven

Use with pages 52–53. 13

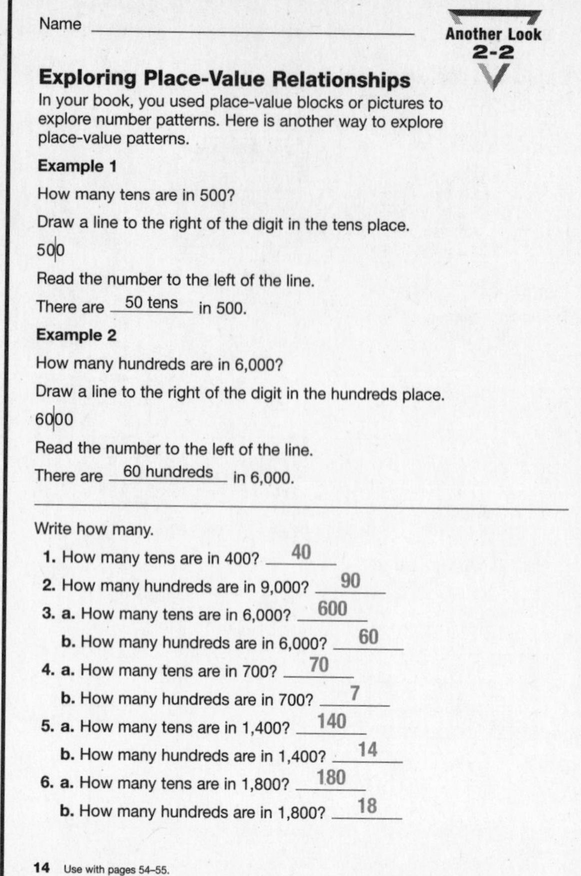

Name ______________________

Another Look 2-2

Exploring Place-Value Relationships

In your book, you used place-value blocks or pictures to explore number patterns. Here is another way to explore place-value patterns.

Example 1

How many tens are in 500?

Draw a line to the right of the digit in the tens place.

50|0

Read the number to the left of the line.

There are 50 tens in 500.

Example 2

How many hundreds are in 6,000?

Draw a line to the right of the digit in the hundreds place.

60|00

Read the number to the left of the line.

There are 60 hundreds in 6,000.

Write how many.

1. How many tens are in 400? 40
2. How many hundreds are in 9,000? 90
3. a. How many tens are in 6,000? 600
   b. How many hundreds are in 6,000? 60
4. a. How many tens are in 700? 70
   b. How many hundreds are in 700? 7
5. a. How many tens are in 1,400? 140
   b. How many hundreds are in 1,400? 14
6. a. How many tens are in 1,800? 180
   b. How many hundreds are in 1,800? 18

14 Use with pages 54–55.

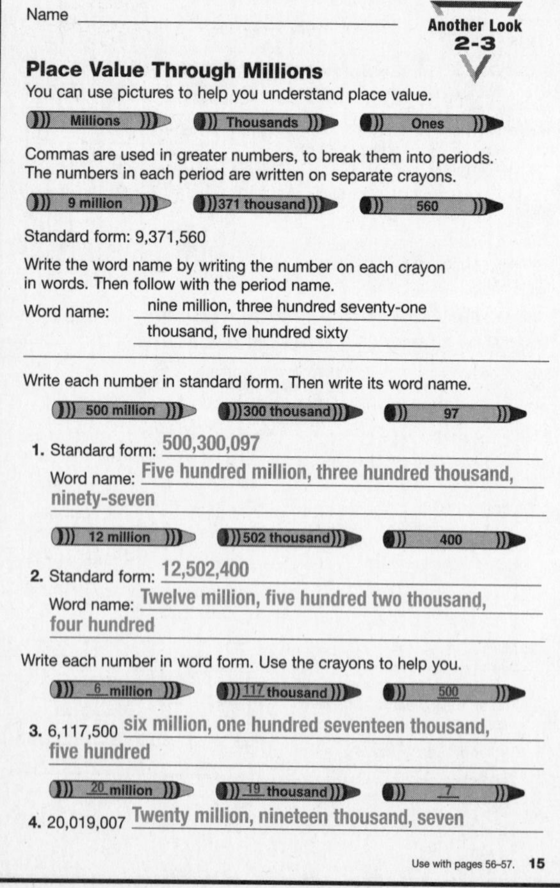

Name ______________________

Another Look 2-3

Place Value Through Millions

You can use pictures to help you understand place value.

Millions | Thousands | Ones

Commas are used in greater numbers, to break them into periods. The numbers in each period are written on separate crayons.

9 million | 371 thousand | 560

Standard form: 9,371,560

Write the word name by writing the number on each crayon in words. Then follow with the period name.

Word name: nine million, three hundred seventy-one thousand, five hundred sixty

Write each number in standard form. Then write its word name.

500 million | 300 thousand | 97

1. Standard form: 500,300,097

   Word name: Five hundred million, three hundred thousand, ninety-seven

12 million | 502 thousand | 400

2. Standard form: 12,502,400

   Word name: Twelve million, five hundred two thousand, four hundred

Write each number in word form. Use the crayons to help you.

6 million | 117 thousand | 500

3. 6,117,500 six million, one hundred seventeen thousand, five hundred

20 million | 19 thousand | 7

4. 20,019,007 Twenty million, nineteen thousand, seven

Use with pages 56–57. 15

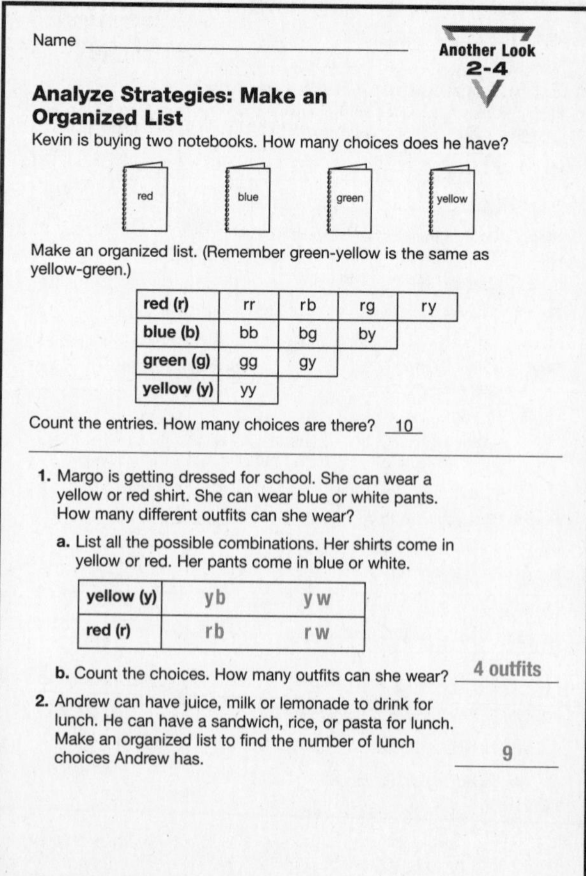

Name ______________________

Another Look 2-4

Analyze Strategies: Make an Organized List

Kevin is buying two notebooks. How many choices does he have?

Make an organized list. (Remember green-yellow is the same as yellow-green.)

red (r)	rr	rb	rg	ry
blue (b)	bb	bg	by	
green (g)	gg	gy		
yellow (y)	yy			

Count the entries. How many choices are there? 10

1. Margo is getting dressed for school. She can wear a yellow or red shirt. She can wear blue or white pants. How many different outfits can she wear?

   a. List all the possible combinations. Her shirts come in yellow or red. Her pants come in blue or white.

yellow (y)	yb	yw
red (r)	rb	rw

   b. Count the choices. How many outfits can she wear? 4 outfits

2. Andrew can have juice, milk or lemonade to drink for lunch. He can have a sandwich, rice, or pasta for lunch. Make an organized list to find the number of lunch choices Andrew has. 9

16 Use with pages 58–61.

Name ____________________

Another Look 2-5

Comparing Numbers

You can use a place-value chart to compare numbers.

Compare 14,260 and 14,306. Find which is greater.

Thousands Period			Ones Period		
hundreds	tens	ones	hundreds	tens	ones
	1	4	2	6	0
	1	4	3	0	6

Begin at the left. Compare.

How many ten thousands does 14,260 have? 1

How many ten thousands does 14,306 have? 1

How many thousands does 14,260 have? 4

How many thousands does 14,306 have? 4

How many hundreds does 14,260 have? 2

How many hundreds does 14,306 have? 3

14,306 > 14,260 because 14,306 has more hundreds than 14,260. 14,306 > 14,260

Compare. Write >, <, or =.

1. 3,210 (<) 3,401

Thousands Period			Ones Period		
hundreds	tens	ones	hundreds	tens	ones
		3	2	1	0
		3	4	0	1

2. 52,348 (>) 51,348

Thousands Period			Ones Period		
hundreds	tens	ones	hundreds	tens	ones
	5	2	3	4	8
	5	1	3	4	8

Name ____________________

Ordering Numbers

You can use a number line to order numbers. Order these numbers from greatest to least:

21,359; 22,491; 19,389

Step 1 Draw a number line.

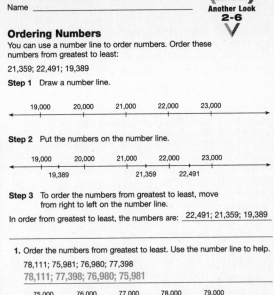

Step 2 Put the numbers on the number line.

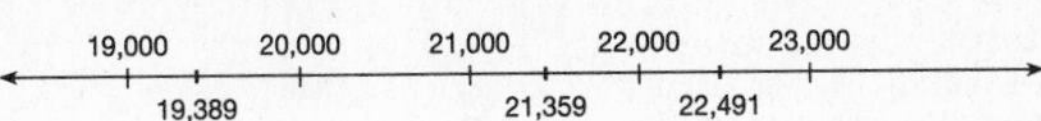

Step 3 To order the numbers from greatest to least, move from right to left on the number line.

In order from greatest to least, the numbers are: 22,491; 21,359; 19,389

1. Order the numbers from greatest to least. Use the number line to help.

78,111; 75,981; 76,980; 77,398

78,111; 77,398; 76,980; 75,981

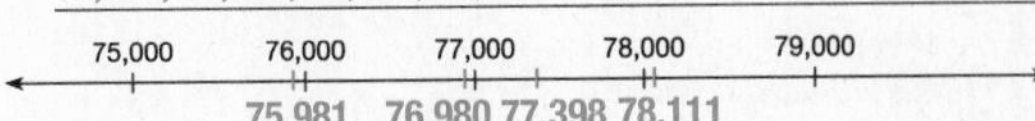

2. Order the numbers from least to greatest (left to right on the number line).

152,000; 155,281; 153,892; 154,389

152,000; 153,892; 154,389; 155,281

152,000 153,000 154,000 155,000 156,000

152,000 153,892 154,389 155,281

Name ____________________

Another Look 2-7

Exploring Rounding

In your book you used halfway numbers on number lines to help you round numbers. Here is another way to round numbers.

Each box shows two numbers and the number halfway between them. Write the **number to be rounded** above or below the halfway number. The number next to your written answer is the rounded number.

Example: Round 178 to the nearest hundred: 200

178	200
- - - - - -	(150)
	100

178 is greater than 150, so 178 is closer to 200 than 100. 178 rounded to the nearest 100 is 200.

1. Round 318 to the nearest hundred: 300

	400
- - - - - -	(350)
318	300

2. Round 6,235 to the nearest hundred: 6,200

	6,300
- - - - - -	(6,250)
6,235	6,200

3. Round 145 to the nearest hundred: 100

	200
- - - - - -	(150)
145	100

4. Round 8,769 to the nearest thousand: 9,000

8,769	9,000
- - - - - -	(8,500)
	8,000

5. Write the halfway number in the box. Then round 478 to the nearest hundred. 500

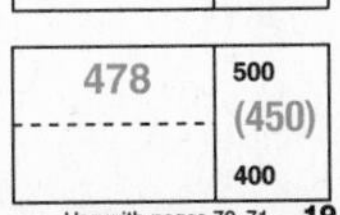

478	500
- - - - - -	(450)
	400

Name ____________________

Another Look 2-8

Telling Time

Read the time on one clock and show it on the other.

Here is the analog clock: Here is the digital clock:

8:15

The longer hand shows the minutes. It is 15 minutes after the hour. The shorter hand points to the hour. The shorter hand is pointing to 8.

You can read the time in 2 ways.

One way: Tell how many minutes after the hour it is. It is eight-fifteen.

Another way: Tell how many minutes until the next hour. It is forty-five minutes before nine.

1. Here is the analog clock: Draw the digital clock:

10:05

2. Here is the analog clock: Draw the digital clock:

1:45

Write each time two ways.

3.

Half past three; 30 minutes before four

4. 6:20 Six-twenty; 40 minutes before seven

Name ______________________

Another Look 2-9

Exploring Time: Exact or Estimate?

It takes about : 1 second to blink your eyes.

1 minute to walk a block.

1 hour to do homework.

1 day to drive across Texas.

1 week for a plant to sprout.

Using this data as reference, you know that you cannot tie your shoe in 1 second. You may not need a full minute either. You can probably tie your shoe in a few seconds. So the most reasonable unit of time to tie your shoe is seconds.

Fill in the blanks with one of the following units of time: seconds, minutes, hours, days, weeks, months, or years.

1. A weekend lasts for 2 __days__.
2. A cup of hot chocolate lasts for about 5 __minutes__.
3. You can keep library books for 2 or 3 __weeks__.
4. Each night, most people sleep for 8–10 __hours__.
5. Most television commercials last for about 20 __seconds__.
6. I threw a ball in the air and I caught it in 2 __seconds__.
7. I rode my bike for 30 __minutes__.
8. Recess lasts 20 __minutes__.
9. Movies are usually about 2 __hours__ long.
10. My summer vacation from school lasts 2 __months__.
11. I have been going to this school for 3 __years__.
12. I put my sweater on in about 5 __seconds__.
13. Your hair grows about an inch in 4 __weeks__.
14. Dentists like to check your teeth every 6 __months__.

Name ______________________

Another Look 2-10

Elapsed Time

Departure Time	Arrival Time
Boston 1:00	Cleveland 4:10

How long does it take to fly from Boston to Cleveland?

Use a clock to help you.

From 1:00 P.M. until 4:00 P.M. is 3 hours. Count 10 minutes from 4:00 P.M. until 4:10 P.M.

It takes __3 hours and 10 minutes__ to fly from Boston to Cleveland.

Write each elapsed time. Use a clock to help you.

1. 9:15 P.M. to 10:30 P.M.
   9:00 P.M. to 10:00 P.M. is __1__ hour(s).
   :15 to :30 is __15__ minutes
   __1 hour and 15 minutes__
2. 5:15 P.M. to 8:30 P.M.
   5:00 P.M. to 8:00 P.M. is __3__ hour(s).
   :15 to :30 is __15__ minutes.
   __3 hours and 15 minutes__
3. 1:00 P.M. to 10:30 P.M. __9 and a half hours__
4. 8:30 P.M. to 9:15 P.M. __45 minutes__
5. 7:20 A.M. to 10:05 A.M. __2 hours and 45 minutes__
6. 10:15 A.M. to 1:00 P.M. __2 hours and 45 minutes__

Name ______________________

Another Look 2-11

Exploring the Calendar

Use the calendar to answer each question.

July

Sun.	Mon.	Tues.	Wed.	Thur.	Fri.	Sat.
				1	2	3
4	5	6	7	8	9	10
11	12	13	14	15	16	17
18	19	20	21	22	23	24
25	26	27	28	29	30	31

How many Fridays are in this month?

Count the squares under Friday. __There are 5__.

Write the date of the third Wednesday.

Count the first 3 Wednesdays and write the date. __July 21__

Write the day of the week of July 7th.

Find the number 7 and look at the top of the column to see the day of the week. __Wednesday__

1. How many Mondays are in July? __4__
2. How many Wednesdays? __4__
3. How many Thursdays? __5__
4. Write the dates of these days.
   a. the fourth Tuesday __July 27__
   b. the second Monday __July 12__
   c. the fifth Friday __July 30__
5. Write the days of the week of these dates.
   a. July 18th __Sunday__
   b. July 1st __Thursday__
   c. July 10th __Saturday__

Name ______________________

Another Look 2-12

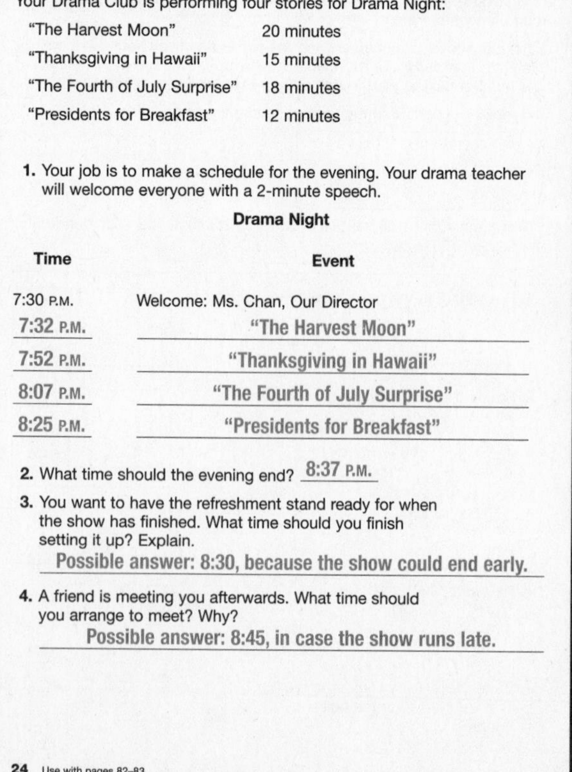

Decision Making

Your Drama Club is performing four stories for Drama Night:

"The Harvest Moon"	20 minutes
"Thanksgiving in Hawaii"	15 minutes
"The Fourth of July Surprise"	18 minutes
"Presidents for Breakfast"	12 minutes

1. Your job is to make a schedule for the evening. Your drama teacher will welcome everyone with a 2-minute speech.

Drama Night

Time	Event
7:30 P.M.	Welcome: Ms. Chan, Our Director
7:32 P.M.	"The Harvest Moon"
7:52 P.M.	"Thanksgiving in Hawaii"
8:07 P.M.	"The Fourth of July Surprise"
8:25 P.M.	"Presidents for Breakfast"

2. What time should the evening end? __8:37 P.M.__
3. You want to have the refreshment stand ready for when the show has finished. What time should you finish setting it up? Explain.
   __Possible answer: 8:30, because the show could end early.__
4. A friend is meeting you afterwards. What time should you arrange to meet? Why?
   __Possible answer: 8:45, in case the show runs late.__

Name ______________________

Another Look 3-1

Exploring Addition and Subtraction Patterns

In your book you used patterns to help you add and subtract mentally. Here is another way using place-value blocks.

Use place-value blocks to find the sum of 60 and 30.

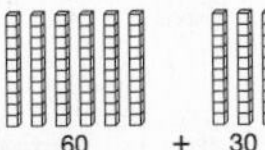

The place-value blocks help you see that 60 + 30 = 90.

You can also use place-value blocks to find the difference between 400 and 200.

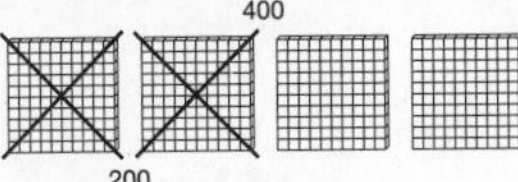

The place-value blocks help you see that 400 − 200 = 200.

Use place-value blocks to help find each sum or difference. Check with a calculator.

1. 70 + 20 = 90
700 + 200 = 900
7,000 + 2,000 = 9,000

2. 70 − 20 = 50
700 − 200 = 500
7,000 − 2,000 = 5,000

3. 40 + 60 = 100
400 + 600 = 1,000
4,000 + 6,000 = 10,000

4. 60 − 40 = 20
600 − 400 = 200
6,000 − 4,000 = 2,000

5. 90 + 50 = 140
900 + 500 = 1,400
9,000 + 5,000 = 14,000

6. 90 − 50 = 40
900 − 500 = 400
9,000 − 5,000 = 4,000

Name ______________________

Another Look 3-2

Exploring Adding and Subtracting on a Thousand Chart

In your book you used counters on a thousand chart to add and subtract. Here is another way to use a thousand chart.

Find 300 − 100.

Put your finger on 100.
How many hundreds do you have to move to get to 300?
You move 2 hundreds.

300 − 100 = 200

Find 380 − 150.

Put your finger on 150.
How many hundreds do you have to move to get to the 300s?
You move 2 hundreds to 350.

How many tens do you have to move to get from 350 to 380?
You move 3 tens.

380 − 150 = 230

Add or subtract. Use a thousand chart.

1. 840 − 310

a. Start at 310. How many hundreds do you have to move to get to the 800s? 5

b. How many tens do you have to move to get from 810 to 840? 3

c. The difference is 5 hundreds and 3 tens.

d. 840 − 310 = 530

2. 130 + 290

a. Put your finger on 290. Move up 1 hundred. On what number did your finger land? 390

b. Move up 3 tens. On what number did your finger land? 420

c. 130 + 290 = 420

3. Find 620 − 210. 410

4. Find 330 + 210. 540

Name ______________________

Another Look 3-3

Estimating Sums and Differences

You can use a number line to help you estimate sums and differences.

Estimate 248 + 457.

Is 248 closer to 200 or 300?
Since 248 $<$ 250, it is closer to 200.

200 225 250 275 300 (248 marked)

Is 457 closer to 400 or 500?
Since 457 $>$ 450, it is closer to 500.

400 425 450 475 500 (457 marked)

Estimate the sum by adding the rounded addends.

200 + 500 = 700

Estimate by rounding to the nearest hundred.

1. 548 − 160

a. Is 548 closer to 500 or 600? 500

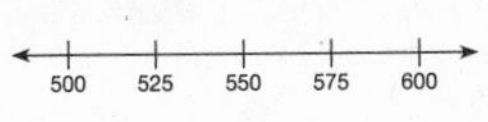

b. Is 160 closer to 100 or 200? 200

100 125 150 175 200

c. 500 − 200 = 300

2. 814 − 335
800 − 300 = 500

3. 329 + 221
300 + 200 = 500

4. 624 + 919
600 + 900 = 1,500

5. 735 + 589
700 + 600 = 1,300

6. 911 − 732
200

7. 852 − 499
400

8. 328 + 271
600

9. 729 − 356
300

10. 615 − 138
500

11. 521 + 411
900

12. 298 − 157
100

13. 362 + 621
1,000

14. 417 + 388
800

Name ______________________

Another Look 3-4

Analyze Word Problems: Exact or Estimate?

Cindy has a dentist's appointment at 4:00. She plans to go shopping and then to the library beforehand. She wants to shop for about an hour and a half and study at the library for about an hour.

Travel Time	
Home → Store	20 min.
Store → Library	18 min.
Library → Dentist	13 min.

Can Cindy estimate the time she should leave, or does she need an exact answer?

Cindy does not know exactly how long she will be shopping or studying, so she doesn't have to leave the house at an exact time. Since she wants to make sure she's at the dentist by 4:00, she should overestimate.

For each problem, tell if you need an exact answer or an estimate.

1. Ron has given 3 recitals this month. At his last recital, he had 118 guests. At the recital before that, he had 180 guests. 165 people came to the first recital. About how many guests have come to Ron's recitals?

Exact or estimate? Estimate

2. Karen is the owner of City Diner. She is planning to bake pies for the upcoming week. Last week 57 people ordered pie. One pie serves 8 people.

a. How many pies should Karen bake?

Exact or estimate? Estimate

b. What is the greatest number of people Karen can serve if she bakes 8 pies?

Exact or estimate? Exact

3. Ann has $3.40. She would like to buy a juice which costs $0.75 and a sandwich which costs $2.55. Does she have enough?

Exact or estimate? Exact

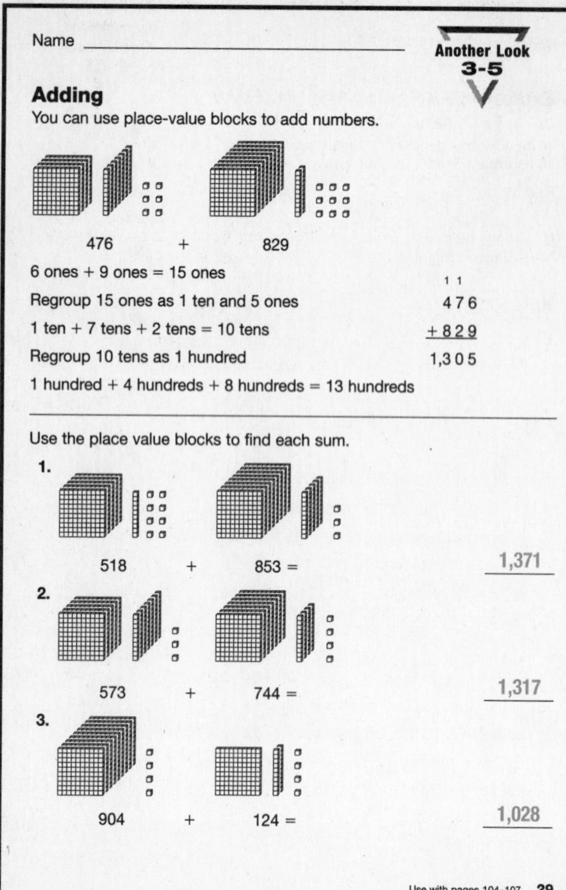

Name ______________________

Another Look 3-5

Adding

You can use place-value blocks to add numbers.

476 + 829

6 ones + 9 ones = 15 ones

Regroup 15 ones as 1 ten and 5 ones

1 ten + 7 tens + 2 tens = 10 tens

Regroup 10 tens as 1 hundred

1 hundred + 4 hundreds + 8 hundreds = 13 hundreds

```
  1 1
  4 7 6
+ 8 2 9
1,3 0 5
```

Use the place value blocks to find each sum.

1. 518 + 853 = 1,371

2. 573 + 744 = 1,317

3. 904 + 124 = 1,028

Use with pages 104–107. 29

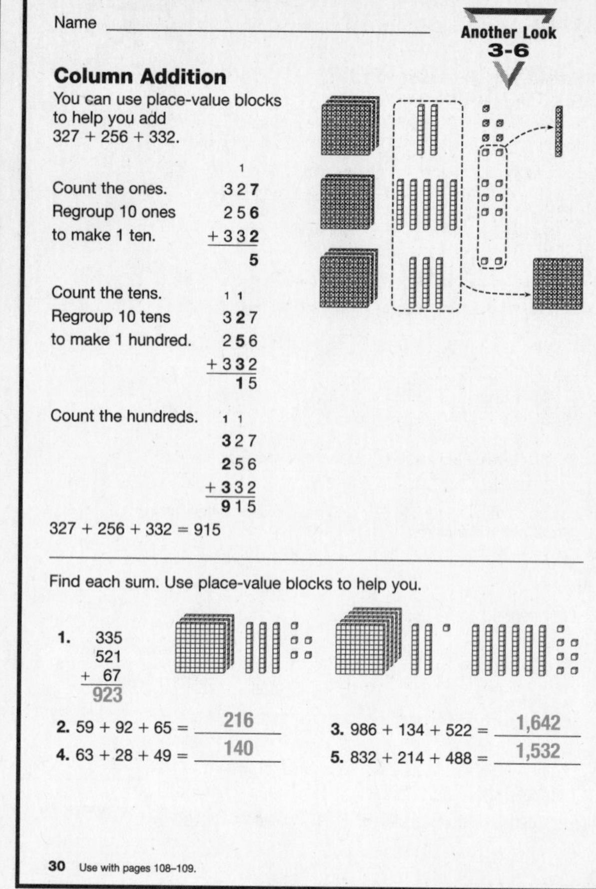

Name ______________________

Another Look 3-6

Column Addition

You can use place-value blocks to help you add 327 + 256 + 332.

Count the ones. Regroup 10 ones to make 1 ten.

```
    1
  3 2 7
  2 5 6
+ 3 3 2
      5
```

Count the tens. Regroup 10 tens to make 1 hundred.

```
  1 1
  3 2 7
  2 5 6
+ 3 3 2
    1 5
```

Count the hundreds.

```
  1 1
  3 2 7
  2 5 6
+ 3 3 2
  9 1 5
```

327 + 256 + 332 = 915

Find each sum. Use place-value blocks to help you.

1.
```
  335
  521
+  67
  923
```

2. 59 + 92 + 65 = 216

3. 986 + 134 + 522 = 1,642

4. 63 + 28 + 49 = 140

5. 832 + 214 + 488 = 1,532

30 Use with pages 108–109.

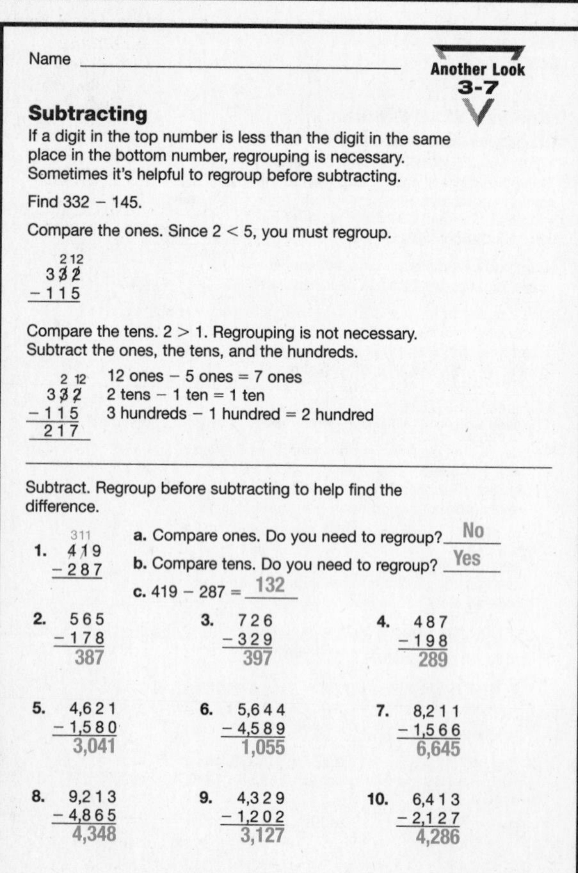

Name ______________________

Another Look 3-7

Subtracting

If a digit in the top number is less than the digit in the same place in the bottom number, regrouping is necessary. Sometimes it's helpful to regroup before subtracting.

Find 332 − 145.

Compare the ones. Since 2 < 5, you must regroup.

```
   2 12
  3 3 2
− 1 1 5
```

Compare the tens. 2 > 1. Regrouping is not necessary. Subtract the ones, the tens, and the hundreds.

```
   2 12
  3 3 2      12 ones − 5 ones = 7 ones
− 1 1 5      2 tens − 1 ten = 1 ten
  2 1 7      3 hundreds − 1 hundred = 2 hundred
```

Subtract. Regroup before subtracting to help find the difference.

1.
```
  311
  4 1 9
− 2 8 7
```
a. Compare ones. Do you need to regroup? No

b. Compare tens. Do you need to regroup? Yes

c. 419 − 287 = 132

2. 565 − 178 = 387

3. 726 − 329 = 397

4. 487 − 198 = 289

5. 4,621 − 1,580 = 3,041

6. 5,644 − 4,589 = 1,055

7. 8,211 − 1,566 = 6,645

8. 9,213 − 4,865 = 4,348

9. 4,329 − 1,202 = 3,127

10. 6,413 − 2,127 = 4,286

Use with pages 110–113. 31

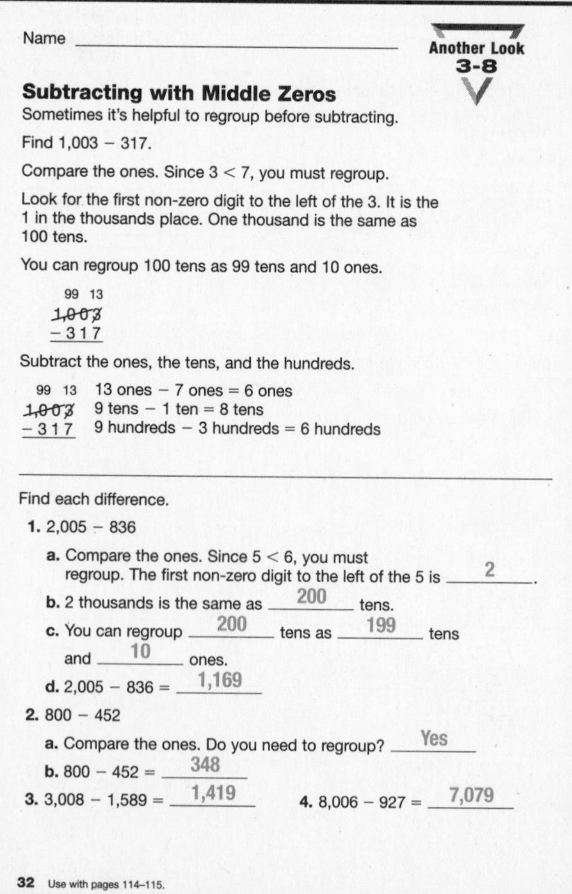

Name ______________________

Another Look 3-8

Subtracting with Middle Zeros

Sometimes it's helpful to regroup before subtracting.

Find 1,003 − 317.

Compare the ones. Since 3 < 7, you must regroup.

Look for the first non-zero digit to the left of the 3. It is the 1 in the thousands place. One thousand is the same as 100 tens.

You can regroup 100 tens as 99 tens and 10 ones.

```
  99 13
  1,0 0 3
−   3 1 7
```

Subtract the ones, the tens, and the hundreds.

```
  99 13
  1,0 0 3      13 ones − 7 ones = 6 ones
−   3 1 7      9 tens − 1 ten = 8 tens
               9 hundreds − 3 hundreds = 6 hundreds
```

Find each difference.

1. 2,005 − 836

a. Compare the ones. Since 5 < 6, you must regroup. The first non-zero digit to the left of the 5 is 2.

b. 2 thousands is the same as 200 tens.

c. You can regroup 200 tens as 199 tens and 10 ones.

d. 2,005 − 836 = 1,169

2. 800 − 452

a. Compare the ones. Do you need to regroup? Yes

b. 800 − 452 = 348

3. 3,008 − 1,589 = 1,419

4. 8,006 − 927 = 7,079

32 Use with pages 114–115.

Name ____________________

Another Look 3-9

Analyze Word Problems: Multiple-Step Problems

Crystal has 436 stamps in her stamp collection. Daryl has 213 stamps in his collection. Kathie has 221 stamps in her collection. Who has more stamps, Kathie and Daryl together or Crystal?

Find the total number of stamps that Kathie and Daryl have together.

221 (Kathie's stamps)
+ 213 (Daryl's stamps)
434 (Kathie and Daryl's total)

Compare the total to Crystal's number of stamps.

434 stamps (Kathie and Daryl) $<$ 436 stamps (Crystal)

Crystal has more stamps than Kathie and Daryl together.

1. There are 346 students in the third grade. There are 662 students in fourth grade and 309 students in fifth grade. How many more students are there in the fourth grade than in the third and fifth grades combined?
   a. How many students are in the third and fifth grades combined? 655 students
   b. How many students are in the fourth grade? 662 students
   c. What is the difference between the number of fourth grade students and the number of students in the third and fifth grades? 7 students
2. On Thursday, 113 people attended the school play. On Friday, 152 people attended. On Saturday, 270 people attended. Did more people see the play on Saturday or on Thursday and Friday combined? Saturday

Name ____________________

Another Look 3-10

Using Mental Math

Follow these steps to mentally add 57 and 42:

First add the tens. 5 + 4 = 9

Then add the ones. 7 + 2 = 9

Write the total as a 2-digit number.

Follow these steps to mentally subtract 53 from 78:

First subtract the tens. 7 − 5 = 2

Then subtract the ones. 8 − 3 = 5

Write the difference as a 2-digit number. 78 − 53 = 25

To add or subtract 3-digit numbers (without regrouping) mentally, add or subtract the hundreds first, then follow the same steps.

Add or subtract mentally.

1. 546 + 213
   a. 5 + 2 = 7
   b. 4 + 1 = 5
   c. 6 + 3 = 9
   546 + 213 = 759
2. 74 − 31
   a. 7 − 3 = 4
   b. 4 − 1 = 3
   c. 74 − 31 = 43
3. 676 + 223 = 899
4. 417 + 82 = 499
5. 89 − 42 = 47
6. 288 − 164 = 124
7. 213 + 424 = 637
8. 679 − 322 = 357
9. 876 − 431 = 445
10. 527 + 332 = 859

Name ____________________

Another Look 3-11

Choosing a Calculation Method

Mental Math	Paper and Pencil	Calculator
47,000 − 5,000 = 42,000	27,515 + 8,021 = 35,536	50,070 − 27,589 = 22,481
Use mental math when there are a lot of zeros in both numbers.	Use paper and pencil when you only need to regroup once or twice.	Use a calculator when there is a lot lot of regrouping to do.

Which method is most appropriate to solve each problem?

Write *mental math*, *paper and pencil*, or *calculator*.

1. 57,211 + 5,314 — Paper and pencil
2. 90,000 − 87,923 — Calculator
3. 59,000 − 18,000 — Mental math

Find each sum or difference. Tell which calculation method you used. Possible methods:

4. 72,000 − 12,000 = 60,000 — Mental math
5. 43,900 + 11,327 = 55,227 — Paper and pencil
6. 42,397 + 56,998 = 99,395 — Calculator
7. 92,187 − 41,023 = 51,164 — Paper and pencil
8. 14,000 + 7,000 = 21,000 — Mental math
9. 64,127 − 5,238 = 58,889 — Calculator

Name ____________________

Another Look 3-12

Counting Money

Counting by 5s, 10s, and 25s can help you count change. Here are some examples.

Example 1 Count nickels by 5s and dimes by 10s.

Say: "10, 20, 30, 40, 45, 50, 55."

You have 55 cents.

Example 2 Count quarters by 25s.

Say: "25, 50, 75, 85, 95, 105, 115, 120."

You have 120 cents.

To write any amount with a dollar sign, put a decimal point to the left of the digit in the tens place.

55 cents is the same as $0.55.

120 cents is the same as $1.20.

Write each amount. Use a dollar sign and decimal point.

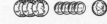

1. $0.85
2. $1.75
3. $0.70
4. $1.60

Solve.

5. Which is more: 3 quarters and 2 dimes, or 2 quarters and 3 dimes? 3 quarters and 2 dimes
6. Which is less: 5 nickels and 3 dimes, or 1 quarter and 2 dimes? 1 quarter and 2 dimes

Name ______________________

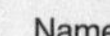

Another Look 3-13

Adding and Subtracting Money

You can use play money to help you add and subtract money amounts.

$12.52
+ 7.67

Start by adding the coins. Count the quarters, then the dimes, then the nickels, then the pennies: "25, 50, 75, 100, 110, 115, 116, 117, 118, 119."

Exchange the coins for dollars. 119 cents is the same as 1 dollar and 19 cents.

Write the amount left in coins after the decimal point.

Count the bills. Count "10, 15, 16, 17, 18, 19, 20."

Write the amount in bills in front of the decimal point.

$12.52 + $7.67 = $20.19

Add or subtract. Use play money to help you.

1. $4.13
+ 5.95
$10.08

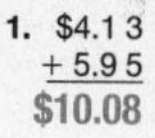

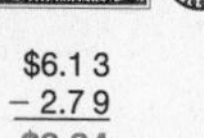

2. $7.13 + 2.27 = $9.40
3. $10.82 − 6.41 = $4.41
4. $6.13 − 2.79 = $3.34
5. $19.32 + 8.74 = $28.06
6. $6.27 − 4.82 = $1.45
7. $12.36 + 7.55 = $19.91
8. $15.47 + 9.08 = $24.55
9. $3.11 − 1.49 = $1.62

Name ______________________

Another Look 3-14

Exploring Making Change

In your book you used play money or drew pictures to make change. Here is another way to make change.

You just bought school supplies that cost $11.42. You gave the store clerk a twenty-dollar bill. How much change should you receive?

Subtract mentally.

Subtracting whole dollar amounts is easier to do mentally. Add an amount of change that will make the purchase price a whole dollar amount.

$20.00	+	0.58	→	20.58
− 11.42	+	0.58	→	− 12.00
				$8.58

Write the change for each purchase.

1. Amount given: $70 — $70.00 + 0.02 → $70.02
Amount due: $67.98 — − 67.98 + 0.02 → −68.00
change: $2.02

2. Amount given: $20.00 — $20.00 + 0.23 → $20.23
Amount due: $15.77 — − $15.77 + $0.23 → −16.00
change: $4.23

3. Amount given: $50.00
Amount due: $36.82
$13.18

4. Amount given: $20.00
Amount due: $6.52
$13.48

5. Amount given: $25.00
Amount due: $21.42
$3.58

6. Amount given: $10.00
Amount due: $8.58
$1.42

Name ______________________

Another Look 3-15

Exploring Algebra: Balancing Number Sentences

In your book you used workmats to balance number sentences. Here is another way to balance number sentences.

$6 + n = 9$

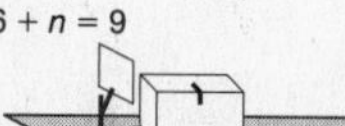

The basketball team has been practicing. They used the same number of basketballs on each side of the court. How many basketballs are in the box?

You can change the picture to solve the problem. Draw Xs over six basketballs on each side of the court.

You took 6 basketballs away from both sides of the basketball court. So, the number of basketballs on either side should be the same. How many basketballs are in the box? 3

---

1. How many basketballs are in the box? 4

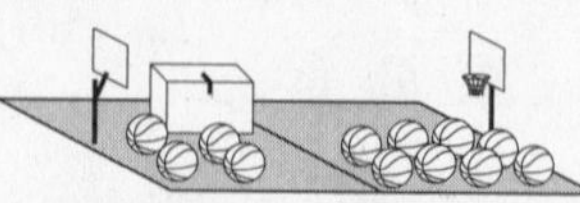

$4 + n = 8$

2. How many tennis balls are in the box? 7

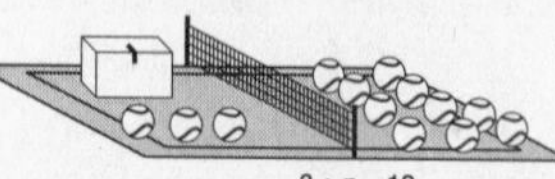

$3 + n = 10$

Draw pictures to show each number sentence. Then find the value of n.

3. $n + 8 = 16$ $n =$ 8

4. $9 + n = 11$ $n =$ 2

Name ______________________

Another Look 3-16

Analyze Strategies: Look for a Pattern

This row of letters follows a pattern:

A E I M Q

What letters of the alphabet are missing?

A bcd E fgh I jkl M nop Q

What is the pattern?

There are 3 letters of the alphabet missing between each letter.

What are the next 2 letters? Q rst U vwx Y

---

1. 4, 10, 16, 22, 28 (differences: 6, 6, 6, 6)

a. Find the difference between each pair of numbers. Fill in the blanks above.

b. What is the rule? Add 6 to each number.

c. What are the next two numbers in the pattern? 34, 40

2. Z YX W VU T SR Q PO N

a. Fill in the blanks to show which letters are missing.

b. What is the rule? Move back 3 letters, or skip 2 letters.

c. What are the next 2 letters in the pattern? K, H

3. 28, 30, 25, 27, 22 (differences: 2, 5, 2, 5)

a. Find the difference between each pair of numbers. Fill in the blanks above.

b. What is the rule? Add 2 then subtract 5.

c. What are the next two numbers in the pattern? 24, 19

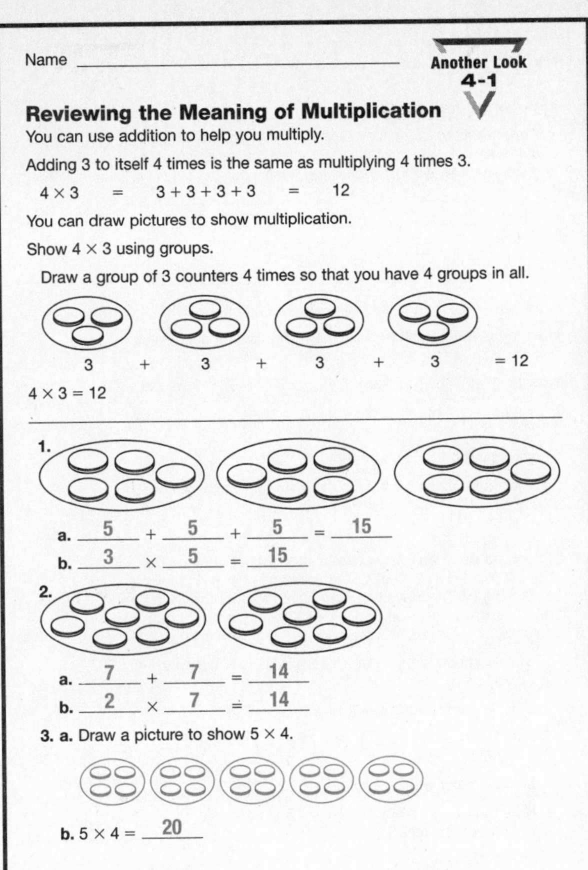

Name ______________________

Another Look 4-1

Reviewing the Meaning of Multiplication

You can use addition to help you multiply.

Adding 3 to itself 4 times is the same as multiplying 4 times 3.

4 × 3 = 3 + 3 + 3 + 3 = 12

You can draw pictures to show multiplication.

Show 4 × 3 using groups.

Draw a group of 3 counters 4 times so that you have 4 groups in all.

3 + 3 + 3 + 3 = 12

4 × 3 = 12

1. a. 5 + 5 + 5 = 15
   b. 3 × 5 = 15

2. a. 7 + 7 = 14
   b. 2 × 7 = 14

3. a. Draw a picture to show 5 × 4.
   b. 5 × 4 = 20

Use with pages 148–149. 41

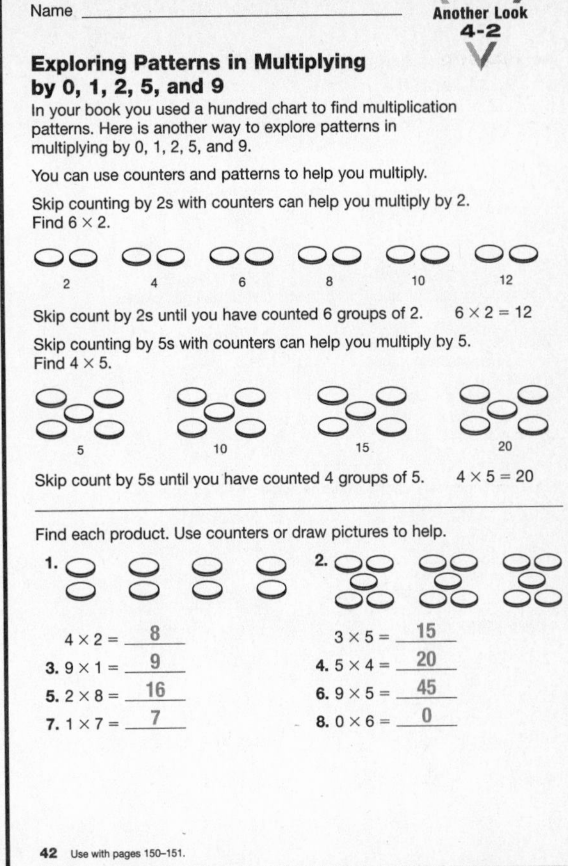

Name ______________________

Another Look 4-2

Exploring Patterns in Multiplying by 0, 1, 2, 5, and 9

In your book you used a hundred chart to find multiplication patterns. Here is another way to explore patterns in multiplying by 0, 1, 2, 5, and 9.

You can use counters and patterns to help you multiply.

Skip counting by 2s with counters can help you multiply by 2.
Find 6 × 2.

2 4 6 8 10 12

Skip count by 2s until you have counted 6 groups of 2. 6 × 2 = 12

Skip counting by 5s with counters can help you multiply by 5.
Find 4 × 5.

5 10 15 20

Skip count by 5s until you have counted 4 groups of 5. 4 × 5 = 20

Find each product. Use counters or draw pictures to help.

1. 4 × 2 = 8
2. 3 × 5 = 15
3. 9 × 1 = 9
4. 5 × 4 = 20
5. 2 × 8 = 16
6. 9 × 5 = 45
7. 1 × 7 = 7
8. 0 × 6 = 0

42 Use with pages 150–151.

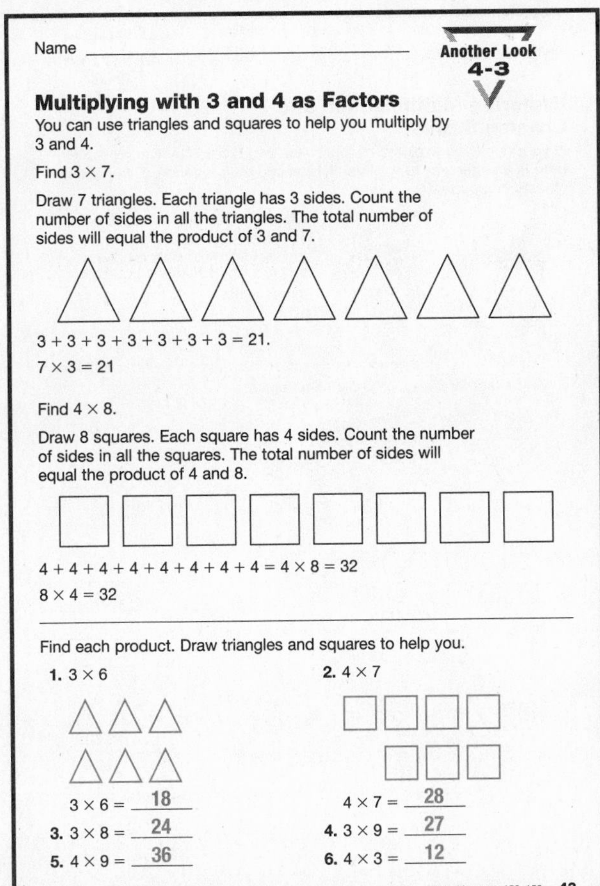

Name ______________________

Another Look 4-3

Multiplying with 3 and 4 as Factors

You can use triangles and squares to help you multiply by 3 and 4.

Find 3 × 7.

Draw 7 triangles. Each triangle has 3 sides. Count the number of sides in all the triangles. The total number of sides will equal the product of 3 and 7.

3 + 3 + 3 + 3 + 3 + 3 + 3 = 21.

7 × 3 = 21

Find 4 × 8.

Draw 8 squares. Each square has 4 sides. Count the number of sides in all the squares. The total number of sides will equal the product of 4 and 8.

4 + 4 + 4 + 4 + 4 + 4 + 4 + 4 = 4 × 8 = 32

8 × 4 = 32

Find each product. Draw triangles and squares to help you.

1. 3 × 6
   3 × 6 = 18
2. 4 × 7
   4 × 7 = 28
3. 3 × 8 = 24
4. 3 × 9 = 27
5. 4 × 9 = 36
6. 4 × 3 = 12

Use with pages 152–153. 43

Name ______________________

Another Look 4-4

Multiplying with 6, 7, and 8 as Factors

You can use 5s to help you multiply by 6s, 7s, and 8s.

Find 6 × 4.

Find 5 × 4 and add 1 more 4.

5 × 4 = 20 20 + 4 = 24

6 × 4 = 24

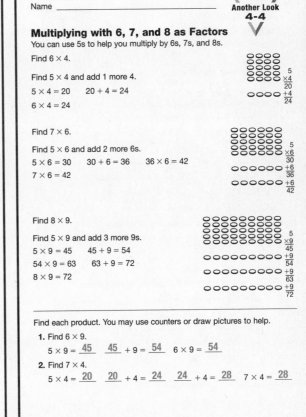

$\begin{array}{r} 5 \\ \times 4 \\ \hline 20 \\ +4 \\ \hline 24 \end{array}$

Find 7 × 6.

Find 5 × 6 and add 2 more 6s.

5 × 6 = 30 30 + 6 = 36 36 × 6 = 42

7 × 6 = 42

$\begin{array}{r} 5 \\ \times 6 \\ \hline 30 \\ +6 \\ \hline 36 \\ +6 \\ \hline 42 \end{array}$

Find 8 × 9.

Find 5 × 9 and add 3 more 9s.

5 × 9 = 45 45 + 9 = 54

54 × 9 = 63 63 + 9 = 72

8 × 9 = 72

$\begin{array}{r} 5 \\ \times 9 \\ \hline 45 \\ +9 \\ \hline 54 \\ +9 \\ \hline 63 \\ +9 \\ \hline 72 \end{array}$

Find each product. You may use counters or draw pictures to help.

1. Find 6 × 9.
   5 × 9 = 45 45 + 9 = 54 6 × 9 = 54
2. Find 7 × 4.
   5 × 4 = 20 20 + 4 = 24 24 + 4 = 28 7 × 4 = 28

44 Use with pages 154–157.

Name

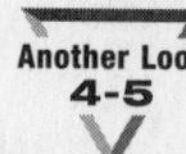

Exploring Patterns in Multiples of 10, 11, and 12

In your book you used a multiplication table to explore patterns multiples of 10, 11, and 12. Here are some patterns that can help you find these multiples.

Find 10 × 6.
When you multiply a number by 10, add **0** to the end of the number being multiplied by 10.
10 × 6 = **60**

Find 11 × 5.
When you multiply a number less than 10 by 11, write the number being multiplied by 11 in the tens and the ones places.
11 × **5** = **55**

When you multiply a number by 12, find the multiple of 10, then add twice the number.
Find 12 × 4.
First find 10 × 4 = 40.
Then add 2 × 4 = 8. 40 + 8 = 48
12 × 4 = 48.

Find each product. Use the patterns above to help.

1. Find 2 × 12.
a. 10 × [2] = [20]
b. 2 × [2] = [4]
c. [20] + [4] = [24]
d. 2 × 12 = [24]

2. Find 9 × 11.
a. 10 × [9] = [90]
b. 9 × [1] = [9]
c. [90] + [9] = [99]
d. 9 × 11 = [99]

3. 11 × 8 = 88
4. 10 × 11 = 110
5. 12 × 5 = 60
6. 10 × 12 = 120
7. 10 × 6 = 60
8. 3 × 10 = 30
9. 4 × 11 = 44
10. 6 × 12 = 72
11. 11 × 6 = 66
12. 12 × 4 = 48

Name

Another Look
4-6

Decision Making

Andrew wants to buy his mother a gift that costs $24. He has 4 weeks to save for the gift. To earn the money for the gift, Andrew can work the following jobs.

Day	Job	Number of Hours	Pay
Monday	Babysitting	2	$4 per hour
Wednesday	Clipping shrubs	1	$3 per hour

How can Andrew earn the money for the gift in 4 weeks?

How much money will Andrew make babysitting each week?
2 × $4 = $8

How long will it take to earn $24? $24 ÷ $8 = 3 weeks

How much money will Andrew make clipping shrubs each week?
1 × $3 = $3

How long will it take to earn $24? $24 ÷ $3 = 8 weeks

Andrew can babysit for 3 weeks to earn the money he needs to buy the gift.

Monica wants to buy new sneakers for school track meets. The first meet is in 8 weeks. The sneakers cost $48. Monica could work on Tuesdays watering plants for 2 hours for $3 per hour. She could work on Fridays walking a dog for 2 hours for $4 per hour. How can Monica earn $48 in 8 weeks?

1. a. How much would Monica earn in a week watering plants? $6
b. How many weeks will it take to earn $48? 8 weeks

2. a. How much would Monica earn in a week walking the dog? $8
b. How many weeks will it take to earn $48? 6 weeks

3. How much would Monica earn in 8 weeks walking the dog each week? $64

Name

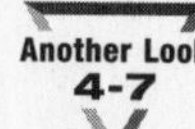

Reviewing the Meaning of Division

You can use counters to help you think about division in 3 different ways.

Find 18 ÷ 6.

Place 18 counters on your desk.

Example 1 Think of division as sharing. Imagine you are sharing the counters with 6 people.

How many counters would each person receive? 3 So, 18 ÷ 6 = 3

Example 2 Think of division as repeated subtraction.

Take away 6 counters from the 18 counters until you have 0. Count how many times you took away 6.

18 − 6 = 12 12 − 6 = 6 6 − 6 = 0
You took away 3 groups of 6. So, 18 ÷ 6 = 3.

Example 3 Think of division as the opposite of multiplication.

Think: What number times 6 equals 18?

3 × 6 = 18 So, 18 ÷ 6 = 3.

Find each quotient. Use the examples above to help.

1. 28 ÷ 4 = 7
2. 36 ÷ 6 = 6
3. 27 ÷ 3 = 9
4. 20 ÷ 5 = 4

Name

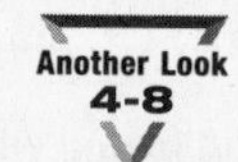

Exploring Multiplication and Division Stories

In your book you explored multiplication and division by writing stories. Here is another way to explore division and multiplication. Think about objects in groups.

Lila has 2 packs of baseball cards. There are 8 cards in each pack. Write the fact family for this problem.
2 × 8 = 16
8 × 2 = 16
16 ÷ 2 = 8
16 ÷ 8 = 2

Write the fact families for the pictures below.

1.

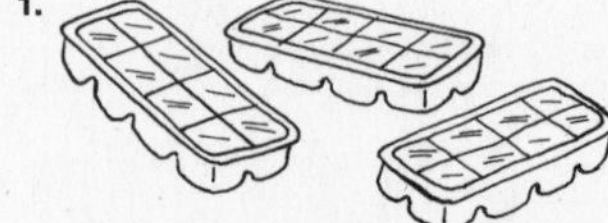

3 × 8 = 24
8 × 3 = 24
24 ÷ 8 = 3
24 ÷ 3 = 8

2.

8 × 4 = 32
4 × 8 = 32
32 ÷ 8 = 4
32 ÷ 4 = 8

3.

6 × 3 = 18
3 × 6 = 18
18 ÷ 6 = 3
18 ÷ 3 = 6

Name ____________________

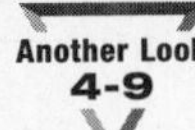

Dividing with 2, 5, and 9

You can use counters to help you divide by 2, 5, and 9.

Example 1 Find $18 \div 2$.
Place 18 counters on your desk.

Divide the counters into 2 equal groups.

How many counters are in each group?

9

So, $18 \div 2 =$ 9.

Example 2 Find $30 \div 5$.
Place 30 counters on your desk.

Divide the counters into 5 equal groups.

How many counters are in each group?

6

So, $30 \div 5 =$ 6.

Find each quotient. Use counters to help.

1. $27 \div 9$
   a. How many counters do you need to start with? 27
   b. Divide the counters into 9 equal groups.
   c. Draw the groups of counters in the space below.

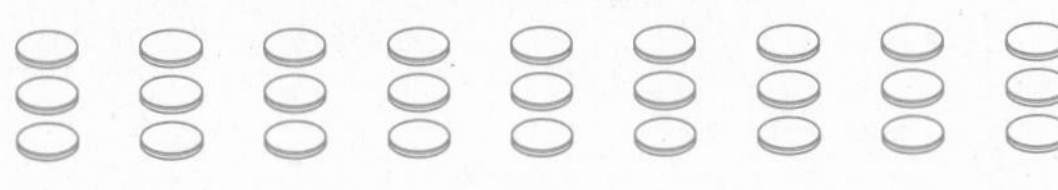

   d. $27 \div 9 =$ 3

2. $14 \div 2 =$ 7 3. $25 \div 5 =$ 5 4. $36 \div 9 =$ 4

Name ____________________

Another Look
4-10

Special Quotients

A full pizza has been divided into 8 slices. If each person receives 1 slice, how many people can be fed?

$8 \div 1 = 8$

Any number divided by 1 is that number. So, 8 people can each eat 1 slice.

Everyone wants a second slice, but there is no more pizza left. How many people will receive a second slice?

$0 \div 8 = 0$

0 divided by any number (except 0) equals 0. It doesn't matter how many people want a second slice. There is no more pizza left to be divided.

Use what you know about dividing with 0s and 1s to find each quotient.

1. $7 \div 7 =$ 1
2. $7 \div 1 =$ 7
3. $0 \div 4 =$ 0
4. $9 \div 1 =$ 9
5. $6 \div 6 =$ 1
6. $0 \div 1 =$ 0
7. $4\overline{)4}$ 1
8. $1\overline{)2}$ 2
9. $3\overline{)0}$ 0
10. $1\overline{)7}$ 7
11. $1\overline{)10}$ 10
12. $5\overline{)5}$ 1
13. $6\overline{)0}$ 0
14. $1\overline{)4}$ 4
15. $3\overline{)3}$ 1

Name ____________________

Another Look
4-11

Dividing with 3 and 4

It's easier to divide by 3 or 4 if you know your multiplication facts.

$3 \times 1 = 3$	$4 \times 1 = 4$
$3 \times 2 = 6$	$4 \times 2 = 8$
$3 \times 3 = 9$ (circled)	$4 \times 3 = 12$
$3 \times 4 = 12$	$4 \times 4 = 16$
$3 \times 5 = 15$	$4 \times 5 = 20$
$3 \times 6 = 18$	$4 \times 6 = 24$
$3 \times 7 = 21$	$4 \times 7 = 28$
$3 \times 8 = 24$	$4 \times 9 = 36$
$3 \times 10 = 30$	$4 \times 10 = 40$

To solve $9 \div 3$, find a multiplication fact that has a product of 9 and a factor of 3.

Since $3 \times \boxed{3} = 9$, $9 \div 3 =$ 3.

Complete each statement.

1. Since $3 \times \boxed{4} = 12$, $12 \div 3 = \boxed{4}$.
2. Since $4 \times \boxed{3} = \boxed{12}$, $12 \div 4 = \boxed{3}$.
3. Since $4 \times 8 = 32$, $32 \div 4 = \boxed{8}$.
4. Since $3 \times 9 = 27$, $27 \div 3 = \boxed{9}$.
5. Since $3 \times 6 = 18$, $18 \div 3 = \boxed{6}$.
6. Since $4 \times 6 = 24$, $24 \div 4 = \boxed{6}$.
7. Since $3 \times 8 = 24$, $24 \div 3 = \boxed{8}$.
8. Since $4 \times 2 = 8$, $8 \div 4 = \boxed{2}$.
9. Since $4 \times 5 = 20$, $20 \div 4 = \boxed{5}$.
10. Since $3 \times 7 = 21$, $21 \div 3 = \boxed{7}$.
11. Since $9 \times 4 = 36$, $36 \div 4 = \boxed{9}$.
12. Since $4 \times 7 = 28$, $28 \div 4 = \boxed{7}$.
13. Since $4 \times 4 = 16$, $16 \div 4 = \boxed{4}$.
14. Since $3 \times 5 = 15$, $15 \div 3 = \boxed{5}$.

Name ____________________

Another Look
4-12

Dividing with 6, 7 and 8

You can use multiplication facts to help you divide by 6, 7, or 8.

To find $18 \div 6$, think 6 times what number equals 18.

$6 \times \square = 18$

$6 \times 1 = 6$

$6 \times 2 = 12$

$6 \times 3 = 18$

To solve $18 \div 6$, find a multiplication fact that has a product of 18 and a factor of 6.

Since $6 \times 3 = 18$, $18 \div 6 =$ 3.

Complete each statement.

1. Since $6 \times \boxed{4} = 24$, $24 \div 6 = \boxed{4}$.
2. Since $8 \times \boxed{3} = \boxed{24}$, $24 \div 8 = \boxed{3}$.
3. Since $7 \times 3 = 21$, $21 \div 7 = \boxed{3}$.
4. Since $6 \times 8 = 48$, $48 \div 6 = \boxed{8}$.
5. Since $7 \times 5 = 35$, $35 \div 7 = \boxed{5}$.
6. Since $8 \times 8 = 64$, $64 \div 8 = \boxed{8}$.
7. Since $6 \times 2 = 12$, $12 \div 6 = \boxed{2}$.
8. Since $7 \times 4 = 28$, $28 \div 7 = \boxed{4}$.
9. Since $8 \times 7 = 56$, $56 \div 8 = \boxed{7}$.
10. Since $6 \times 9 = 54$, $54 \div 6 = \boxed{9}$.
11. Since $5 \times 8 = 40$, $40 \div 8 = \boxed{5}$.
12. Since $7 \times 7 = 49$, $49 \div 7 = \boxed{7}$.
13. Since $6 \times 6 = 36$, $36 \div 6 = \boxed{6}$.

Name ______________________

Another Look 4-13

Exploring Even and Odd Numbers

In your book you used counters to explore even and odd numbers. Here is another way to explore even and odd.

Is 17 odd or even?

Below are 17 stars. Draw a ring around each pair of stars. If there are no stars left over, 17 is even. If there is one star left over, 17 is odd.

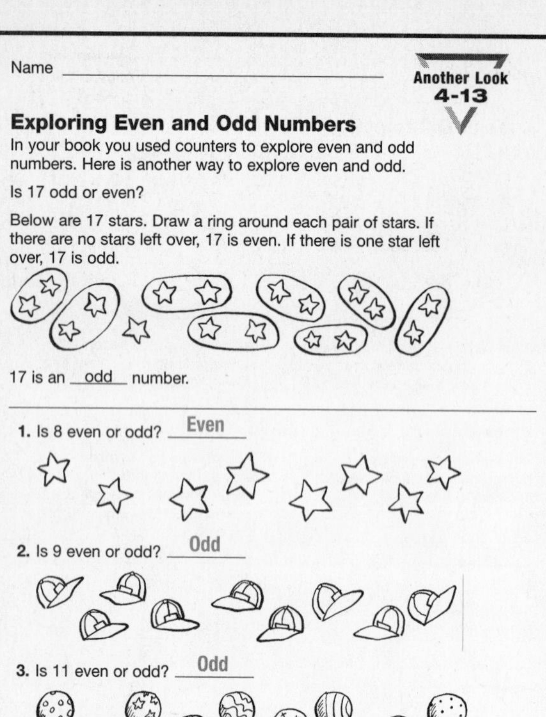

17 is an odd number.

1. Is 8 even or odd? Even
2. Is 9 even or odd? Odd
3. Is 11 even or odd? Odd
4. Is 16 even or odd? Even

Name ______________________

Another Look 4-14

Exploring Factors

In your book you used rectangles to find factors. Here is another way to explore factors.

To find *all* the factors for a number, make an organized list of multiplication sentences. Write sentences until your factors start to repeat. (Ignore any sentences that won't work.) Then list the factors.

Find all the factors of 48.

48 = 1 × 48
2 × 24
3 × 16
4 × 12
~~5 ×~~
6 × 8
~~7 ×~~
8 × 6 (← STOP! Repeat of 6 × 8).

The factors of 48 are 1, 2, 3, 4, 6, 8, 12, 16, 24 and 48.

The factors of 48 are 1, 2, 3, 4, 6, 8, 12, 16, 24, and 48.

1. Find all the factors of 15.
   15 = 1 × 15
   ~~2 ×~~ ☐
   3 × 5
   ~~4 ×~~ ☐
   5 × 3
   1, 3, 5, 15
2. Find all the factors of 24.
   1, 2, 3, 4, 6, 8, 12, 24
3. Find all the factors of 56.
   1, 2, 4, 7, 8, 14, 28, 56
4. Find all factors of 32.
   1, 2, 4, 8, 16, 32

Name ______________________

Another Look 4-15

Analyze Word Problems: Too Much or Too Little Information

To solve a word problem, look carefully at the information. Does it give you enough information to find the answer?

Example Julie bought milk, cereal, and juice today. How much did she spend if the milk cost $1.85 and the cereal cost $4.25.

a. What does the problem tell you? the cost of the milk and cereal
   What does it leave out? the total cost; the cost of the juice
b. Can you figure out the answer? Explain. No. I don't know how much the juice cost so I can't figure the total cost.

1. Central Middle School has 450 students in 7th, 8th, and 9th grade. There are 185 students in the 7th grade and 115 students in the 8th grade. How many students are in the 9th grade?
   a. What does the problem tell you? The total number of students, the number of students in 7th grade, the number of students in 8th grade
      What does it leave out? The number of students in 9th grade
   b. Can you figure out the answer? Explain. Yes; I can subtract the number of students in 7th and 8th grade from the total number to find the number of students in 9th grade.
2. Central High School has 215 students in 10th grade and 158 students in 11th grade. How many students are in 10th, 11th, and 12th grade?
   a. What does the problem tell you? The number of students in 10th grade, the number of students in 11th grade
      What does it leave out? The number of students in 12th grade, the total number of students
   b. Can you figure out the answer? Explain. No; I need to know how many students are in the 12th grade.

Name ______________________

Another Look 4-16

Compare Strategies: Guess and Check/Draw a Picture

Together, Janie and Howard brought 15 fruit tarts to a party. If Howard brought 3 more tarts than Janie, how many fruit tarts did they each bring?

JANIE | HOWARD

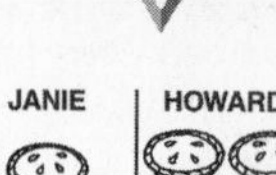

You can solve the problem by drawing a picture. First write the names "Janie" and "Howard". Draw 1 tart under "Janie" and 4 tarts under "Howard." Howard has 3 more tarts than Janie, but the picture doesn't show 15 tarts.

JANIE | HOWARD

Now add one tart to Janie's and one tart to Howard's until you have 15 tarts in all.

This drawing shows that Janie brought 6 tarts and Howard brought 9.

Marla and Ahmed brought 18 beach shells to show and tell. If Marla brought 4 more shells than Ahmed, how many did they each bring?

1. What do you need to find out?
   How many shells Ahmed and Marla each brought
2. Draw a picture to show the number of shells each person brought to show. Check students' drawings.
3. How many shells did Ahmed bring? 7 shells
4. How many shells did Marla bring? 11 shells

Name ______________________

Another Look 5-1

Multiplying Tens

Place-value blocks can help you multiply.

Example 1 Find 3×4.

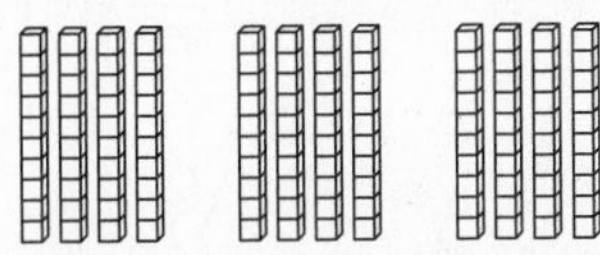

The place-value blocks show 3 groups of 4 tens.

3×4 tens = 12 tens = 120

$3 \times 40 = 120$

Example 2 Find 4×50.

4×5 tens = 20 tens = 200

Use place-value blocks to help you find each product.

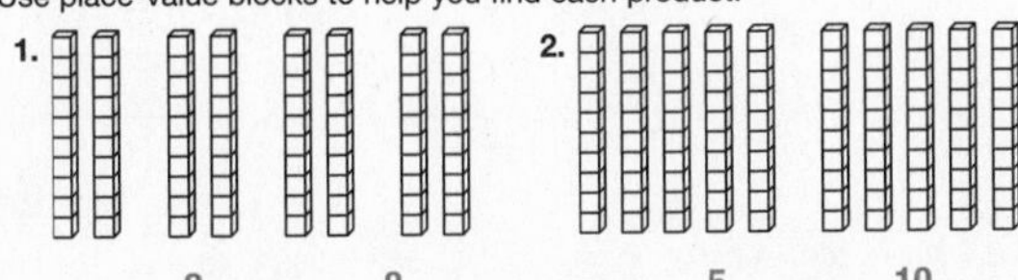

1. **a.** $4 \times$ __2__ tens = __8__ tens
b. $4 \times 20 =$ __80__

2. **a.** $2 \times$ __5__ tens = __10__ tens
b. $2 \times 50 =$ __100__

3. **a.** 4×4 tens = __16__ tens
b. $4 \times 40 =$ __160__

4. **a.** 6×3 tens = __18__ tens
b. $6 \times 30 =$ __180__

5. $5 \times 10 =$ __50__ **6.** $8 \times 70 =$ __560__ **7.** $7 \times 70 =$ __490__

8. $40 \times 7 =$ __280__ **9.** $30 \times 8 =$ __240__ **10.** $80 \times 7 =$ __560__

11. $3 \times 50 =$ __150__ **12.** $20 \times 6 =$ __120__ **13.** $9 \times 6 =$ __540__

Name ______________________

Another Look 5-2

Exploring Multiplication Patterns

In your book you multiplied using patterns. Here is another way to multiply.

4×4 ones = $4 \times 4 = 16$ 4×4 tens = $4 \times 40 = 160$

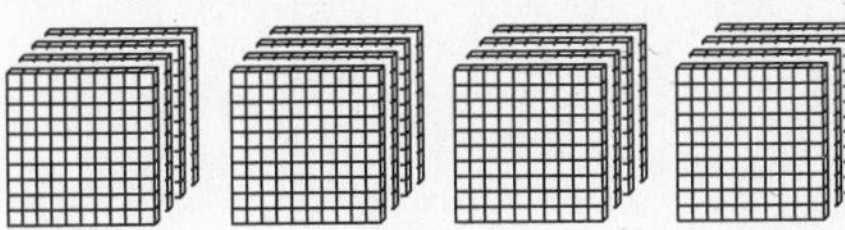

So, 4×4 hundreds = $4 \times 400 = 1{,}600$

Complete each multiplication sentence. Think of place-value blocks and look for patterns.

1. $5 \times 5 = 25$
5×5 tens = __250__
5×5 hundreds = 2,500

2. $4 \times 3 =$ __12__
4×3 tens = 120
4×3 hundreds = 1,200

Use patterns to complete each multiplication sentence.

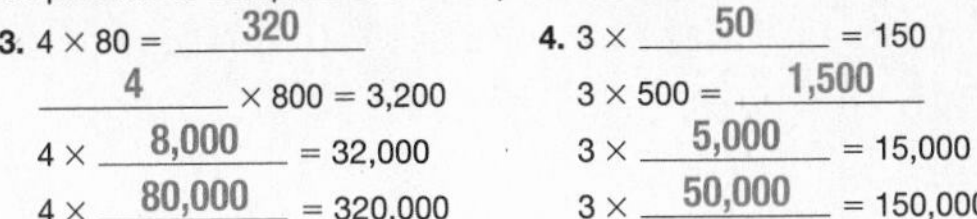

3. $4 \times 80 =$ __320__
__4__ $\times 800 = 3{,}200$
$4 \times$ __8,000__ = 32,000
$4 \times$ __80,000__ = 320,000

4. $3 \times$ __50__ = 150
$3 \times 500 =$ __1,500__
$3 \times$ __5,000__ = 15,000
$3 \times$ __50,000__ = 150,000

Find each product.

5. $6 \times 400 =$ __2,400__ **6.** $3 \times 200 =$ __600__

7. $5 \times 700 =$ __3,500__ **8.** $8 \times 2{,}000 =$ __16,000__

9. $4 \times 3{,}000 =$ __12,000__ **10.** $6 \times 5{,}000 =$ __30,000__

Name ______________________

Another Look 5-3

Estimating Products

Estimate.

Example 1 3×12

Round 12 to nearest multiple of 10.

Think of the multiples of 10.

0, 10, 20, 30, 40, 50, 60, 70, 80, ...
↑
12

Which number is nearest to 12?

Replace 12 in the problem with 10.

$3 \times$ ~~12~~
↓
$3 \times 10 = 30$

Example 2 4×570

Round 570 to nearest multiple of 100.

570 is closer to 600.

Replace 570 with 600.

$4 \times$ ~~570~~
↓
$4 \times 600 = 2{,}400$

Write the nearest multiple of ten for each number.

1. 83 __80__ **2.** 46 __50__ **3.** 57 __60__ **4.** 48 __50__

Write the nearest multiple of 100 for each number.

5. 120 __100__ **6.** 280 __300__ **7.** 940 __900__ **8.** 350 __400__

Estimate each product by rounding each two-digit number to the nearest multiple of 10. Round each three-digit number to the nearest multiple of 100.

9. 2×93
$2 \times$ __90__ = __180__

10. 37×7
__40__ $\times 7 =$ __280__

11. 6×49
$6 \times$ __50__ = __300__

12. 5×14 __50__ **13.** 42×5 __200__ **14.** 85×4 __360__

15. 47×8 __400__ **16.** 26×9 __270__ **17.** 7×81 __560__

Name ______________________

Another Look 5-4

Exploring Multiplication with Arrays

In your book you used place-value blocks to multiply. Here is another way to multiply. Drawing a rectangular array on grid paper can help you find the product. Here is how you can use an array to find the product of 3×25.

a. Draw a rectangle 25 boxes wide and 3 boxes long.

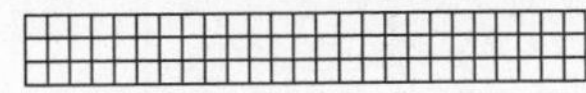

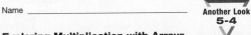

b. Outline groups of ten boxes in each row.

c. How many ones are there? 15

d. How many tens are there? 6

e. How many ones boxes are there in all? 75

Draw an array to help you find each product. Use a separate sheet of grid paper.

1.
$$\begin{array}{r} 23 \\ \times\ 6 \\ \hline 18 \\ +\ 120 \\ \hline 138 \end{array}$$
a. How many ones are there? __18__
b. How many tens are there? __12__
c. How many ones boxes in all? __138__

2.
$$\begin{array}{r} 37 \\ \times\ 8 \\ \hline 56 \\ +\ 240 \\ \hline 296 \end{array}$$
a. How many ones are there? __56__
b. How many tens are there? __24__
c. How many ones boxes in all? __296__

3.
$$\begin{array}{r} 28 \\ \times\ 3 \\ \hline 24 \\ +\ 60 \\ \hline 84 \end{array}$$
a. How many ones are there? __24__
b. How many tens are there? __6__
c. How many ones boxes in all? __84__

Name ______________________________

Multiplying 2-Digit Numbers

Step 1 Multiply the ones.

73
× 7
21   7 × 3 = 21

24
× 9
36   9 × 4 = 36

Step 2 Multiply the tens.

73
× 7
21
490   7 × 7 tens = 49 tens or 490

24
× 9
36
180   9 × 2 tens = 180

Step 3 Add.

73
× 7
21
490
511

24
× 9
36
180
216

Step 4 Estimate to check the answer.

73 × 7 is close to 70 × 7.

70 × 7 = 490

511 is close to 490, so the answer is reasonable.

24 × 9 is close to 20 × 9.

20 × 9 = 180

180 is close to 216, so the answer is reasonable.

Complete. Show your ones and tens products.

1. 23
× 3
9
60
69

2. 21
× 4
4
80
84

3. 44
× 3
12
120
132

4. 59
× 5
250
45
295

5. 33
× 2
6
60
66

6. 64
× 8
32
480
512

7. 24
× 4
16
80
96

8. 54
× 6
24
300
324

Name ______________________________

Another Look
5-6

Multiplying 3-Digit Numbers

Breaking numbers apart can make them easier to multiply.

Find the product of 547 and 4.

You can break 547 into hundreds, tens, and ones.

Step 1 547 = 500 + 40 + 7

Step 2 Multiply each part by 4.

4 × 7 = 28
4 × 40 = 160
4 × 500 = 2,000

Step 3 Add. 2,188

Find each product. Break numbers apart to help you.

1. 566 × 4 = 500 + 60 + 6
4 × 6 = 24
4 × 60 = 240
4 × 500 = 2,000
2,264

2. 601 × 5 = 600 + 1
5 × 1 = 5
5 × 600 = 3,000
3,005

3. 789 × 3 = 700 + 80 + 9
3 × 9 = 27
3 × 80 = 240
3 × 700 = 2,100
2,367

4. 342 × 8 = 300 + 40 + 2
8 × 2 = 16
8 × 40 = 320
8 × 300 = 2,400
2,736

Name ______________________________

Decision Making

A group of sea otters is called a raft. Several rafts of sea otters live off the coast of California. Scientists who study sea otters often tag a few otters of different ages in each raft. They often tag 1 of 10 otters in each raft. They make conclusions based on what they notice about the tagged otters.

65 otters
× 7 rafts
455

Seven rafts had 65 sea otters each.

How many otters are there all together? 455

How many tens are there in 455? 45 tens

How many sea otters will be tagged? 45

1. In another area, there are 8 rafts with 82 sea otters in each raft.
   a. How many otters are there all together? 656
   b. How many tens are there? 65 tens
   c. How many sea otters will be tagged? 65
2. By one island, there are 6 rafts of 72 sea otters.
   a. How many otters are there all together? 432
   b. How many tens are there? 43 tens
   c. How many sea otters will be tagged? 43
3. How many otters will be tagged in each of the following:
   a. 5 rafts of 42 21
   b. 4 rafts of 53? 21
   c. 7 rafts of 25? 17

Name ______________________________

Choosing a Calculation Method

Place-value blocks can help you find the product of 3 and 1,032.

1,032
× 3
6 = 3 × 2 ones
90 = 3 × 3 tens
3,000 = 3 × 1 thousand
3,096

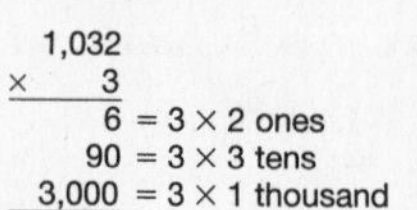

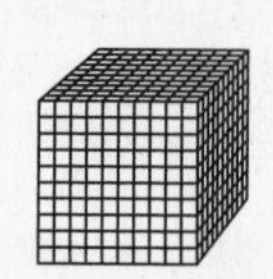

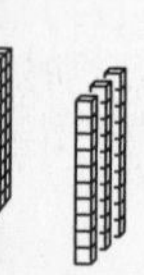

Or, you can multiply using a short cut. Multiply each digit in 1,032 by 3. Write your answer.

1,032
× 3
3,096

A calculator can be helpful for harder problems.

2,378 × 9 = 21,102

Multiply by drawing place-value blocks.

1. 1,223 × 3 3,669

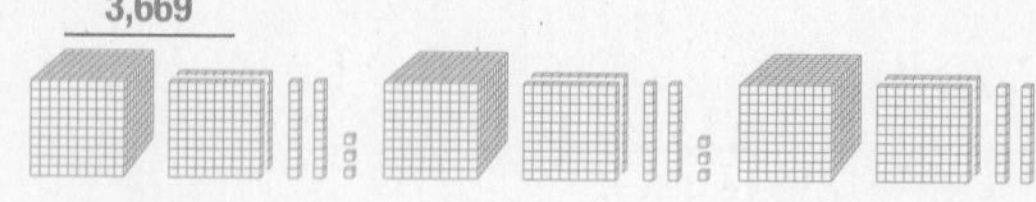

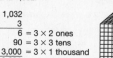

2. 1,120 × 4 4,480

Multiply. Use place-value blocks if needed. Try using the short-cut method, or use a calculator.

3. 1,025
× 3
3,075

4. 2,432
× 4
9,728

5. 2,056
× 6
12,336

6. 3,127
× 7
21,889

Name ______________________ **Another Look 5-9**

Multiplying Money

Draw a picture to help you find the product of $1.40 × 3.

How many dimes do you need to have 3 stacks of $1.40?

```
  $1.40
×     3
  $4.20  (42 dimes)
```

Complete each problem.

1. $2.35 × 2 = $4.70	**2.** $1.09 × 4 = $4.36	**3.** $4.50 × 3 = $13.50	**4.** $2.23 × 6 = $13.38

Multiply.

5. $3.45 × 4 = $13.80	**6.** $5.50 × 5 = $27.50	**7.** $8.04 × 2 = $16.08	**8.** $4.33 × 7 = $30.31
9. $7.15 × 3 = $21.45	**10.** $1.13 × 6 = $6.78	**11.** $6.60 × 5 = $33.00	**12.** $3.97 × 4 = $15.88
13. $4.23 × 4 = $16.92	**14.** $2.74 × 7 = $19.18	**15.** $1.85 × 3 = $5.55	**16.** $5.05 × 9 = $45.45

Name ______________________ **Another Look 5-10**

Mental Math: Special Products

Here is a way to solve problems mentally when one number is even. Cutting an even number in half and doubling the other number can help you do mental math.

6 × 15 =

Half of 6 is: 3

Double 15 is: 30

3 × 30 = 90

If one number is still too large, you can keep cutting it in half to make it easier, but don't forget to double your other number! Try 13 × 16.

Double		Half
26	×	8
52	×	4
104	×	2 = 208

Use mental math to solve these problems. If necessary, cut one number in half and double the other.

1. 4 × 18 = 72	**2.** 6 × 35 = 210
3. 8 × 42 = 336	**4.** 45 × 4 = 180
5. 25 × 6 = 150	**6.** 49 × 4 = 196
7. 22 × 8 = 176	**8.** 44 × 6 = 264
9. 4 × 36 = 144	**10.** 55 × 8 = 440
11. 6 × 27 = 162	**12.** 4 × 29 = 116
13. 32 × 4 = 128	**14.** 54 × 8 = 432
15. 43 × 6 = 258	**16.** 34 × 4 = 136

Name ______________________ **Another Look 5-11**

Multiplying 3 Factors

Here is a way you can find the product when there are 3 factors. Multiply the least numbers or use the easy facts first. Use parentheses to show what to multiply first.

5 × 9 × 3 = (5 × 3) × 9
↓
15 × 9 = 135

Write each product. Multiply the least numbers first and use parentheses.

1. 6 × 2 × 8
   (2 × 6) × 8 = 12 × 8 = 96
2. 5 × 7 × 3
   (3 × 5) × 7 = 15 × 7 = 105
3. 4 × 9 × 2
   (2 × 4) × 9 = 8 × 9 = 72
4. 3 × 6 × 4
   (3 × 4) × 6 = 12 × 6 = 72
5. 9 × 5 × 7
   (5 × 7) × 9 = 35 × 9 = 315
6. 4 × 1 × 8
   (1 × 4) × 8 = 4 × 8 = 32
7. 3 × 7 × 2
   (2 × 3) × 7 = 6 × 7 = 42
8. 5 × 2 × 6
   (2 × 5) × 6 = 10 × 6 = 60

Name ______________________ **Another Look 5-12**

Analyze Word Problems: Multiple-Step Problems

Grocery Items
loaf of bread – $2.25
box of cereal – $4.29
bar of soap – $1.69

How much money would you need to buy 4 loaves of bread and 3 boxes of cereal?

What do you know? You need: 4 loaves of bread at $2.25 each, 3 boxes of cereal at $4.29 each

What do you need to find out? The total cost of the groceries

How can you find the cost of 4 loaves of bread? Multiply 4 × $2.25.
How can you find the cost of 3 boxes of cereal? Multiply 3 × $4.29.
How can you find the total cost? Add.

Step 1 Multiply.

bread	**cereal**
$2.25	$4.29
× 4	× 3
$9.00	$12.87

Step 2 Add. $9.00 + $12.87 = $21.87

What's the answer? You need $ 21.87 to buy the groceries.

How can you check if your answer makes sense?

Estimate. $2 × 4 = $8
$4 × 3 = + $12
$20

1. What is the total cost of 4 bars of soap, 3 loaves of bread, and 5 boxes of cereal?
   a. What is the cost of 4 bars of soap? $6.76
   b. What is the cost of 3 loaves of bread? $6.75
   c. What is the cost of 5 boxes of cereal? $21.45
   d. What is the total cost of all of the groceries above? $34.96
5. How much change would you receive if you paid for 2 bars of soap with a $5 bill? $1.62

Name 

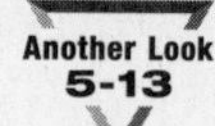

Analyze Strategies: Make a Table

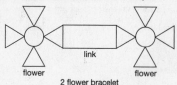

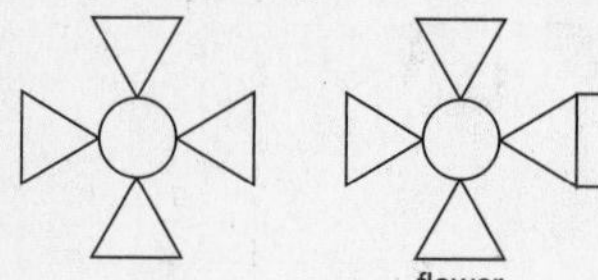

How many pattern pieces do you need to make a bracelet with 3 flowers?

Understand What do you know? There are 5 pieces in a flower. There are 11 pieces in a 2-flower bracelet.

What do you need to find out? How many pieces are there in a 3-flower bracelet?

Plan Make a table to organize the data.

Solve Fill in the table. You can use power polygons or draw a picture to help you see a pattern. Complete the table to find the pattern.

Number of Flowers	Number of Pieces
1	5
2	11
3	17

When there are 3 flowers, there are 17 pieces in all.

Look Back How can you check your answer? Possible answer: Draw a picture.

Use the pattern above to answer the questions.

1. If you continue the pattern until you have a 4-flower bracelet, how many pieces will you need? 23
2. If your bracelet has 6 flowers, how many pieces will it have in all? 35

Name

Exploring Multiplication Patterns

In your book you used a calculator to explore patterns. Here is another way to find patterns. Basic fact and place-value patterns can help you multiply by multiples of 10; 100; or 1,000.

Example 1 70×50
Basic Fact: $7 \times 5 = 35$
Total number of zeros in factors: 2
Therefore, $70 \times 50 = 3{,}500$ (basic fact: 35; 2 zeros)

Example 2 700×500
Basic Fact: $7 \times 5 = 35$
Total number of zeros in factors: 4
Therefore, $700 \times 500 = 350{,}000$ (basic fact: 35; 4 zeros)

Use patterns to find each product.

1. 30×70
   a. Find the product of the basic fact: $3 \times 7 =$ 21
   b. Count the number of zeros in the factors. 2
   c. Write the final product. 2,100
2. 600×500
   a. Find the product of the basic fact: $6 \times 5 =$ 30
   b. Count the number of zeros in the factors. 4
   c. Write the final product. 300,000

3. $80 \times 30 =$ 2,400
4. $900 \times 300 =$ 270,000
5. $40 \times 500 =$ 20,000
6. $800 \times 500 =$ 400,000
7. $20 \times 700 =$ 14,000
8. $300 \times 600 =$ 180,000
9. $400 \times 400 =$ 160,000
10. $200 \times 800 =$ 160,000

Name

Another Look
6-2

Estimating Products

Estimate the product of 43 and 57.

Step 1 Round each number to the nearest ten.

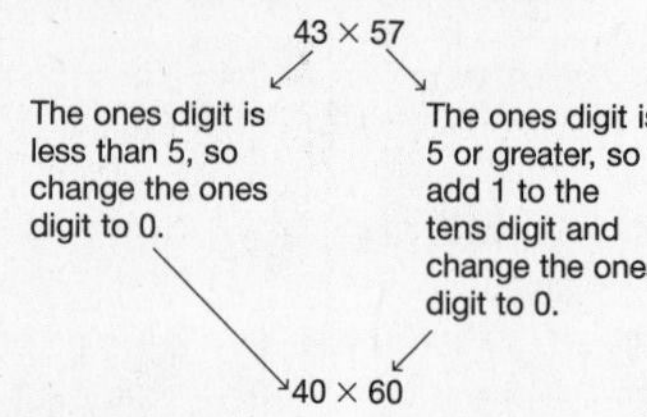

43 × 57
The ones digit is less than 5, so change the ones digit to 0.
The ones digit is 5 or greater, so add 1 to the tens digit and change the ones digit to 0.
40 × 60

Step 2 Multiply. $40 \times 60 =$ 2,400

Estimate the product.

1. 36 × 82 → 40 × 80 = 3,200
2. 68 × 32 → 70 × 30 = 2,100
3. 93 × 75 → 90 × 80 = 7,200
4. 36 × 57 → 40 × 60 = 2,400
5. 34 × 65 → 30 × 70 = 2,100
6. 66 × 42 → 70 × 40 = 2,800
7. 38 × 67 → 40 × 70 = 2,800
8. 78 × 23 → 80 × 20 = 1,600
9. 48 × 58 → 50 × 60 = 3,000
10. 14 × 18 → 10 × 20 = 200
11. 93 × 26 → 90 × 30 = 2,700
12. 77 × 44 → 80 × 40 = 3,200

Name

Another Look
6-3

Multiplying by Multiples of 10

You can break apart each multiple of 10 to help you multiply.

Example 1 60×43

Think: 60 is 10×6 → $10 \times 6 \times 43$

Multiply. $6 \times 43 = 258$ → 10×258

Multiply by the product of 10. $10 \times 258 = 2{,}580$

Example 2 40×78 → $10 \times 4 \times 78$ → $10 \times 312 = 3{,}120$

Find each product.

1. 30×48
   a. $10 \times$ 3 $\times 48$
   b. $10 \times$ 144 $=$ 1,440
2. 50×78
   a. $10 \times$ 5 $\times 78$
   b. $10 \times$ 390 $=$ 3,900
3. $86 \times 20 =$ 1,720
4. $24 \times 40 =$ 960
5. $64 \times 70 =$ 4,480
6. $73 \times 50 =$ 3,650
7. $51 \times 60 =$ 3,060
8. $32 \times 90 =$ 2,880

Name ______________________

Another Look 6-4

Exploring Multiplication with 2-Digit Factors

In your book you multiplied using place-value blocks. Here is another way to show multiplication.

Draw rectangles on grid paper to show partial products.

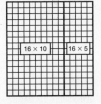

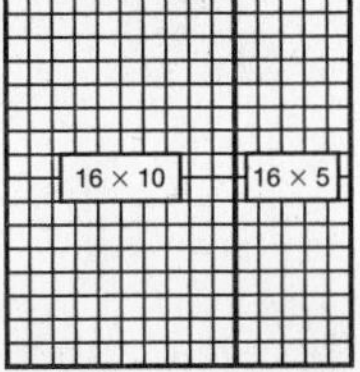

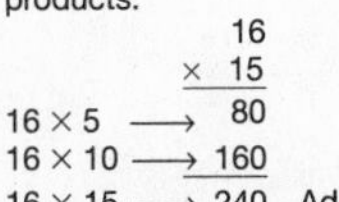

```
              16
            × 15
16 × 5  →     80
16 × 10 →    160
16 × 15 →    240   Add.
```

1. Draw lines to show the multiplication. Find 11 × 16.

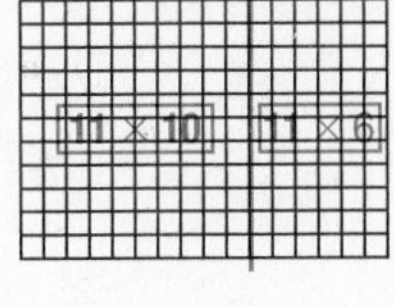

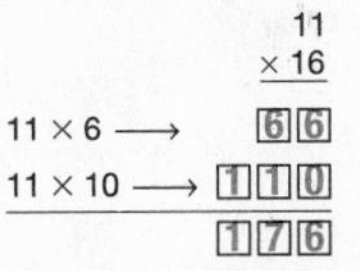

```
              11
            × 16
11 × 6  →     66
11 × 10 →    110
             176
```

2.
```
              18
            × 32
18 × 2  →     36
18 × 30 →    540
             576
```

3.
```
              18
            × 43
18 × 3  →     54
18 × 40 →    720
             774
```

Find each product.

4. 32 × 15 = 480

5. 73 × 32 = 2,336

6. 46 × 55 = 2,530

Name ______________________

Another Look 6-5

Multiplying with 2-Digit Factors

Multiply 34 × 36.

Step 1 Multiply 6 ones and 34.

```
   3 4   Regroup.
 × 3 6
 2 0 4 ← 6 × 34
```

Step 2 Multiply 3 tens and 34.

```
     3 4   Regroup.
   × 3 6
   2 0 4
 1 0 2 0 ← 30 × 34
```

Step 3 Add the partial products.

```
     3 4
   × 3 6
   2 0 4
 1 0 2 0
 1 2 2 4 ← 204 + 1,020
```

Step 4 Check by estimating.

```
34 × 36
↓    ↓
30 × 40 = 1,200
```

Since 1,224 is close to 1,200, the answer is reasonable.

Complete.

1.
```
     2 4
   × 1 7
   1 6 8 ← 7 × 24
   2 4 0 ← 10 × 24
   4 0 8
```

2.
```
     4 2
   × 5 3
   1 2 6 ← 3 × 42
 2 1 0 0 ← 50 × 42
 2 2 2 6
```

3. 76 × 23 = 1,748

4. 63 × 34 = 2,142

5. 45 × 25 = 1,125

6. 56 × 43 = 2,408

Name ______________________

Another Look 6-6

Estimating Greater Products

Estimate 37 × 592

Step 1 Round each number to its greatest place.
37 × 592 → 40 × 600

Step 2 Multiply the non-zero digits.
40 × **6**00 4 × 6 = 24

Step 3 Count the zeros in the factors.
40 × 600 — 3 zeros

Step 4 Write them after the product in **Step 2**.
24**,000**

The product of 37 × 592 is about 24,000.

Estimate each product.

1. 489 × 73
   a. Round: 500 × 70
   b. 5 × 7 = 35
   c. 3 zeros in the factors
   d. 500 × 70 = 35,000

2. 365 × 47
   a. Round: 400 × 50
   b. 4 × 5 = 20
   c. 3 zeros in the factors
   d. 400 × 50 = 20,000

3. 683 × 28
   700 × 30 = 21,000

4. 835 × 62
   800 × 60 = 48,000

5. 176 × 38
   200 × 40 = 8,000

6. 342 × 78
   300 × 80 = 24,000

7. 491 × 87
   500 × 90 = 45,000

8. 947 × 52
   900 × 50 = 45,000

Name ______________________

Another Look 6-7

Choosing a Calculation Method

The table below shows 3 ways of thinking about different calculation methods.

Method	When to Use It	Examples
Paper and pencil	to work out a long problem on your own	2,700 × 19: 24,300 + 27,000 = 51,300
Calculator	to get a quick but accurate answer to check your figures from the long method	2,700 × 19 = 51,300
Estimation	to make sure your answer is reasonable	2,700 × 19 = 51,300 3,000 × 20 = 60,000 The answer is reasonable.

Find each product. Tell which method you used.

Methods will vary. Look for reasonable methods.

1. 373 × 21 = 7,833
   Method: ________

2. 407 × 18 = 7,326
   Method: ________

3. 6,000 × 30 = 180,000
   Method: ________

4. 243 × 61 = 14,823
   Method: ________

5. 162 × 25 = 4,050
   Method: ________

6. 278 × 40 = 11,120
   Method: ________

Name ______________________

Another Look 6-8

Decision Making

Len is making snacks and drinks for his friends to take to the beach. He only has $\frac{1}{2}$ hour to get the food ready. He wants to take 3 different items. Here is a list of possible choices and the time they take to get ready.

- cheese sandwiches: 10 minutes
- fruit punch: 10 minutes
- chips and dip: 10 minutes
- tuna sandwiches: 15 minutes
- drink mix: 5 minutes
- trail mix: 5 minutes
- fruit salad: 5 minutes
- frosted cake: 15 minutes

Len asked himself the following questions to help him make his decision:

What are my top 6 choices in order?
tuna sandwiches, cake, fruit punch, drink mix, chips and dip, fruit salad

How long will my top 3 choices take to prepare?
40 minutes

Should I take only my top 2 items?
No, drinks are important to have at the beach.

Len decides to bring tuna sandwiches, chips and dip, and drink mix.

1. Which sandwiches are fastest to make? How much time could Len save?
Cheese sandwiches; 5 minutes
2. What drink is the fastest to make? How much time could Len save?
Drink mix; 5 minutes
3. What 3 items could Len bring that would take the least time to make?
Drink mix, trail mix, and fruit salad
4. If you want to take two different kinds of sandwiches, what else would you have time to prepare in the 30 minutes?
Drink mix, trail mix, or fruit salad

Use with pages 270–271. 77

Name ______________________

Another Look 6-9

Multiplying Money

You can multiply money in the same way you multiply whole numbers.

To multiply $7.89 and 15, multiply the whole numbers 789 and 15.

```
            789
         ×   15
789 × 5  =  3945
789 × 10 =  7890
           11835
```

Place a dollar sign in front of the answer and a decimal point to the left of the tens digit.

$7.89 × 15 = $118.35

Find the product of the whole number amount and place the dollar sign and decimal point.

1. $4.47 × 11

```
   4 4 7
 ×   1 1
    447  ← 447 × 1
   4470  ← 447 × 10
   4917
```

$4.47 × 11 = **$49.17**

2. $36.19 × 47

```
    3 6 1 9
  ×     4 7
    25333  ← 3619 × 7
   144760  ← 3619 × 40
   170093
```

$36.19 × 47 = **$1,700.93**

3. $6.31 × 15 = **$94.65**

4. $59.80 × 4 = **$239.20**

5. $15.11 × 6 = **$90.66**

78 Use with pages 274–275.

Name ______________________

Another Look 6-10

Analyze Word Problems: Overestimating and Underestimating

Asking a series of questions can help you decide when to overestimate and when to underestimate.

Jasmine invites 22 friends to a party. She plans to spend about $0.45 per person on favors. Should she overestimate or underestimate the total cost of favors?

How many people are expected at the party?
22 friends plus Jasmine, 23 people in all

How much does Jasmine plan to spend? $0.45 per person

How do you figure the total cost?
Multiply the cost of favors per person by the number of people.

What will happen if she underestimates?
She may not plan for enough money.

What if she overestimates?
She will have money left over.

Should she overestimate or underestimate?
She should overestimate. She can round the cost per favor to a greater amount, $0.50.

23 × $0.50 = $11.50

Jasmine will need about $11.50 for favors.

1. The captain is planning a kick-off meeting for her 16-member team. She plans to buy a headband for each person. The headbands cost $0.57 each. Should she overestimate or underestimate the total cost? Explain. How much money should she take when she goes shopping?
Possible answer: She should overestimate to be sure she has enough money; $0.60 × 16 = $9.60.

Use with pages 278–279. 79

Name ______________________

Another Look 6-11

Analyze Strategies: Draw a Picture

A filled auditorium has 6 rows with 15 seats per row. José is seated in row 5. How many people are in front of José? How many in all?

Here is a picture to help you.

15 seats per row José in row 5 6 rows in all

	1	2	3	4	5	6	7	8	9	10	11	12	13	14	15
1															
2															
3															
4															
5								J							
6															

Use the picture to solve the problem.

How many people are in front of José?
There are 4 rows in front of him.
15 seats per row
So, 4 × 15 = 60 people in front of José.

How many people in all?
6 rows in all
15 seats per row
So, 6 × 15 = 90 people in all

Check your answer.

Each ☐ = 1 person

Count the ☐ in the grid.

There are 90 ☐ in all.

1. How many people are behind José? **15 people**
2. Ahmed is 3 rows in front of José. How many people are behind Ahmed? **60 people**

80 Use with pages 280–281.

Name ____________________

Another Look 7-1

Exploring Division Patterns

In your book you used basic facts and place-value patterns to divide numbers. Here is another way to divide using place-value.

280 ÷ 7 = ?

Divide 28 tens into 7 equal groups.

28 tens ÷ 7 = 4 tens

280 ÷ 7 = 40

Divide. Use the place-value blocks to help.

1. 160 ÷ 8

a. 1 hundred and 6 tens is the same as 16 tens.

b. 16 tens ÷ 8 = 2 tens

c. 160 ÷ 8 = 20

2. 2,000 ÷ 5

a. 2 thousands is the same as 20 hundreds.

b. 20 hundreds ÷ 5 = 4 hundreds.

c. 2,000 ÷ 5 = 400

Find each quotient.

3. 120 ÷ 3 = 40

4. 600 ÷ 3 = 200

5. 2,400 ÷ 8 = 300

6. 3,600 ÷ 9 = 400

7. 3,000 ÷ 6 = 500

8. 120 ÷ 2 = 60

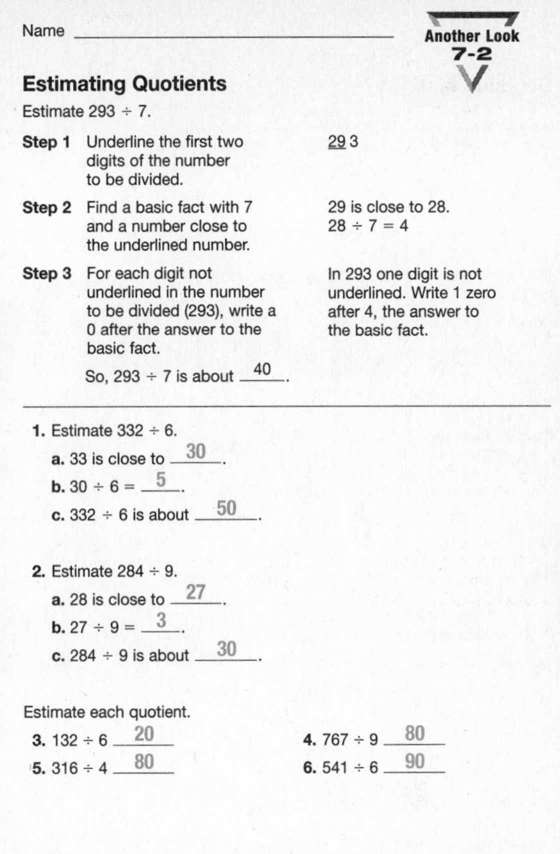

Name ____________________

Another Look 7-2

Estimating Quotients

Estimate 293 ÷ 7.

Step 1 Underline the first two digits of the number to be divided. — <u>29</u>3

Step 2 Find a basic fact with 7 and a number close to the underlined number. — 29 is close to 28. 28 ÷ 7 = 4

Step 3 For each digit not underlined in the number to be divided (293), write a 0 after the answer to the basic fact. — In 293 one digit is not underlined. Write 1 zero after 4, the answer to the basic fact.

So, 293 ÷ 7 is about 40.

1. Estimate 332 ÷ 6.

a. 33 is close to 30.

b. 30 ÷ 6 = 5.

c. 332 ÷ 6 is about 50.

2. Estimate 284 ÷ 9.

a. 28 is close to 27.

b. 27 ÷ 9 = 3.

c. 284 ÷ 9 is about 30.

Estimate each quotient.

3. 132 ÷ 6 20

4. 767 ÷ 9 80

5. 316 ÷ 4 80

6. 541 ÷ 6 90

Name ____________________

Another Look 7-3

Exploring Division with Remainders

In your book, you used counters to explore division with remainders. Here is another way to divide.

Find 7)52.

Using grid paper, draw a box around 52 squares. Circle groups of 7 squares.

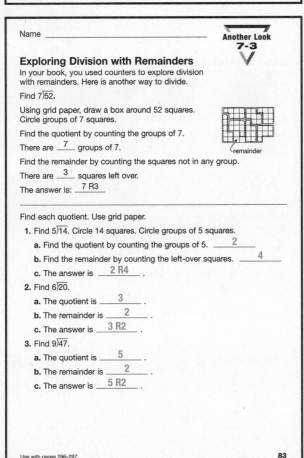

remainder

Find the quotient by counting the groups of 7.

There are 7 groups of 7.

Find the remainder by counting the squares not in any group.

There are 3 squares left over.

The answer is: 7 R3

Find each quotient. Use grid paper.

1. Find 5)14. Circle 14 squares. Circle groups of 5 squares.

a. Find the quotient by counting the groups of 5. 2

b. Find the remainder by counting the left-over squares. 4

c. The answer is 2 R4.

2. Find 6)20.

a. The quotient is 3.

b. The remainder is 2.

c. The answer is 3 R2.

3. Find 9)47.

a. The quotient is 5.

b. The remainder is 2.

c. The answer is 5 R2.

Name ____________________

Another Look 7-4

Exploring Division

In your book you used place-value blocks to explore division. Here is another way to divide.

Find 73 ÷ 3.

You can use coins to show division.

Show 73 using dimes and pennies.

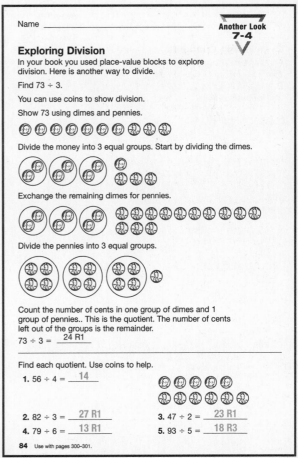

Divide the money into 3 equal groups. Start by dividing the dimes.

Exchange the remaining dimes for pennies.

Divide the pennies into 3 equal groups.

Count the number of cents in one group of dimes and 1 group of pennies.. This is the quotient. The number of cents left out of the groups is the remainder.

73 ÷ 3 = 24 R1

Find each quotient. Use coins to help.

1. 56 ÷ 4 = 14

2. 82 ÷ 3 = 27 R1

3. 47 ÷ 2 = 23 R1

4. 79 ÷ 6 = 13 R1

5. 93 ÷ 5 = 18 R3

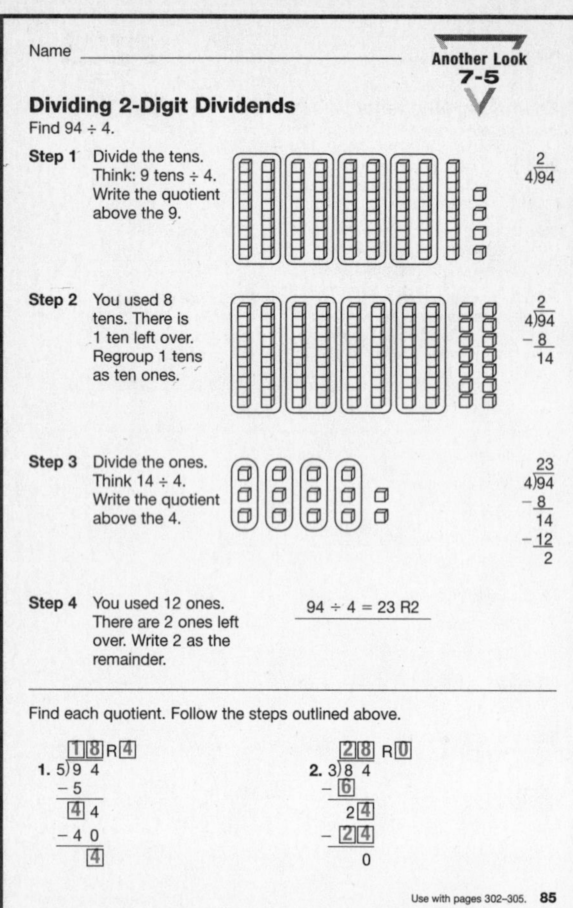

Name ______________________

Another Look 7-5

Dividing 2-Digit Dividends

Find 94 ÷ 4.

Step 1 Divide the tens. Think: 9 tens ÷ 4. Write the quotient above the 9.

```
  2
4)94
```

Step 2 You used 8 tens. There is 1 ten left over. Regroup 1 tens as ten ones.

```
  2
4)94
 -8
  14
```

Step 3 Divide the ones. Think 14 ÷ 4. Write the quotient above the 4.

```
  23
4)94
 -8
  14
 -12
   2
```

Step 4 You used 12 ones. There are 2 ones left over. Write 2 as the remainder.

94 ÷ 4 = 23 R2

Find each quotient. Follow the steps outlined above.

```
1.  18 R4          2.  28 R0
   5)9 4              3)8 4
    -5                 -6
     4 4                2 4
    -4 0               -2 4
       4                  0
```

Use with pages 302–305. 85

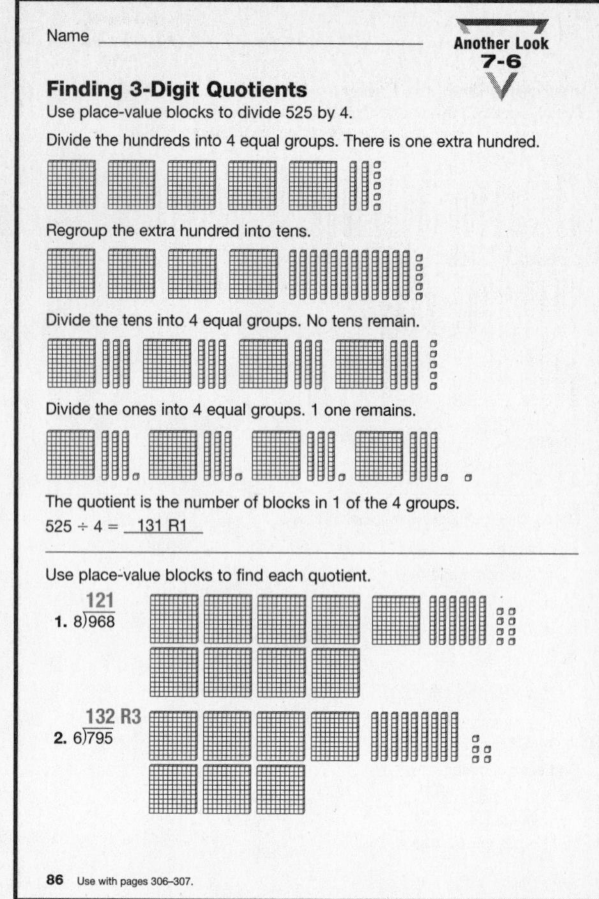

Name ______________________

Another Look 7-6

Finding 3-Digit Quotients

Use place-value blocks to divide 525 by 4.

Divide the hundreds into 4 equal groups. There is one extra hundred.

Regroup the extra hundred into tens.

Divide the tens into 4 equal groups. No tens remain.

Divide the ones into 4 equal groups. 1 one remains.

The quotient is the number of blocks in 1 of the 4 groups.

525 ÷ 4 = 131 R1

Use place-value blocks to find each quotient.

1. 8)968 — 121

2. 6)795 — 132 R3

86 Use with pages 306–307.

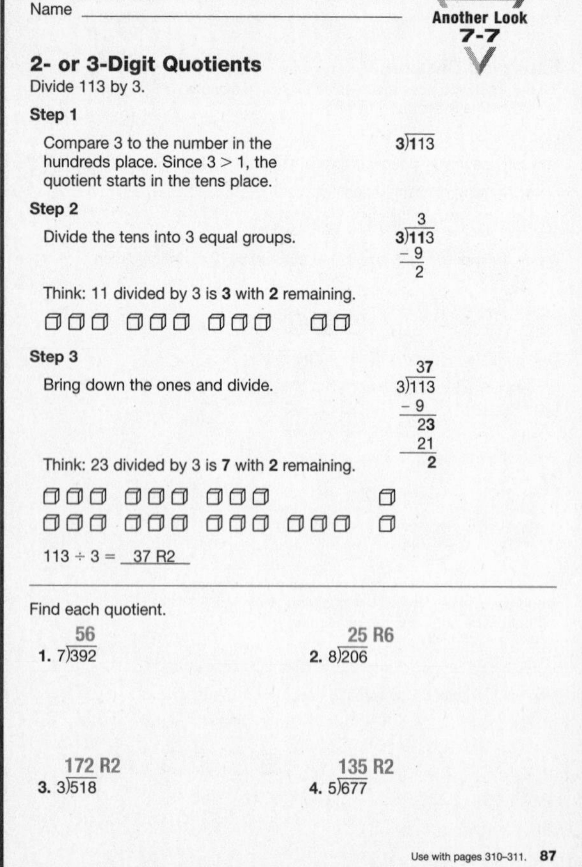

Name ______________________

Another Look 7-7

2- or 3-Digit Quotients

Divide 113 by 3.

Step 1

Compare 3 to the number in the hundreds place. Since 3 > 1, the quotient starts in the tens place.

```
3)113
```

Step 2

Divide the tens into 3 equal groups.

```
   3
3)113
  -9
   2
```

Think: 11 divided by 3 is **3** with **2** remaining.

Step 3

Bring down the ones and divide.

```
   37
3)113
  -9
   23
   21
    2
```

Think: 23 divided by 3 is **7** with **2** remaining.

113 ÷ 3 = 37 R2

Find each quotient.

1. 7)392 — 56
2. 8)206 — 25 R6
3. 3)518 — 172 R2
4. 5)677 — 135 R2

Use with pages 310–311. 87

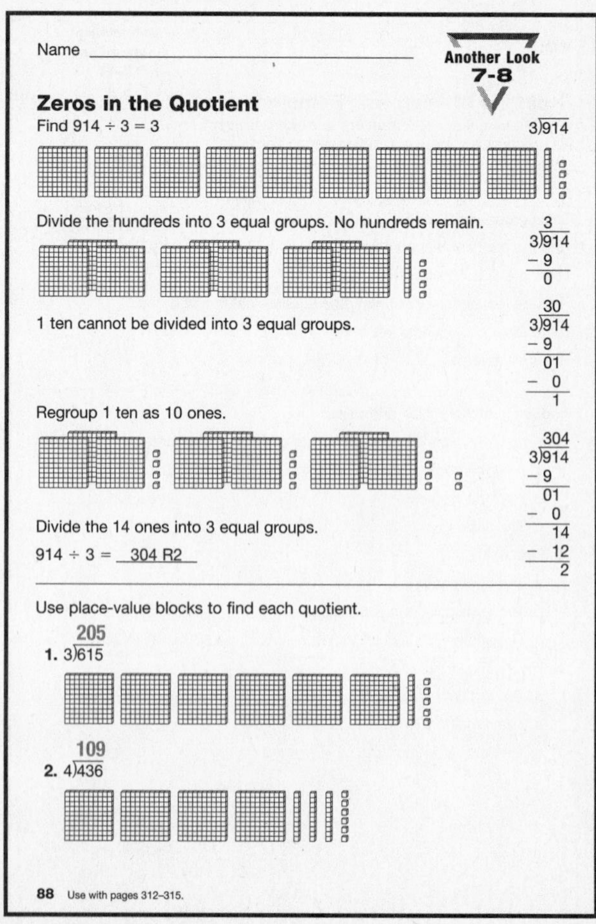

Name ______________________

Another Look 7-8

Zeros in the Quotient

Find 914 ÷ 3 = 3

```
3)914
```

Divide the hundreds into 3 equal groups. No hundreds remain.

```
   3
3)914
  -9
   0
```

1 ten cannot be divided into 3 equal groups.

```
   30
3)914
  -9
   01
  - 0
    1
```

Regroup 1 ten as 10 ones.

Divide the 14 ones into 3 equal groups.

```
  304
3)914
  -9
   01
  - 0
    14
  - 12
     2
```

914 ÷ 3 = 304 R2

Use place-value blocks to find each quotient.

1. 3)615 — 205
2. 4)436 — 109

88 Use with pages 312–315.

Name ________________________________

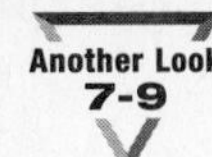

Analyze Word Problems: Interpreting Remainders

Marci is making punch for a party. The recipe makes 27 cups of punch. If each guest drinks 2 cups of punch, how many guests will the recipe serve?

Write a division sentence for this problem. 27 ÷ 2 = 13 R1

13 guests can each have 2 cups. There is 1 cup of punch left over.

The Rotary Club is holding its annual fashion show. A total of 435 people will be attending. Each table at the fashion show seats 8 people. How many tables should be set up for the show?

1. How many people will be attending the fashion show? 435 people
2. How many people can sit at one table? 8
3. Write a division sentence for this problem. 435 ÷ 8 = 54 R3
4. How many full groups of 8 will be seated? 54
5. What does the remainder represent? 3 people not at one of the 54 tables
6. How many tables should be set up for the show? 55 tables

Name ________________________________

Exploring Division with Money

In your book you used money to show division with money. Here is another way to divide with money.

Find $2.65 ÷ 5.

Step 1 Show the first two digits as dimes. Show the rest as pennies. 26 dimes and 5 pennies = $2.65

Step 2 Draw circles around groups of 5 dimes. Write the number of groups after a decimal point. $0.5

Step 3 Regroup the left over dime as 10 pennies

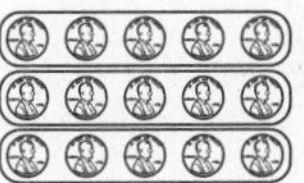

Step 4 Draw circles around groups of 5 pennies. Write the number of groups of pennies as the second digit after the decimal point. $0.53

$2.65 ÷ 5 = $0.53

Find each quotient. Draw rings around groups of money to help.

1. $2.25 ÷ 3 = $0.75

2. $1.88 ÷ 4 = $0.47

Name ________________________________

Dividing Money Amounts

Find $4.52 ÷ 4.

Divide the way you would with whole numbers. Change 4)$4.52 to 4)452.

Divide hundreds.	Bring down the tens and divide.	Bring down the ones and divide.
1 4)452 − 4 0	11 4)452 − 4 **05** − 4 1	113 4)452 − 4 05 − 4 **12** − 12 0
Divide. 4 ÷ 4 = 1 Multiply. 1 × 4 = 4 Subtract. 4 − 4 = 0 Compare. 0 < 4	Divide. 5 ÷ 4 = 1 Multiply. 1 × 4 = 4 Subtract. 5 − 4 = 1 Compare. 1 < 4	Divide. 12 ÷ 4 = 3 Multiply. 3 × 4 = 12 Subtract. 12 − 12 = 0 Compare. 0 < 4

So: 452 ÷ 4 = 113

Now show dollars and cents in the quotient. $4.52 ÷ 4 = $1.13

Divide.

1. $5.34 ÷ 3
   a. First change 3)$5.34 to 3)534
   b. 534 ÷ 3 = 178
   c. $5.34 ÷ 3 = $1.78
2. $6.50 ÷ 5 = $1.30
3. $4.72 ÷ 2 = $2.36
4. $3.24 ÷ 4 = $0.81
5. $7.23 ÷ 3 = $2.41
6. $6.15 ÷ 5 = $1.23
7. $7.56 ÷ 6 = $1.26

Name ________________________________

Another Look
7-12

Exploring Mean

In your book you found the mean using paper strips. Here is another way to find the mean.

Find the mean of 12, 5, 9, and 10.

Use counters to help you find the mean. Place the 4 groups of counters on your desk.

Group 1 | Group 2 | Group 3 | Group 4

How many counters all together do you have? 36

Mix up the counters and place them into 4 equal groups.

How many counters are in each group now? 9

The mean of 12, 5, 9, and 10 is 9.

Use counters to find the mean for each set of data.

1. 3, 4, 10, and 7.
   a. How many counters in all will you put on your desk? 24
   b. How many groups of counters will you have? 4
   c. Place the counters into equal groups. How many are in each group? 6
   d. What is the mean of 3, 4, 10, and 7? 6
2. 11, 13, and 6.
   a. How many counters in all will you put on your desk? 30
   b. How many groups of counters will you have? 3
   c. Place the counters into equal groups. How many are in each group? 10
   d. What is the mean of 11, 13, and 6? 10
3. What is the mean of 11, 7, 5, 10, and 12? 9

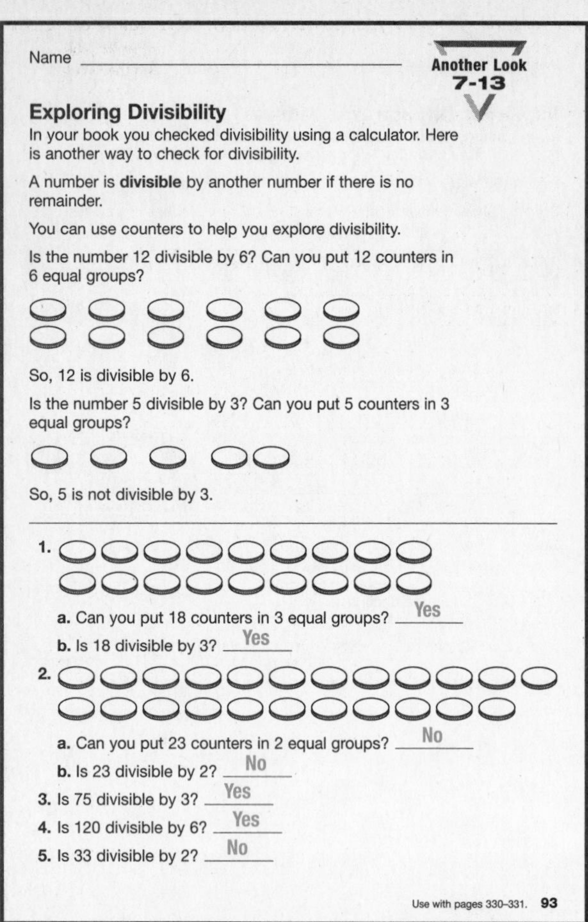

Name ______________________

Another Look 7-13

Exploring Divisibility

In your book you checked divisibility using a calculator. Here is another way to check for divisibility.

A number is **divisible** by another number if there is no remainder.

You can use counters to help you explore divisibility.

Is the number 12 divisible by 6? Can you put 12 counters in 6 equal groups?

So, 12 is divisible by 6.

Is the number 5 divisible by 3? Can you put 5 counters in 3 equal groups?

So, 5 is not divisible by 3.

1. a. Can you put 18 counters in 3 equal groups? Yes
   b. Is 18 divisible by 3? Yes
2. a. Can you put 23 counters in 2 equal groups? No
   b. Is 23 divisible by 2? No
3. Is 75 divisible by 3? Yes
4. Is 120 divisible by 6? Yes
5. Is 33 divisible by 2? No

Use with pages 330–331. **93**

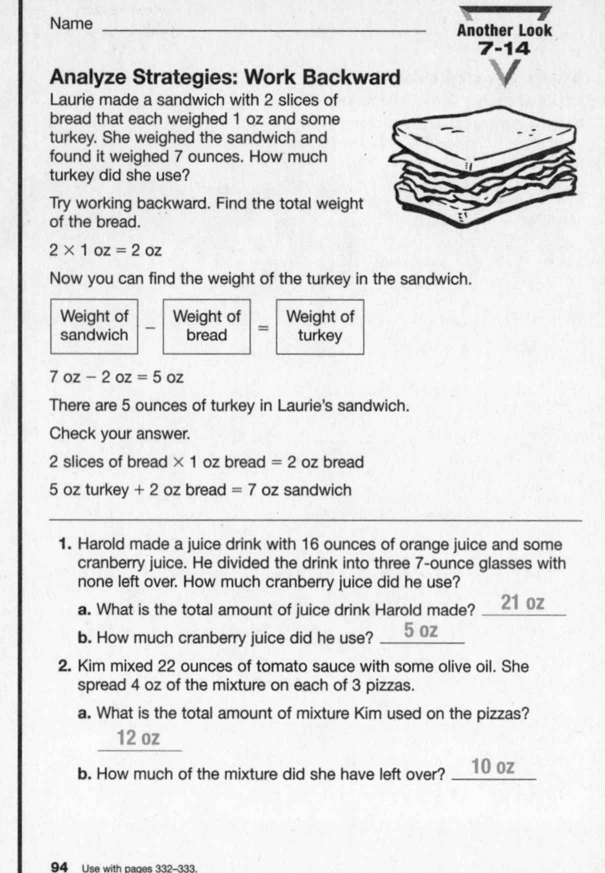

Name ______________________

Another Look 7-14

Analyze Strategies: Work Backward

Laurie made a sandwich with 2 slices of bread that each weighed 1 oz and some turkey. She weighed the sandwich and found it weighed 7 ounces. How much turkey did she use?

Try working backward. Find the total weight of the bread.

2×1 oz = 2 oz

Now you can find the weight of the turkey in the sandwich.

Weight of sandwich − Weight of bread = Weight of turkey

7 oz − 2 oz = 5 oz

There are 5 ounces of turkey in Laurie's sandwich.

Check your answer.

2 slices of bread × 1 oz bread = 2 oz bread

5 oz turkey + 2 oz bread = 7 oz sandwich

1. Harold made a juice drink with 16 ounces of orange juice and some cranberry juice. He divided the drink into three 7-ounce glasses with none left over. How much cranberry juice did he use?
   a. What is the total amount of juice drink Harold made? 21 oz
   b. How much cranberry juice did he use? 5 oz
2. Kim mixed 22 ounces of tomato sauce with some olive oil. She spread 4 oz of the mixture on each of 3 pizzas.
   a. What is the total amount of mixture Kim used on the pizzas? 12 oz
   b. How much of the mixture did she have left over? 10 oz

94 Use with pages 332–333.

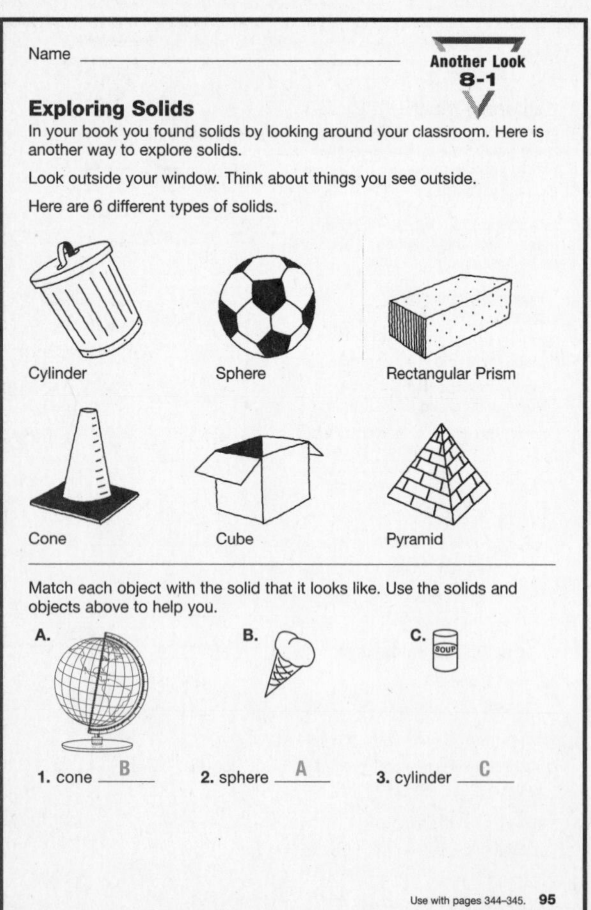

Name ______________________

Another Look 8-1

Exploring Solids

In your book you found solids by looking around your classroom. Here is another way to explore solids.

Look outside your window. Think about things you see outside.

Here are 6 different types of solids.

Cylinder Sphere Rectangular Prism

Cone Cube Pyramid

Match each object with the solid that it looks like. Use the solids and objects above to help you.

A. B. C.

1. cone B
2. sphere A
3. cylinder C

Use with pages 344–345. **95**

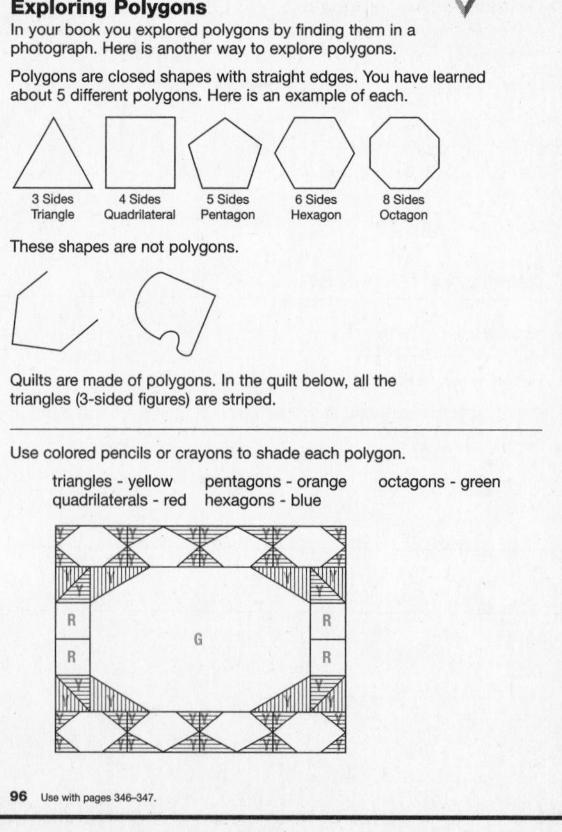

Name ______________________

Another Look 8-2

Exploring Polygons

In your book you explored polygons by finding them in a photograph. Here is another way to explore polygons.

Polygons are closed shapes with straight edges. You have learned about 5 different polygons. Here is an example of each.

3 Sides Triangle	4 Sides Quadrilateral	5 Sides Pentagon	6 Sides Hexagon	8 Sides Octagon

These shapes are not polygons.

Quilts are made of polygons. In the quilt below, all the triangles (3-sided figures) are striped.

Use colored pencils or crayons to shade each polygon.

triangles - yellow pentagons - orange octagons - green
quadrilaterals - red hexagons - blue

96 Use with pages 346–347.

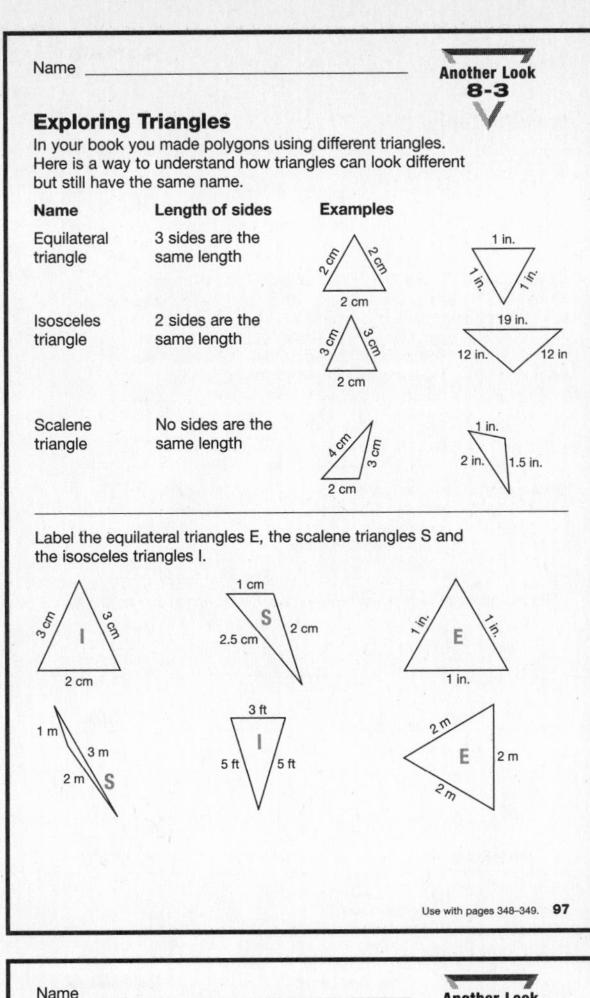

Name ______________________

Another Look 8-3

Exploring Triangles

In your book you made polygons using different triangles. Here is a way to understand how triangles can look different but still have the same name.

Name	Length of sides	Examples
Equilateral triangle	3 sides are the same length	2 cm, 2 cm, 2 cm; 1 in., 1 in., 1 in.
Isosceles triangle	2 sides are the same length	3 cm, 3 cm, 2 cm; 19 in., 12 in., 12 in
Scalene triangle	No sides are the same length	4 cm, 3 cm, 2 cm; 1 in., 2 in., 1.5 in.

Label the equilateral triangles E, the scalene triangles S and the isosceles triangles I.

Use with pages 348–349. 97

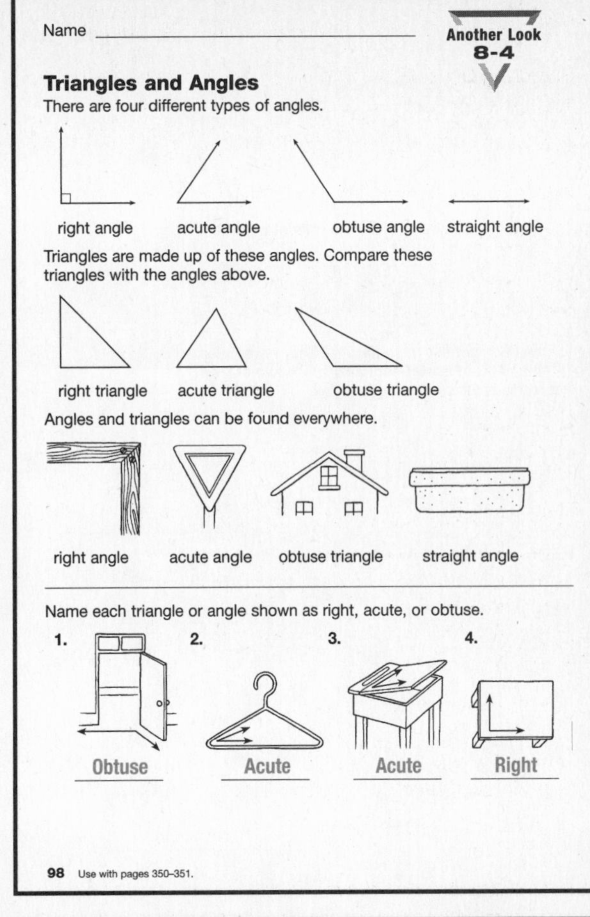

Name ______________________

Another Look 8-4

Triangles and Angles

There are four different types of angles.

Triangles are made up of these angles. Compare these triangles with the angles above.

Angles and triangles can be found everywhere.

Name each triangle or angle shown as right, acute, or obtuse.

1. Obtuse
2. Acute
3. Acute
4. Right

98 Use with pages 350–351.

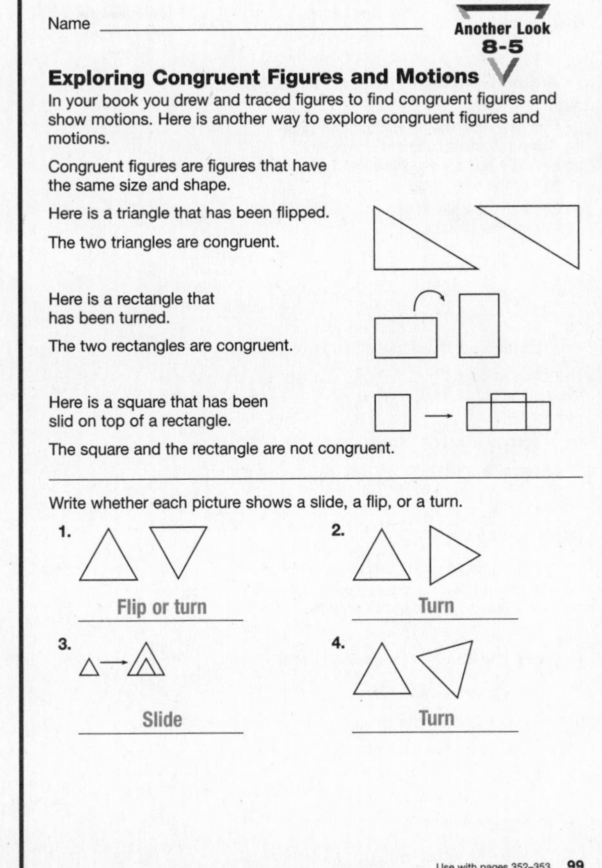

Name ______________________

Another Look 8-5

Exploring Congruent Figures and Motions

In your book you drew and traced figures to find congruent figures and show motions. Here is another way to explore congruent figures and motions.

Congruent figures are figures that have the same size and shape.

Here is a triangle that has been flipped.

The two triangles are congruent.

Here is a rectangle that has been turned.

The two rectangles are congruent.

Here is a square that has been slid on top of a rectangle.

The square and the rectangle are not congruent.

Write whether each picture shows a slide, a flip, or a turn.

1. Flip or turn
2. Turn
3. Slide
4. Turn

Use with pages 352–353. 99

Name ______________________

Another Look 8-6

Exploring Similar Figures

In your book you made similar shapes, using geoboards. Here is another way to explore what makes shapes congruent, similar, or neither. Similar figures have the same shape but not necessarily the same size.

Polygon **Congruent** **Similar** **Neither**

Write whether each set of figures appears to be congruent, similar or neither.

1. similar
2. neither
3. congruent
4. similar

100 Use with pages 354–355.

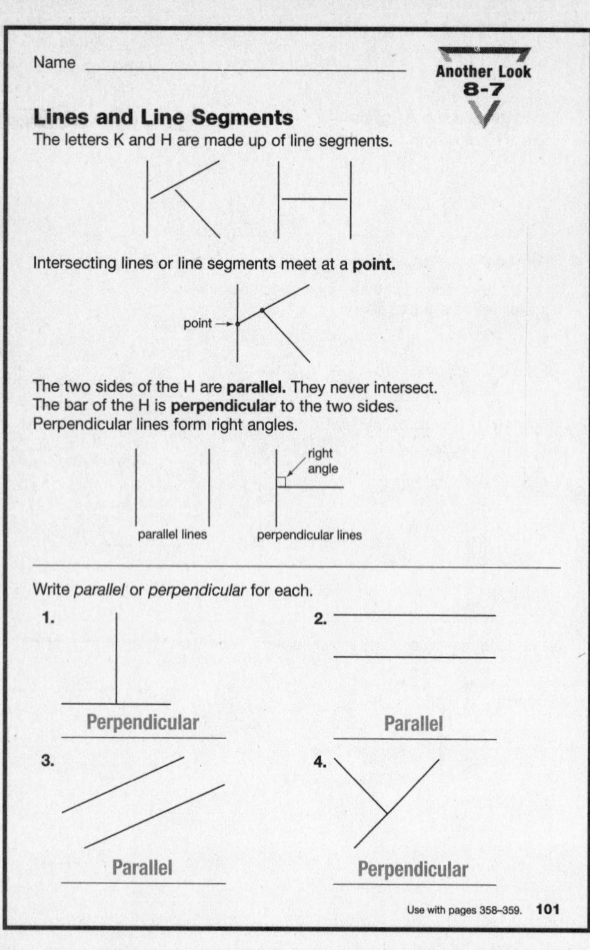
Name ______________________

Another Look 8-7

Lines and Line Segments

The letters K and H are made up of line segments.

Intersecting lines or line segments meet at a **point.**

point

The two sides of the H are **parallel.** They never intersect. The bar of the H is **perpendicular** to the two sides. Perpendicular lines form right angles.

right angle

parallel lines   perpendicular lines

Write *parallel* or *perpendicular* for each.

1. Perpendicular
2. Parallel
3. Parallel
4. Perpendicular

Use with pages 358–359. 101

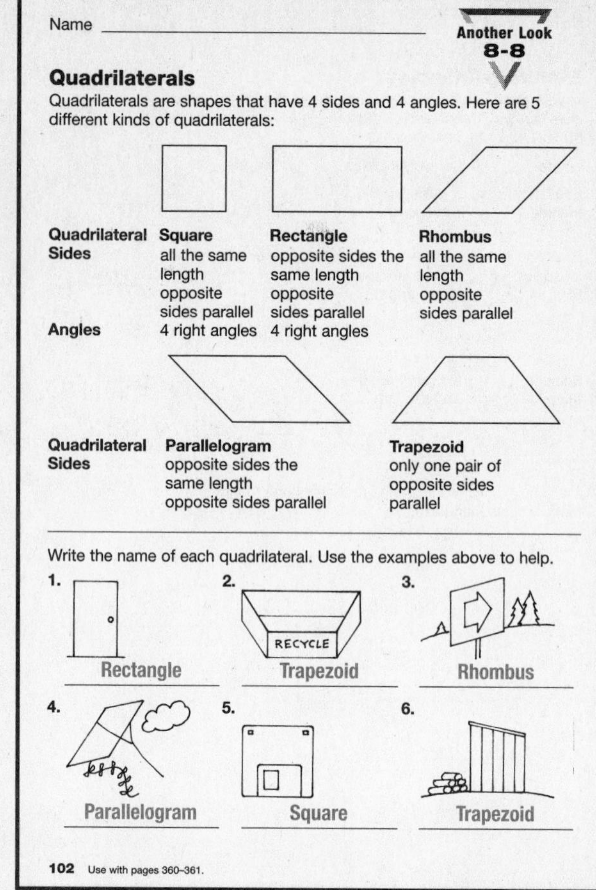
Name ______________________

Another Look 8-8

Quadrilaterals

Quadrilaterals are shapes that have 4 sides and 4 angles. Here are 5 different kinds of quadrilaterals:

Quadrilateral	Square	Rectangle	Rhombus
Sides	all the same length opposite sides parallel	opposite sides the same length opposite sides parallel	all the same length opposite sides parallel
Angles	4 right angles	4 right angles	

Quadrilateral	Parallelogram	Trapezoid
Sides	opposite sides the same length opposite sides parallel	only one pair of opposite sides parallel

Write the name of each quadrilateral. Use the examples above to help.

1. Rectangle
2. RECYCLE Trapezoid
3. Rhombus
4. Parallelogram
5. Square
6. Trapezoid

102 Use with pages 360–361.

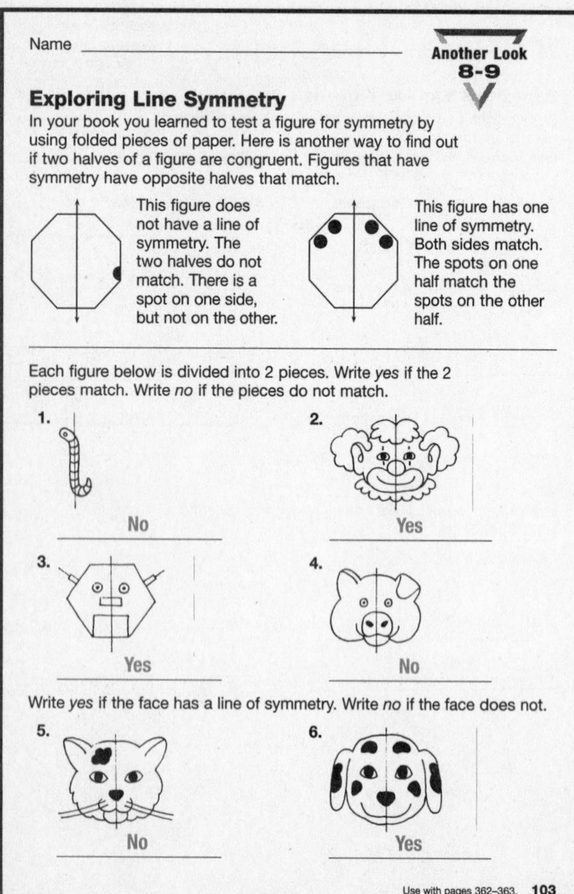
Name ______________________

Another Look 8-9

Exploring Line Symmetry

In your book you learned to test a figure for symmetry by using folded pieces of paper. Here is another way to find out if two halves of a figure are congruent. Figures that have symmetry have opposite halves that match.

This figure does not have a line of symmetry. The two halves do not match. There is a spot on one side, but not on the other.

This figure has one line of symmetry. Both sides match. The spots on one half match the spots on the other half.

Each figure below is divided into 2 pieces. Write *yes* if the 2 pieces match. Write *no* if the pieces do not match.

1. No
2. Yes
3. Yes
4. No

Write *yes* if the face has a line of symmetry. Write *no* if the face does not.

5. No
6. Yes

Use with pages 362–363. 103

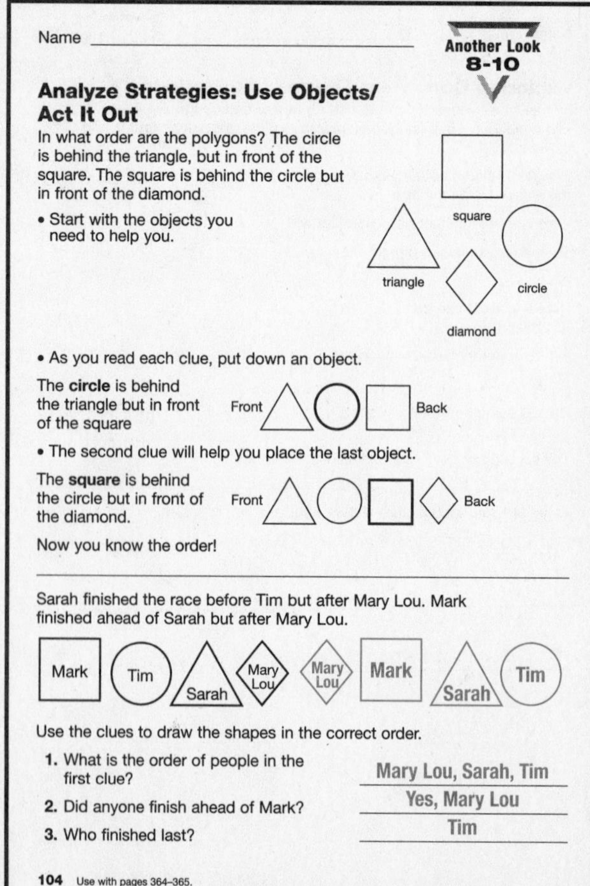
Name ______________________

Another Look 8-10

Analyze Strategies: Use Objects/ Act It Out

In what order are the polygons? The circle is behind the triangle, but in front of the square. The square is behind the circle but in front of the diamond.

- Start with the objects you need to help you.

square   triangle   circle   diamond

- As you read each clue, put down an object.

The **circle** is behind the triangle but in front of the square   Front   Back

- The second clue will help you place the last object.

The **square** is behind the circle but in front of the diamond.   Front   Back

Now you know the order!

Sarah finished the race before Tim but after Mary Lou. Mark finished ahead of Sarah but after Mary Lou.

Mark   Tim   Sarah   Mary Lou   Mary Lou   Mark   Sarah   Tim

Use the clues to draw the shapes in the correct order.

1. What is the order of people in the first clue? Mary Lou, Sarah, Tim
2. Did anyone finish ahead of Mark? Yes, Mary Lou
3. Who finished last? Tim

104 Use with pages 364–365.

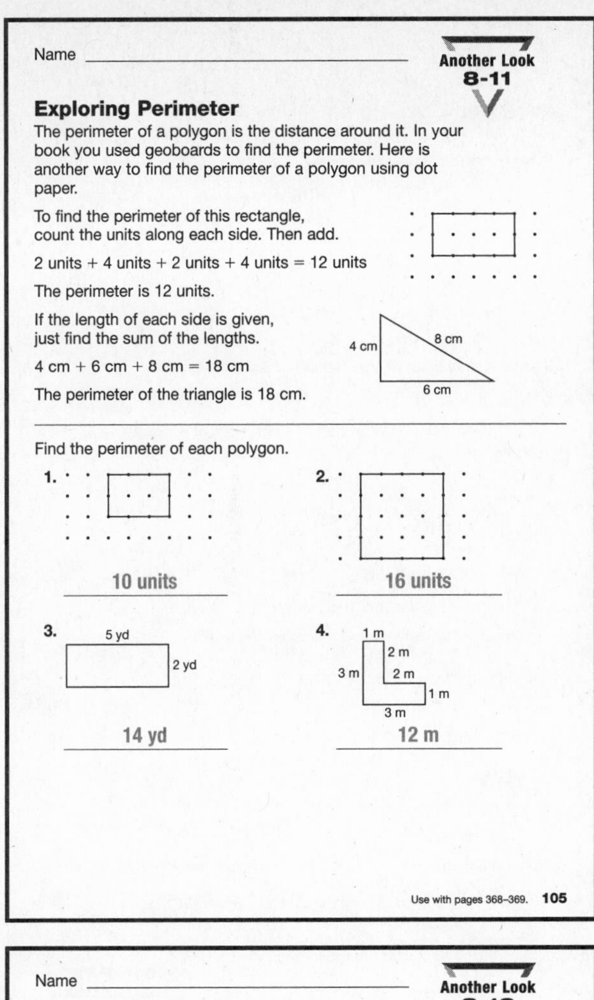

Name ______________________

Another Look 8-11

Exploring Perimeter

The perimeter of a polygon is the distance around it. In your book you used geoboards to find the perimeter. Here is another way to find the perimeter of a polygon using dot paper.

To find the perimeter of this rectangle, count the units along each side. Then add.

2 units + 4 units + 2 units + 4 units = 12 units

The perimeter is 12 units.

If the length of each side is given, just find the sum of the lengths.

4 cm + 6 cm + 8 cm = 18 cm

The perimeter of the triangle is 18 cm.

Find the perimeter of each polygon.

1. 10 units
2. 16 units
3. (5 yd, 2 yd) 14 yd
4. (1 m, 2 m, 3 m, 2 m, 1 m, 3 m) 12 m

Use with pages 368–369. 105

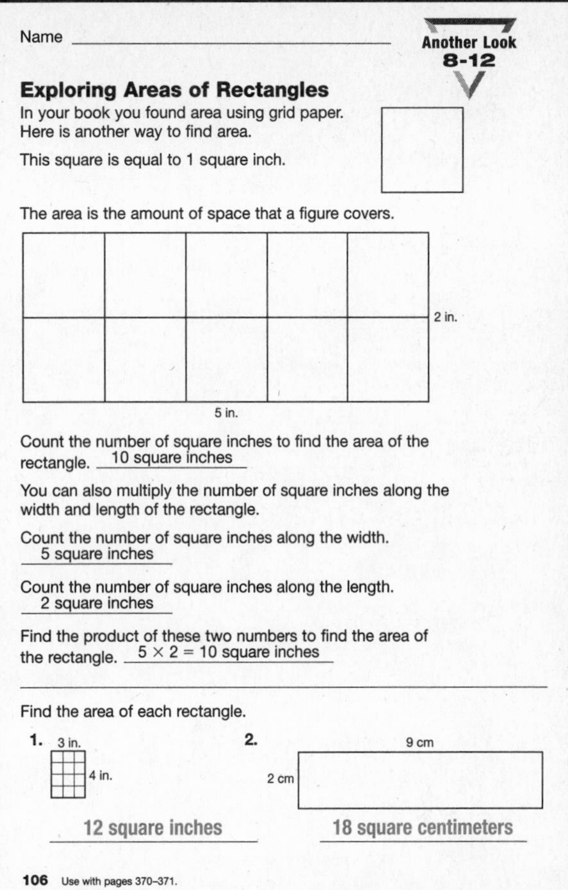

Name ______________________

Another Look 8-12

Exploring Areas of Rectangles

In your book you found area using grid paper. Here is another way to find area.

This square is equal to 1 square inch.

The area is the amount of space that a figure covers.

Count the number of square inches to find the area of the rectangle. 10 square inches

You can also multiply the number of square inches along the width and length of the rectangle.

Count the number of square inches along the width. 5 square inches

Count the number of square inches along the length. 2 square inches

Find the product of these two numbers to find the area of the rectangle. $5 \times 2 = 10$ square inches

Find the area of each rectangle.

1. (3 in., 4 in.) 12 square inches
2. (9 cm, 2 cm) 18 square centimeters

106 Use with pages 370–371.

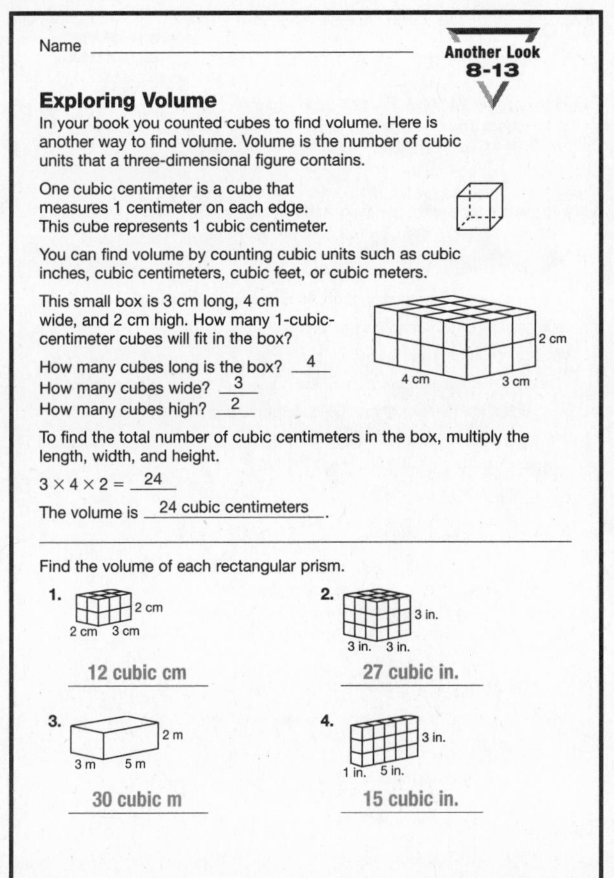

Name ______________________

Another Look 8-13

Exploring Volume

In your book you counted cubes to find volume. Here is another way to find volume. Volume is the number of cubic units that a three-dimensional figure contains.

One cubic centimeter is a cube that measures 1 centimeter on each edge. This cube represents 1 cubic centimeter.

You can find volume by counting cubic units such as cubic inches, cubic centimeters, cubic feet, or cubic meters.

This small box is 3 cm long, 4 cm wide, and 2 cm high. How many 1-cubic-centimeter cubes will fit in the box?

How many cubes long is the box? 4
How many cubes wide? 3
How many cubes high? 2

To find the total number of cubic centimeters in the box, multiply the length, width, and height.

$3 \times 4 \times 2 =$ 24

The volume is 24 cubic centimeters.

Find the volume of each rectangular prism.

1. (2 cm, 2 cm, 3 cm) 12 cubic cm
2. (3 in., 3 in., 3 in.) 27 cubic in.
3. (2 m, 3 m, 5 m) 30 cubic m
4. (3 in., 1 in., 5 in.) 15 cubic in.

Use with pages 372–373. 107

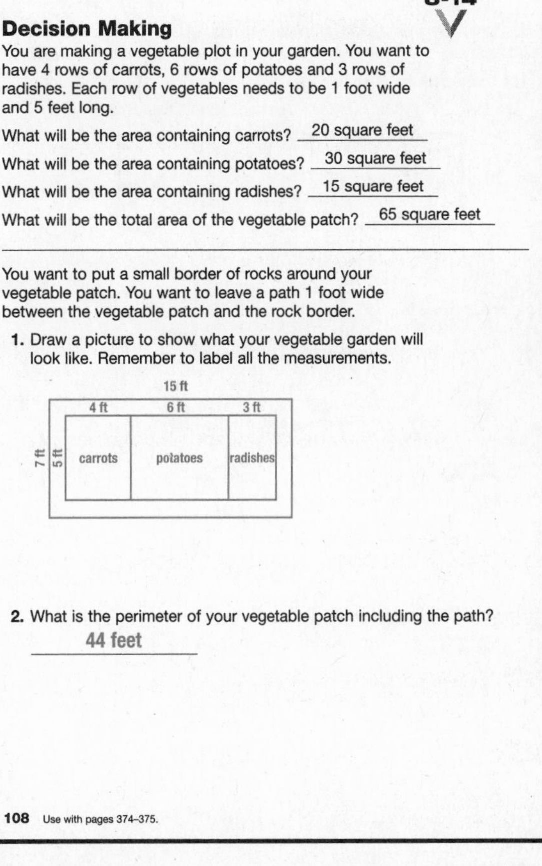

Name ______________________

Another Look 8-14

Decision Making

You are making a vegetable plot in your garden. You want to have 4 rows of carrots, 6 rows of potatoes and 3 rows of radishes. Each row of vegetables needs to be 1 foot wide and 5 feet long.

What will be the area containing carrots? 20 square feet

What will be the area containing potatoes? 30 square feet

What will be the area containing radishes? 15 square feet

What will be the total area of the vegetable patch? 65 square feet

You want to put a small border of rocks around your vegetable patch. You want to leave a path 1 foot wide between the vegetable patch and the rock border.

1. Draw a picture to show what your vegetable garden will look like. Remember to label all the measurements.

2. What is the perimeter of your vegetable patch including the path?
44 feet

108 Use with pages 374–375.

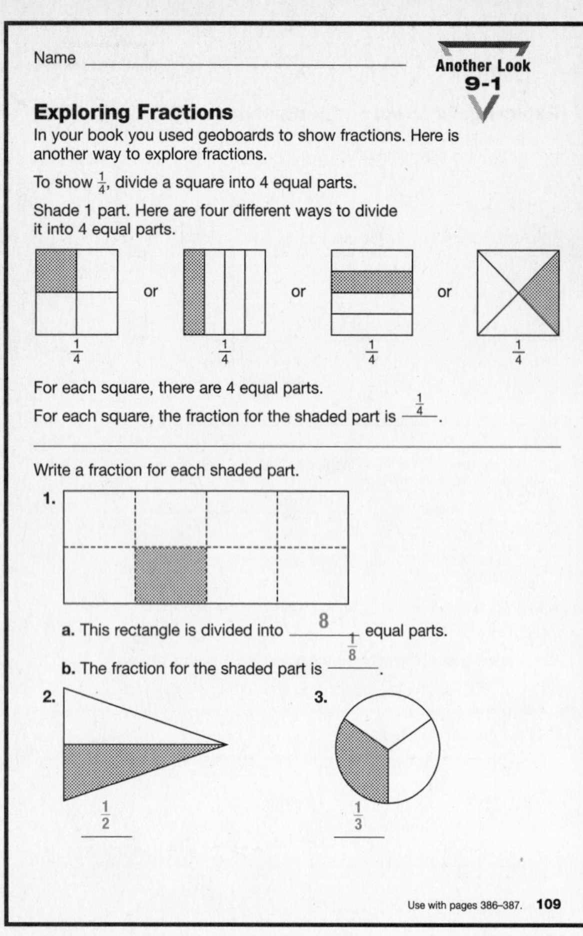
Name ____________

Another Look 9-1

Exploring Fractions

In your book you used geoboards to show fractions. Here is another way to explore fractions.

To show $\frac{1}{4}$, divide a square into 4 equal parts.

Shade 1 part. Here are four different ways to divide it into 4 equal parts.

$\frac{1}{4}$ or $\frac{1}{4}$ or $\frac{1}{4}$ or $\frac{1}{4}$

For each square, there are 4 equal parts.

For each square, the fraction for the shaded part is $\frac{1}{4}$.

Write a fraction for each shaded part.

1.

a. This rectangle is divided into 8 equal parts.

b. The fraction for the shaded part is $\frac{1}{8}$.

2. $\frac{1}{2}$

3. $\frac{1}{3}$

Use with pages 386–387. 109

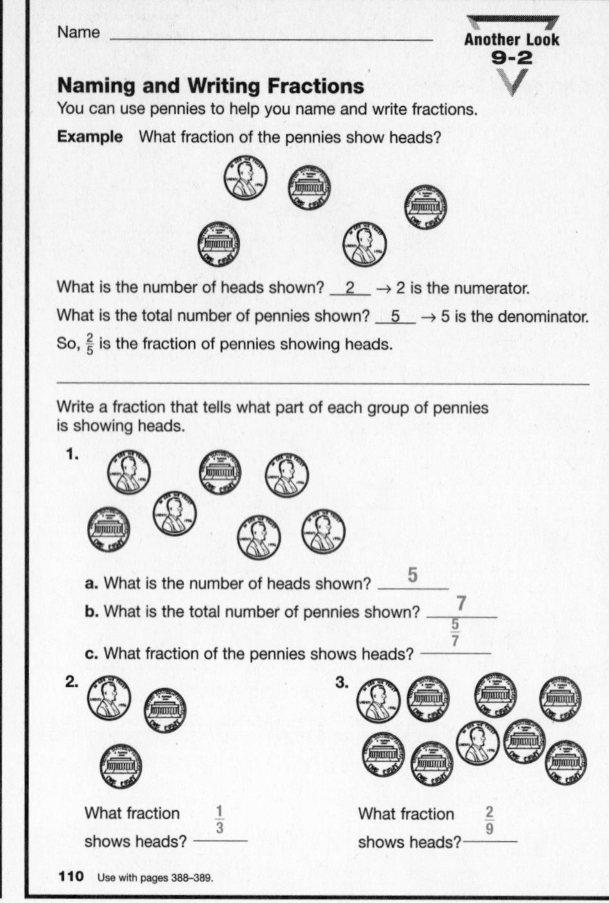
Name ____________

Another Look 9-2

Naming and Writing Fractions

You can use pennies to help you name and write fractions.

Example What fraction of the pennies show heads?

What is the number of heads shown? 2 → 2 is the numerator.

What is the total number of pennies shown? 5 → 5 is the denominator.

So, $\frac{2}{5}$ is the fraction of pennies showing heads.

Write a fraction that tells what part of each group of pennies is showing heads.

1.

a. What is the number of heads shown? 5

b. What is the total number of pennies shown? 7

c. What fraction of the pennies shows heads? $\frac{5}{7}$

2. What fraction shows heads? $\frac{1}{3}$

3. What fraction shows heads? $\frac{2}{9}$

110 Use with pages 388–389.

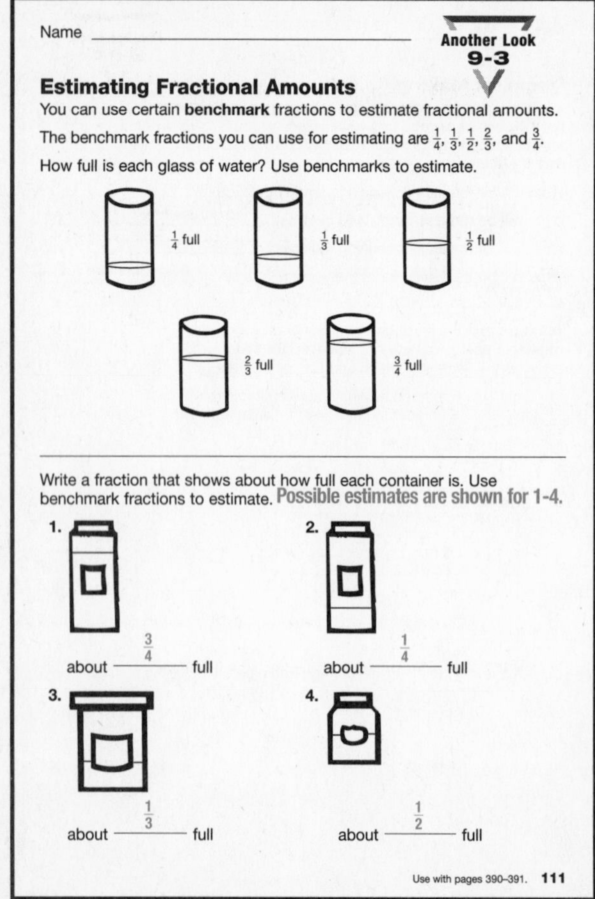
Name ____________

Another Look 9-3

Estimating Fractional Amounts

You can use certain **benchmark** fractions to estimate fractional amounts.

The benchmark fractions you can use for estimating are $\frac{1}{4}$, $\frac{1}{3}$, $\frac{1}{2}$, $\frac{2}{3}$, and $\frac{3}{4}$.

How full is each glass of water? Use benchmarks to estimate.

$\frac{1}{4}$ full $\frac{1}{3}$ full $\frac{1}{2}$ full

$\frac{2}{3}$ full $\frac{3}{4}$ full

Write a fraction that shows about how full each container is. Use benchmark fractions to estimate. Possible estimates are shown for 1-4.

1. about $\frac{3}{4}$ full

2. about $\frac{1}{4}$ full

3. about $\frac{1}{3}$ full

4. about $\frac{1}{2}$ full

Use with pages 390–391. 111

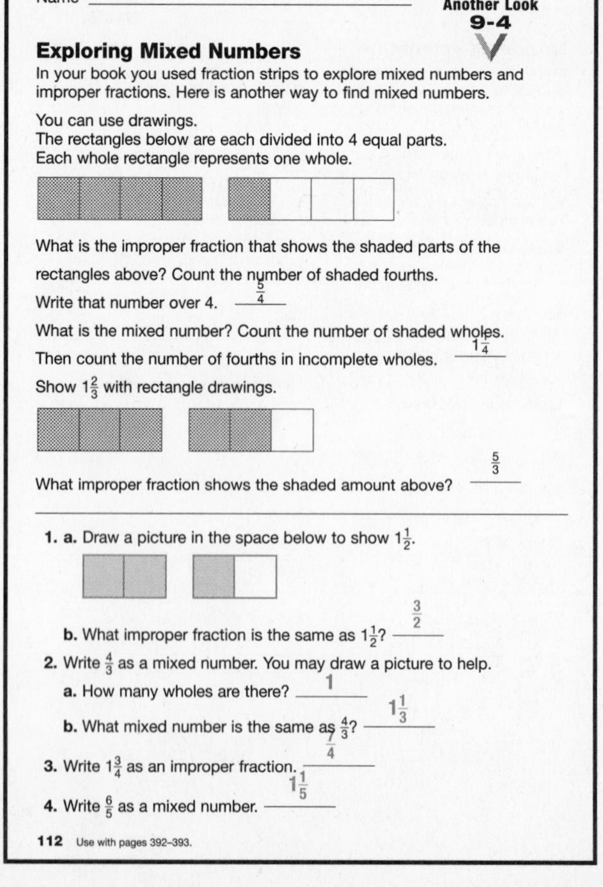
Name ____________

Another Look 9-4

Exploring Mixed Numbers

In your book you used fraction strips to explore mixed numbers and improper fractions. Here is another way to find mixed numbers.

You can use drawings.
The rectangles below are each divided into 4 equal parts.
Each whole rectangle represents one whole.

What is the improper fraction that shows the shaded parts of the rectangles above? Count the number of shaded fourths.

Write that number over 4. $\frac{5}{4}$

What is the mixed number? Count the number of shaded wholes.

Then count the number of fourths in incomplete wholes. $1\frac{1}{4}$

Show $1\frac{2}{3}$ with rectangle drawings.

What improper fraction shows the shaded amount above? $\frac{5}{3}$

1. **a.** Draw a picture in the space below to show $1\frac{1}{2}$.

b. What improper fraction is the same as $1\frac{1}{2}$? $\frac{3}{2}$

2. Write $\frac{4}{3}$ as a mixed number. You may draw a picture to help.

a. How many wholes are there? 1

b. What mixed number is the same as $\frac{4}{3}$? $1\frac{1}{3}$

3. Write $1\frac{3}{4}$ as an improper fraction. $\frac{7}{4}$

4. Write $\frac{6}{5}$ as a mixed number. $1\frac{1}{5}$

112 Use with pages 392–393.

Name ______________________

Another Look 9-5

Decision Making

Akbar wants to plant a vegetable garden. In his area, he can plant the vegetables at the time shown:

Beets: February through August
Carrots: January 1 through the middle of September
Parsnips: March 15 through August 31
Rhubarb: January through March
Peas: August 1 through November 15
Shallots: November and December

Make a table to help Akbar plan his garden. Since beets can be planted February through August, on the row next to beets, shade in the boxes under the months from February through August.

	Jan	Feb	Mar	Apr	May	June	July	Aug	Sept	Oct	Nov	Dec
Beets		■	■	■	■	■	■	■				
Carrots	■	■	■	■	■	■	■	■	■			
Parsnips			■	■	■	■	■	■				
Rhubarb	■	■	■									
Peas								■	■	■	■	
Shallots											■	■

1. Complete the table above with the data given.
2. Akbar has some free time on March 21. What can he plant on that day?
   Beets, carrots, parsnips, rhubarb
3. On November 1, Akbar is at the garden store. What should he buy for immediate planting?
   Peas, shallots
4. What vegetables can Akbar plant at the very beginning of the year?
   Carrots, rhubarb

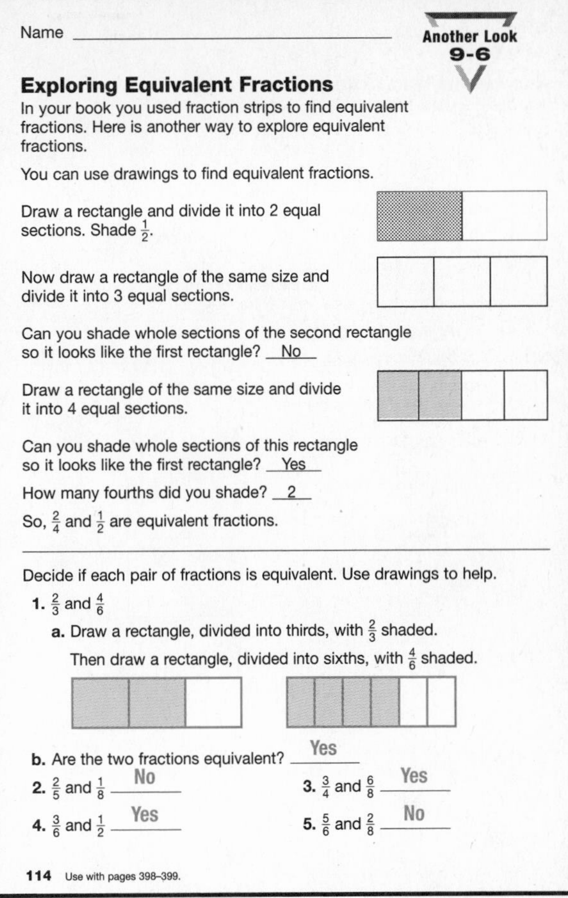

Name ______________________

Another Look 9-6

Exploring Equivalent Fractions

In your book you used fraction strips to find equivalent fractions. Here is another way to explore equivalent fractions.

You can use drawings to find equivalent fractions.

Draw a rectangle and divide it into 2 equal sections. Shade $\frac{1}{2}$.

Now draw a rectangle of the same size and divide it into 3 equal sections.

Can you shade whole sections of the second rectangle so it looks like the first rectangle? No

Draw a rectangle of the same size and divide it into 4 equal sections.

Can you shade whole sections of this rectangle so it looks like the first rectangle? Yes

How many fourths did you shade? 2

So, $\frac{2}{4}$ and $\frac{1}{2}$ are equivalent fractions.

Decide if each pair of fractions is equivalent. Use drawings to help.

1. $\frac{2}{3}$ and $\frac{4}{6}$
   a. Draw a rectangle, divided into thirds, with $\frac{2}{3}$ shaded. Then draw a rectangle, divided into sixths, with $\frac{4}{6}$ shaded.
   b. Are the two fractions equivalent? Yes
2. $\frac{2}{5}$ and $\frac{1}{8}$ No
3. $\frac{3}{4}$ and $\frac{6}{8}$ Yes
4. $\frac{3}{6}$ and $\frac{1}{2}$ Yes
5. $\frac{5}{6}$ and $\frac{2}{8}$ No

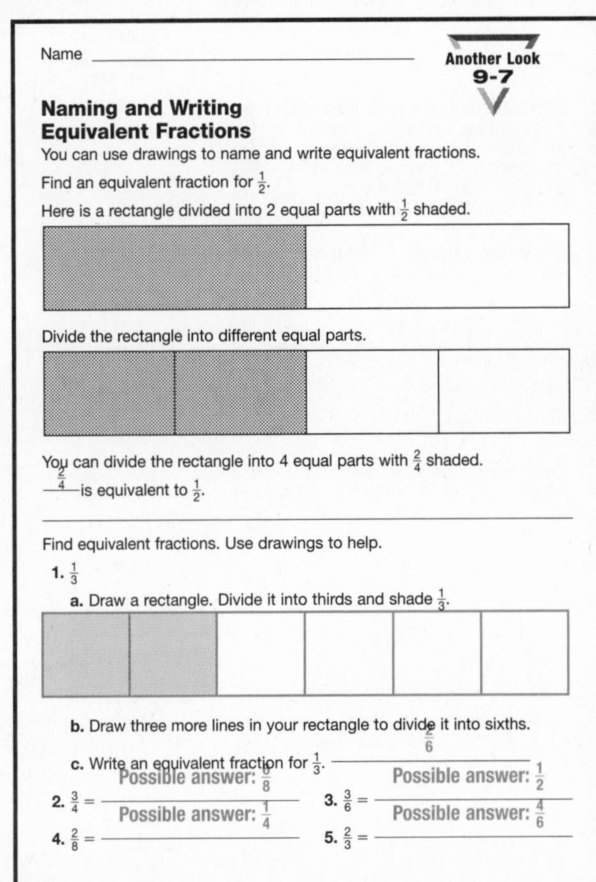

Name ______________________

Another Look 9-7

Naming and Writing Equivalent Fractions

You can use drawings to name and write equivalent fractions.

Find an equivalent fraction for $\frac{1}{2}$.

Here is a rectangle divided into 2 equal parts with $\frac{1}{2}$ shaded.

Divide the rectangle into different equal parts.

You can divide the rectangle into 4 equal parts with $\frac{2}{4}$ shaded.

$\frac{2}{4}$ is equivalent to $\frac{1}{2}$.

Find equivalent fractions. Use drawings to help.

1. $\frac{1}{3}$
   a. Draw a rectangle. Divide it into thirds and shade $\frac{1}{3}$.
   b. Draw three more lines in your rectangle to divide it into sixths.
   c. Write an equivalent fraction for $\frac{1}{3}$. $\frac{2}{6}$
2. $\frac{3}{4}$ = Possible answer: $\frac{6}{8}$
3. $\frac{3}{6}$ = Possible answer: $\frac{1}{2}$
4. $\frac{2}{8}$ = Possible answer: $\frac{1}{4}$
5. $\frac{2}{3}$ = Possible answer: $\frac{4}{6}$

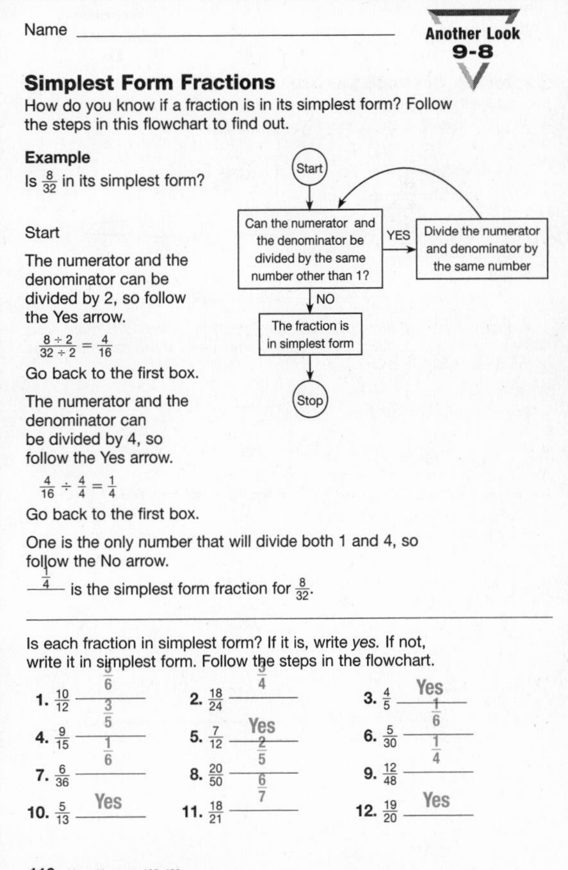

Name ______________________

Another Look 9-8

Simplest Form Fractions

How do you know if a fraction is in its simplest form? Follow the steps in this flowchart to find out.

Example

Is $\frac{8}{32}$ in its simplest form?

Start

The numerator and the denominator can be divided by 2, so follow the Yes arrow.

$\frac{8 \div 2}{32 \div 2} = \frac{4}{16}$

Go back to the first box.

The numerator and the denominator can be divided by 4, so follow the Yes arrow.

$\frac{4}{16} \div \frac{4}{4} = \frac{1}{4}$

Go back to the first box.

One is the only number that will divide both 1 and 4, so follow the No arrow.

$\frac{1}{4}$ is the simplest form fraction for $\frac{8}{32}$.

Is each fraction in simplest form? If it is, write *yes*. If not, write it in simplest form. Follow the steps in the flowchart.

1. $\frac{10}{12}$ $\frac{5}{6}$
2. $\frac{18}{24}$ $\frac{3}{4}$
3. $\frac{4}{5}$ Yes
4. $\frac{9}{15}$ $\frac{3}{5}$
5. $\frac{7}{12}$ Yes
6. $\frac{5}{30}$ $\frac{1}{6}$
7. $\frac{6}{36}$ $\frac{1}{6}$
8. $\frac{20}{50}$ $\frac{2}{5}$
9. $\frac{12}{48}$ $\frac{1}{4}$
10. $\frac{5}{13}$ Yes
11. $\frac{18}{21}$ $\frac{6}{7}$
12. $\frac{19}{20}$ Yes

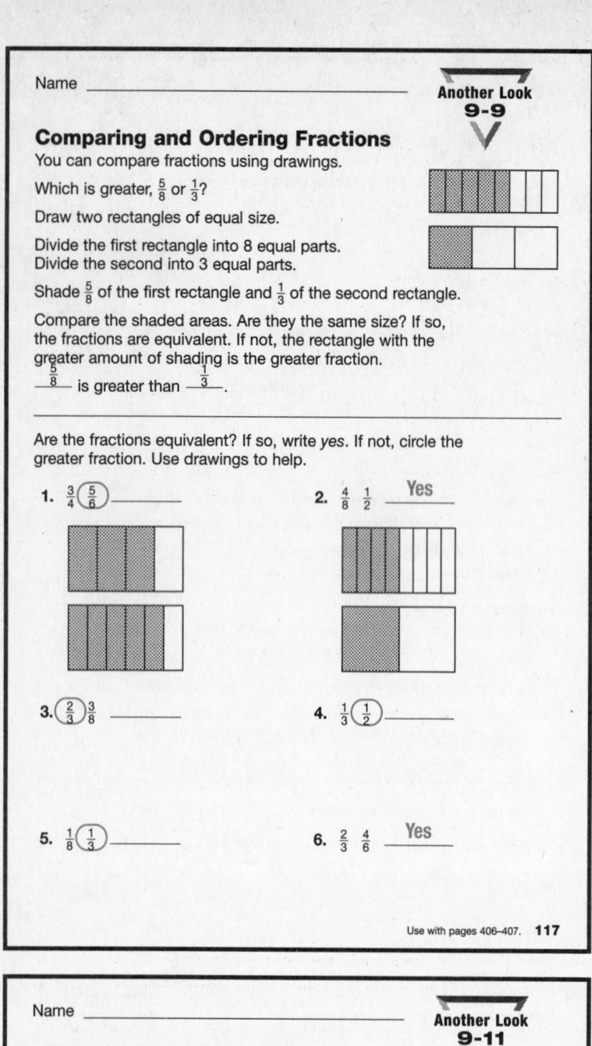

Name ______________________

Another Look 9-9

Comparing and Ordering Fractions

You can compare fractions using drawings.

Which is greater, $\frac{5}{8}$ or $\frac{1}{3}$?

Draw two rectangles of equal size.

Divide the first rectangle into 8 equal parts.
Divide the second into 3 equal parts.

Shade $\frac{5}{8}$ of the first rectangle and $\frac{1}{3}$ of the second rectangle.

Compare the shaded areas. Are they the same size? If so, the fractions are equivalent. If not, the rectangle with the greater amount of shading is the greater fraction.

$\frac{5}{8}$ is greater than $\frac{1}{3}$.

Are the fractions equivalent? If so, write *yes*. If not, circle the greater fraction. Use drawings to help.

1. $\frac{3}{4}$ ($\frac{5}{6}$) ______
2. $\frac{4}{8}$ $\frac{1}{2}$ Yes
3. ($\frac{2}{3}$) $\frac{3}{8}$ ______
4. $\frac{1}{3}$ ($\frac{1}{2}$) ______
5. $\frac{1}{8}$ ($\frac{1}{3}$) ______
6. $\frac{2}{3}$ $\frac{4}{6}$ Yes

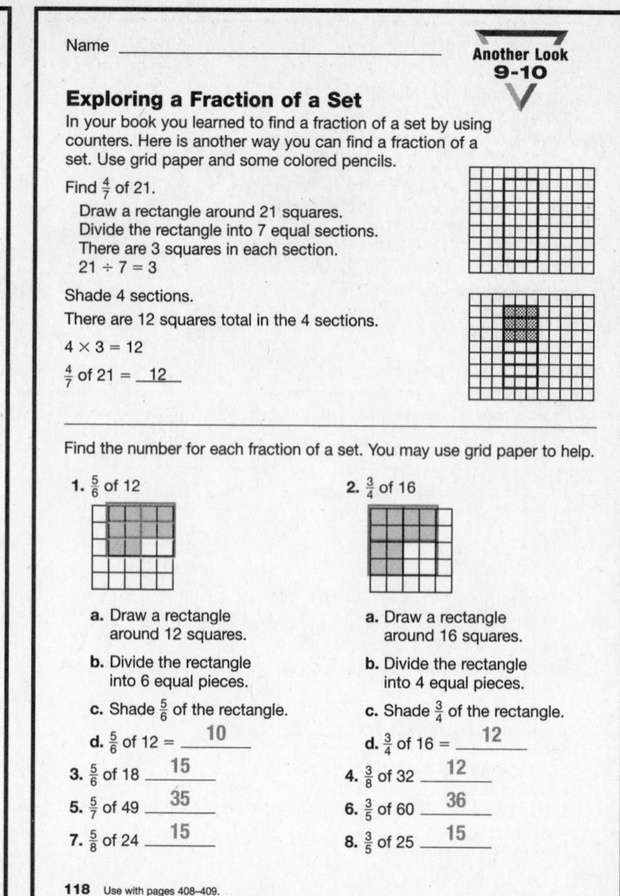

Name ______________________

Another Look 9-10

Exploring a Fraction of a Set

In your book you learned to find a fraction of a set by using counters. Here is another way you can find a fraction of a set. Use grid paper and some colored pencils.

Find $\frac{4}{7}$ of 21.

Draw a rectangle around 21 squares.
Divide the rectangle into 7 equal sections.
There are 3 squares in each section.
$21 \div 7 = 3$

Shade 4 sections.

There are 12 squares total in the 4 sections.

$4 \times 3 = 12$

$\frac{4}{7}$ of 21 = 12

Find the number for each fraction of a set. You may use grid paper to help.

1. $\frac{5}{6}$ of 12
   a. Draw a rectangle around 12 squares.
   b. Divide the rectangle into 6 equal pieces.
   c. Shade $\frac{5}{6}$ of the rectangle.
   d. $\frac{5}{6}$ of 12 = 10
2. $\frac{3}{4}$ of 16
   a. Draw a rectangle around 16 squares.
   b. Divide the rectangle into 4 equal pieces.
   c. Shade $\frac{3}{4}$ of the rectangle.
   d. $\frac{3}{4}$ of 16 = 12
3. $\frac{5}{6}$ of 18 15
4. $\frac{3}{8}$ of 32 12
5. $\frac{5}{7}$ of 49 35
6. $\frac{3}{5}$ of 60 36
7. $\frac{5}{8}$ of 24 15
8. $\frac{3}{5}$ of 25 15

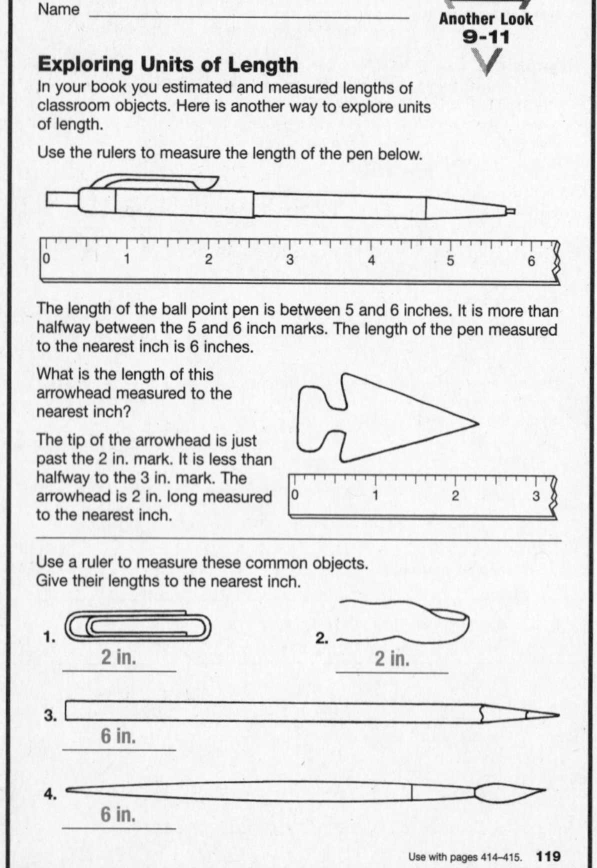

Name ______________________

Another Look 9-11

Exploring Units of Length

In your book you estimated and measured lengths of classroom objects. Here is another way to explore units of length.

Use the rulers to measure the length of the pen below.

The length of the ball point pen is between 5 and 6 inches. It is more than halfway between the 5 and 6 inch marks. The length of the pen measured to the nearest inch is 6 inches.

What is the length of this arrowhead measured to the nearest inch?

The tip of the arrowhead is just past the 2 in. mark. It is less than halfway to the 3 in. mark. The arrowhead is 2 in. long measured to the nearest inch.

Use a ruler to measure these common objects. Give their lengths to the nearest inch.

1. 2 in.
2. 2 in.
3. 6 in.
4. 6 in.

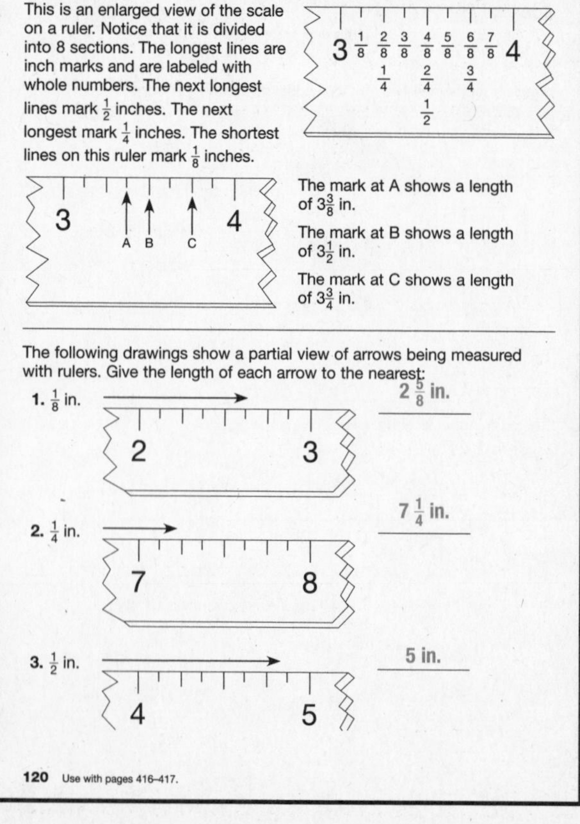

Name ______________________

Another Look 9-12

Measuring Fractional Parts of an Inch

This is an enlarged view of the scale on a ruler. Notice that it is divided into 8 sections. The longest lines are inch marks and are labeled with whole numbers. The next longest lines mark $\frac{1}{2}$ inches. The next longest mark $\frac{1}{4}$ inches. The shortest lines on this ruler mark $\frac{1}{8}$ inches.

The mark at A shows a length of $3\frac{3}{8}$ in.

The mark at B shows a length of $3\frac{1}{2}$ in.

The mark at C shows a length of $3\frac{3}{4}$ in.

The following drawings show a partial view of arrows being measured with rulers. Give the length of each arrow to the nearest:

1. $\frac{1}{8}$ in. $2\frac{5}{8}$ in.
2. $\frac{1}{4}$ in. $7\frac{1}{4}$ in.
3. $\frac{1}{2}$ in. 5 in.

Name ______________________

Another Look 9-13

Exploring Feet, Yards, and Miles

In your book you used a calculator to explore distances. Here is another way to understand feet, yards, and miles.

1 mile = 5,280 feet   1 mile = 1,760 yards

The track at Merrimack Middle School is 500 yards. If Marianne runs 2 laps, has she run more or less than 1 mile?

1 lap is 500 yards.
So, 2 laps is 500 + 500 = 1,000 yards
1,000 is less than 1,760.
So, 2 laps is __less than__ 1 mile.

Solve. Use the picture to help.

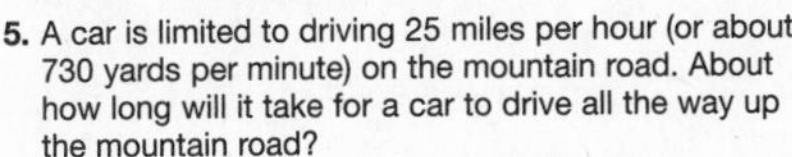

1. How many yards would you have to drive or walk to reach the top of the mountain?
   2,809 yards
2. If it took you 5 minutes to walk 25 yards, about how long would it take you to walk from the picnic area to the top of the mountain?
   About 170 minutes or 3 hours
3. About how many miles is it from the base of the mountain to the picnic area?
   About 1 mile
4. About how many miles long is the mountain road from the base of the mountain to the very top?
   About 2 miles
5. A car is limited to driving 25 miles per hour (or about 730 yards per minute) on the mountain road. About how long will it take for a car to drive all the way up the mountain road?
   About 4 minutes

Name ______________________

Guided Problem Solving 9-14

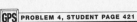

GPS PROBLEM 4, STUDENT PAGE 421

A group of 50 climbers took part in this year's mountain cleanup. For 29 climbers this was their second year helping. 10 had never helped before. How many of the 50 climbers had helped before last year?

Understand

1. What do you know?
   50 climbers participated this year, 29 climbers participated the year before, 10 climbers never participated before this year.
2. What do you need to find out? The number of climbers who participated before last year

Plan

3. Describe how you can solve the problem. Use Logical Reasoning.
4. Of the 50 climbers, how many helped last year? 29
5. How many climbers had participated in a cleanup before? Write the number sentence. 50 − 10 = 40

Solve

6. How many of the 50 climbers had helped before last year? Write the number sentence. 11; 40 − 29 = 11

Look Back

7. How can you check your answer?
   Possible answer: Work Backward

SOLVE ANOTHER PROBLEM

A crew of 28 people picked up trash in a local park. 18 people picked up trash along the hiking trails. 15 people picked up trash in the picnic areas. How many people helped in both areas?

5 people

Name ______________________

Another Look 10-1

Exploring Adding Fractions with Like Denominators

In your book you used fraction strips to add fractions with like denominators. Here is another way to add fractions.

Use the denominator as the number of equal sections to divide a rectangle. Use the numerators to shade in sections. Then count the number of shaded sections you have.

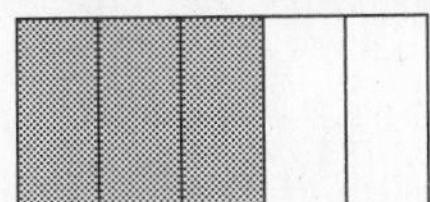

Find $\frac{1}{5} + \frac{2}{5}$.

Divide the rectangle into 5 equal sections.

Shade $\frac{1}{5}$. Then shade $\frac{2}{5}$.

What is the total amount shaded?

$\frac{3}{5}$ are shaded, so $\frac{1}{5} + \frac{2}{5} =$ __$\frac{3}{5}$__

Use the rectangles to help find each sum.

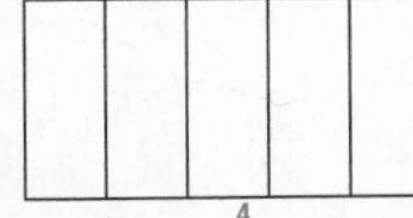

1. $\frac{2}{5} + \frac{2}{5} =$ __$\frac{4}{5}$__

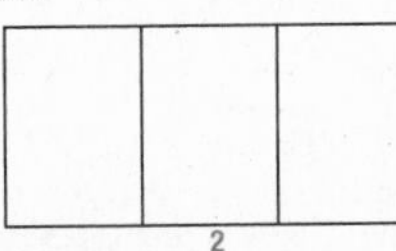

2. $\frac{1}{3} + \frac{1}{3} =$ __$\frac{2}{3}$__

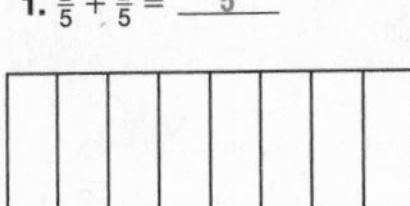

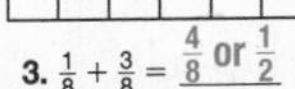

3. $\frac{1}{8} + \frac{3}{8} =$ __$\frac{4}{8}$ or $\frac{1}{2}$__

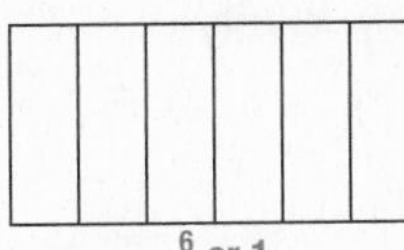

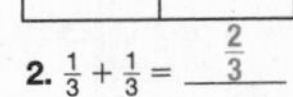

4. $\frac{1}{6} + \frac{5}{6} =$ __$\frac{6}{6}$ or 1__

Name ______________________

Another Look 10-2

Exploring Adding Fractions with Unlike Denominators

In your book you added two fractions with unlike denominators by renaming a fraction. Here is a closer look at renaming fractions.

How do you rename a fraction?
Multiply the numerator and denominator by the same number to make a new, equivalent fraction.

The fraction $\frac{1}{2}$ can be renamed as $\frac{2}{4}, \frac{3}{6}, \frac{4}{8}$, and so on.

$\frac{1 \times 2}{2 \times 2} = \frac{2}{4}$ $\frac{1 \times 3}{2 \times 3} = \frac{3}{6}$ $\frac{1 \times 4}{2 \times 4} = \frac{4}{8}$

Add $\frac{1}{3}$ and $\frac{1}{6}$. $\frac{1 \times 2}{3 \times 2} = \frac{2}{6}$, $+\frac{1}{6} = \frac{1}{6}$, total $\frac{3}{6}$

Simplify. $\frac{3 \div 3}{6 \div 3} = \frac{1}{2}$

Complete.

1. $\frac{3 \times 2}{5 \times 2} = \frac{6}{10}$
2. $\frac{1 \times 3}{8 \times 3} = \frac{3}{24}$
3. $\frac{2 \times 2}{9 \times 2} = \frac{4}{18}$

Write equivalent fractions with the given denominator.

4. $\frac{1}{4} = \frac{2}{8}$
5. $\frac{2}{3} = \frac{6}{9}$
6. $\frac{5}{6} = \frac{10}{12}$

Find each sum.

7. $\frac{1}{8} = \frac{1}{8}$; $+\frac{1}{2} = \frac{4}{8}$; $\frac{5}{8}$
8. $\frac{2}{9} = \frac{2}{9}$; $+\frac{1}{3} = \frac{3}{9}$; $\frac{5}{9}$
9. $\frac{3}{5} = \frac{6}{10}$; $+\frac{3}{10} = \frac{3}{10}$; $\frac{9}{10}$
10. $\frac{1}{3} + \frac{1}{9} =$ __$\frac{4}{9}$__
11. $\frac{3}{8} + \frac{1}{4} =$ __$\frac{5}{8}$__
12. $\frac{1}{2} + \frac{1}{6} =$ __$\frac{4}{6}$ or $\frac{2}{3}$__
13. $\frac{4}{5} + \frac{1}{10} =$ __$\frac{9}{10}$__
14. $\frac{2}{5} + \frac{1}{10} =$ __$\frac{5}{10}$ or $\frac{1}{2}$__
15. $\frac{1}{6} + \frac{2}{3} =$ __$\frac{5}{6}$__

Name ____________________

Adding Fractions

Only fractions with like denominators can be added. Before adding fractions with unlike denominators, you must rename the fractions so their denominators "match."

Decide whether or not to rename a fraction. Then solve the problem.

Example: $\frac{1}{5} + \frac{2}{5} = ?$

a. Do you need to rename a fraction? If so, which one? Explain.

No. Both fractions already have the same denominator.

b. Solve the problem. $\frac{1}{5} + \frac{2}{5} = \frac{3}{5}$

Example: $\frac{1}{5} + \frac{1}{10} = ?$

a. Do you need to rename a fraction? If so, which one? Explain.

Yes. Rename $\frac{1}{5}$ as $\frac{2}{10}$ so it can be added to $\frac{1}{10}$.

b. Solve the problem. $\frac{2}{10} + \frac{1}{10} = \frac{3}{10}$

1. $\frac{1}{6} + \frac{5}{6} = ?$

a. Do you need to rename a fraction? If so, which one? Explain.

No. Both fractions already have the same denominator.

b. Solve the problem: $\frac{1}{6} + \frac{5}{6} = \frac{6}{6}$ (or 1)

2. $\frac{1}{6} + \frac{5}{18} = ?$

a. Do you need to rename a fraction? If so, which one? Explain.

Yes. Rename $\frac{1}{6}$ as $\frac{3}{18}$ so it can be added to $\frac{5}{18}$.

b. Solve the problem: $\frac{3}{18} + \frac{5}{18} = \frac{8}{18}$ (or $\frac{4}{9}$)

Find each sum. Simplify.

3. $\frac{1}{8} + \frac{3}{8} =$ $\frac{4}{8} = \frac{1}{2}$ **4.** $\frac{2}{3} + \frac{2}{9} =$ $\frac{8}{9}$

Name ____________________

Another Look
10-4

Decision Making

Your class wants to paint a design on the courtyard wall. The principal will let you use left-over paint from the supply closet. Here is what you have available:

Yellow	$\frac{1}{2}$ can	White	$\frac{1}{2}$ can
Red	$\frac{1}{2}$ can	Black	1 can
Blue	1 can	Green	$\frac{1}{2}$ can
Each can holds a gallon of paint. One gallon will cover about 100 square feet.			

If the wall measures 100 square feet, is there enough yellow and red paint to cover it?

$\frac{1}{2}$ can yellow + $\frac{1}{2}$ can red = 1.

Since 1 whole can will cover 100 square feet, there is enough paint.

1. If the wall measures 200 square feet, is there enough yellow, red, white, and green paint to cover it? Explain.

Yes. There is $\frac{1}{2}$ can each of yellow, red, white and green paint. $\frac{1}{2} + \frac{1}{2} = 1$ and $\frac{1}{2} + \frac{1}{2} = 1$, so there are 1 + 1 or 2 cans of paint total. Two cans hold 2 gallons of paint, enough for 200 square feet.

2. If the wall measures 200 square feet, is there enough black and white paint to cover it? Explain.

No. There is $\frac{1}{2}$ can of white and 1 can of black; $1\frac{1}{2}$ cans of paint, total. That's not enough. You need 2 cans (2 gallons) for 200 square feet.

Name ____________________

Exploring Subtracting Fractions

In your book you subtracted fractions with like and unlike denominators using fraction strips. Here is a closer look at how to subtract fractions. For fractions with like denominators, follow these steps:

Find $\frac{7}{8} - \frac{3}{8}$.

Step 1 Use fraction strips that match the denominators. $\frac{1}{8}$

Step 2 Model the larger fraction.

$\frac{1}{8}$ $\frac{1}{8}$ $\frac{1}{8}$ $\frac{1}{8}$ $\frac{1}{8}$ $\frac{1}{8}$ $\frac{1}{8}$

Step 3 Model the smaller fraction.

$\frac{1}{8}$ $\frac{1}{8}$ $\frac{1}{8}$

Step 4 Line the strips up. Take away pairs of fractions. Count the remaining fraction strips.

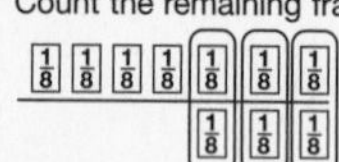

$\frac{7}{8} - \frac{3}{8} = \frac{4}{8}$ $\frac{4 \div 4}{8 \div 4} = \frac{1}{2}$

Use fraction strips or draw a picture to solve each problem.

1. $\frac{8}{9} - \frac{2}{9} =$ $\frac{6}{9}$, or $\frac{2}{3}$ **2.** $\frac{3}{4} - \frac{1}{4} =$ $\frac{2}{4}$, or $\frac{1}{2}$

3. $\frac{5}{8} - \frac{1}{8} =$ $\frac{4}{8}$, or $\frac{1}{2}$ **4.** $\frac{11}{12} - \frac{5}{12} =$ $\frac{6}{12}$, or $\frac{1}{2}$

5. $\frac{4}{5} - \frac{2}{5} =$ $\frac{2}{5}$ **6.** $\frac{2}{3} - \frac{1}{3} =$ $\frac{1}{3}$

7. $\frac{5}{6} - \frac{1}{6} =$ $\frac{4}{6}$, or $\frac{2}{3}$ **8.** $\frac{6}{7} - \frac{3}{7} =$ $\frac{3}{7}$

9. $\frac{7}{10} - \frac{3}{10} =$ $\frac{4}{10}$, or $\frac{2}{5}$ **10.** $\frac{8}{9} - \frac{5}{9} =$ $\frac{3}{9}$, or $\frac{1}{3}$

Name ____________________

Subtracting Fractions

Only fractions with like denominators can be subtracted. Before subtracting fractions with unlike denominators, you must rename the fractions so their denominators "match."

Example: $\frac{2}{5} - \frac{1}{5} = ?$

a. Do you need to rename a fraction? If so, which one? Explain.

No. Both fractions already have the same denominator.

b. Solve the problem. $\frac{2}{5} - \frac{1}{5} = \frac{1}{5}$

Example: $\frac{1}{5} - \frac{1}{10} = ?$

a. Do you need to rename a fraction? If so, which one? Explain.

Yes. Rename $\frac{1}{5}$ as $\frac{2}{10}$ so you can subtract $\frac{1}{10}$.

b. Solve the problem. $\frac{2}{10} - \frac{1}{10} = \frac{1}{10}$

1. $\frac{5}{6} - \frac{1}{6} = ?$

a. Do you need to rename a fraction? If so, which one? Explain.

No. Both fractions already have the same denominator.

b. Solve the problem. $\frac{5}{6} - \frac{1}{6} = \frac{4}{6}$, or $\frac{2}{3}$

2. $\frac{1}{6} - \frac{1}{18}$

a. Do you need to rename a fraction? If so, which one? Explain.

Yes. Rename $\frac{1}{6}$ as $\frac{3}{18}$ so you can subtract $\frac{1}{18}$.

b. Solve the problem $\frac{3}{18} - \frac{1}{18} = \frac{2}{18}$, or $\frac{1}{9}$

Find each difference.

3. $\frac{1}{2} - \frac{1}{4} =$ $\frac{1}{4}$ **4.** $\frac{5}{8} - \frac{1}{8} =$ $\frac{4}{8}$ or $\frac{1}{2}$ **5.** $\frac{2}{3} - \frac{1}{9} =$ $\frac{5}{9}$

Name ______________________

Another Look 10-7

Analyze Word Problems: Choose an Operation

Len has a collection of baseball cards. Pitchers make up $\frac{1}{12}$ of his collection while outfielders make up $\frac{2}{3}$ of his collection. What fractional part of his collection are pitchers and outfielders?

Since you want to combine the fractional parts of pitchers and outfielders, you have to add $\frac{1}{12}$ and $\frac{2}{3}$.

The denominators are unlike.

Rename $\frac{2}{3}$. $\frac{2}{3} = \frac{8}{12}$

$\frac{2}{3} \overset{\times 4}{=} \frac{8}{12}$

Find the sum and simplify.

$\frac{1}{12} + \frac{8}{12} = \frac{9}{12} = \frac{3}{4}$

$\frac{3}{4}$ of Len's baseball cards are pitchers and outfielders.

Solve.

1. Maria has a coin collection. Nickels make up $\frac{3}{8}$ of her collection. Pennies make up $\frac{1}{4}$ of her collection. What fractional part of her collection are pennies and nickels? $\frac{5}{8}$
2. Patsy has $\frac{7}{8}$ yd of red ribbon and $\frac{3}{4}$ yd of yellow ribbon.
   a. How much more red ribbon does she have than yellow ribbon? $\frac{1}{8}$ yd
   b. If Patsy uses $\frac{1}{2}$ yd of each color ribbon, how much ribbon of each color will Patsy have left over?
   Red: $\frac{3}{8}$ yd
   Yellow: $\frac{1}{4}$ yd
3. Simon has $\frac{7}{8}$ of a bag of marbles. He gives $\frac{1}{4}$ of them to his friend. How much of the bag does he have left?  $\frac{5}{8}$

Name ______________________

Another Look 10-8

Exploring Weight

In your book you chose the better estimate for the weight of certain items. Another way is to match items that weigh about the same.

Look at each item. Imagine trying to pick up each item. Think, "Which items would require about the same amount of strength to pick up?"

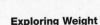

You could pick up a salad bowl and a dinner plate with one hand. You would need both hands or help from a friend to pick up the chair.

Circle the two items that weigh about the same.

1\.

2\.

3\.

4\.

5\.

Name ______________________

Another Look 10-9

Exploring Capacity

In your book you chose the better estimate for the capacity of certain items. Another way is to match items that have about the same capacity.

Look at each container. Imagine filling each container with water. Think, "Which containers would hold about the same amount of water?"

A few drops would fill the teaspoon. The glass and the coffee cup hold about 1 cup each.

Circle the two items that have about the same capacity.

1\. 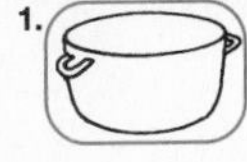  

2\. 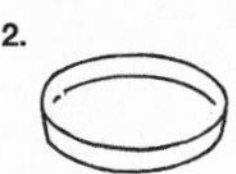 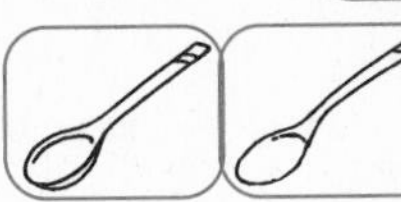

3\. 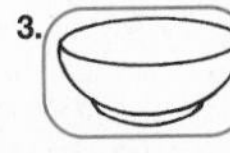  

4\.    

5\.   

Name ______________________

Another Look 10-10

Changing Units: Length, Weight, and Capacity

12 qt = ☐ gal

A quart is smaller than a gallon.

When you change from smaller units to larger units, you divide.

4 qt = 1 gal

12 qt ÷ 4 = 3 gal

12 qt = 3 gal

6 lb = ☐ oz

A pound weighs more than an ounce.

When you change from larger units to smaller units, you multiply.

1 lb = 16 oz

6 lb × 16 = 96 oz

6 lb = 96 oz

---

1. 5 qt = ☐ pt
   a. Is a quart larger or smaller than a pint? Larger
   b. Should you multiply or divide? Multiply
   c. 1 qt = 2 pt
   d. 5 qt = 10 pt
2. 80 oz = ☐ lb
   a. Is an ounce larger or smaller than a pound? Smaller
   b. Should you multiply or divide? Divide
   c. 1 lb = 16 oz
   d. 80 oz = 5 lb
3. 14 c = 7 pt **4.** 6 yd = 18 ft **5.** 7 ft = 84 in.

Name ______________________

Another Look 10-11

Compare Strategies: Draw a Picture/Make a Table

Make a table and draw a picture to solve the problem. Decide which strategy you prefer.

For every 12 cans of food donated to the food drive, Belmont Market donates 3 pounds of apples. By the end of the week, 84 cans of food had been donated. How many pounds of apples will Belmont Market donate?

You can solve this problem by making a table. Find a pattern to complete the table.

Number of cans	12	24	36	48	60	72	84
Pounds of apples	3	6	9	12	15	18	21

Add 12 more cans and 3 more pounds of apples for each column in the table. Continue until you find the answer.

Another way to solve this problem is to draw a picture. Use squares for cans and circles for pounds of apples. Count the number of pounds of apples in your drawing.

12 12 12 12 12 12 12

3 3 3 3 3 3 3

$3 \times 7 =$ 21, so Belmont Market will donate 21 pounds of apples.

Use any strategy to solve each problem.

1. Belmont Market has also decided to donate 5 lb of fresh fruit for every 15 lb of canned goods donated. How many pounds of fresh fruit will Belmont Market donate if 90 lb of canned goods are donated? 30 lb
2. Jenny likes to swim laps. After every 12 laps, she takes 4 dives. On Saturday, she swam 48 laps. How many dives did she take? 16 dives
3. For every 2 miles Russell walks, he takes a rest. How many rests does he take on a 12-mile walk? 6 rests

Name ______________________

Another Look 10-12

Exploring Algebra: Using a Balance Scale Model

In your book you used a balance scale model to help find an unknown value in an equation. Here is another way to find the unknown value.

Find the value of n.

6 + ✉ = 11

Suppose a closed envelope holds the unknown number. You can find the unknown value.

$6 + n = 11$

Ask yourself, "What must be in the envelope to make the equation true?"

Count up from 6 to 11 to find the answer.

7, 8, 9, 10, 11

You counted up 5 numbers. So, $n = 5$

Find the value of each ✉.

1. 9 + ✉ = 17 $n = 8$
2. 8 + ✉ = 21 $n = 13$
3. 11 + ✉ = 12 $n = 1$
4. 6 + ✉ = 14 $n = 8$
5. ✉ + 12 = 18 $n = 6$
6. ✉ + 3 = 7 $n = 4$
7. ✉ + 4 = 11 $n = 7$
8. ✉ + 16 = 21 $n = 5$
9. 10 + 7 = ✉ $n = 17$
10. 3 + 4 = ✉ $n = 7$
11. 8 + 11 = ✉ $n = 19$
12. 12 + 11 = ✉ $n = 23$

Name ______________________

Another Look 11-1

Reading and Writing Decimals

You see decimals every day. Money amounts are often written as decimals.

\$2.43 is read "2 dollars and 43 cents."

To read the same decimal as a non-money amount, drop "dollars" and change "cents" to "hundredths."

2.43 is read as "2 and 43 hundredths."

If there is only one number after the decimal point, use "tenths" instead of "hundredths."

2.4 is read as "2 and 4 tenths."

1. \$4.57 is read as "4 dollars and 57 cents."
2. 4.57 is read as "4 and 57 hundredths."
3. 4.5 is read as "4 and 5 tenths."

Write the word name for each decimal.

4. 3.65 3 and 65 hundredths
5. 4.39 4 and 39 hundredths
6. 17.1 17 and 1 tenth
7. 21.35 21 and 35 hundredths
8. 142.6 142 and 6 tenths
9. 67.35 67 and 35 hundredths

Write the decimal for each word name.

10. 4 and 6 tenths 4.6
11. 3 and 44 hundredths 3.44
12. 42 and 1 tenth 42.1
13. 6 and 52 hundredths 6.52
14. 7 and 9 tenths 7.9
15. 4 and 98 hundredths 4.98

Name ______________________

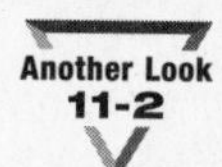

Another Look 11-2

Exploring Decimal Place-Value Relationships

In your book you used grids to show decimals.
Here is another way to explore decimal place-value relationships.

Use simple fractions to look at decimals.

$0.1 = $ one tenth $= \frac{1}{10}$

$0.10 = $ ten hundredths $= \frac{10}{100}$

Can you reduce $\frac{10}{100}$? Yes.

Divide the numerator and denominator by 10. $\frac{10 \div 10}{100 \div 10} = \frac{1}{10}$

So, $\frac{1}{10} = \frac{10}{100}$, one tenth equals ten hundredths, and $0.1 = 0.10$.

Write 0.5 in hundredths. $0.5 = 5$ tenths $= \frac{5}{10}$

Multiply the numerator and the denominator by 10 to change tenths to hundredths. $\frac{5 \times 10}{10 \times 10} = \frac{50}{100}$ $\frac{50}{100} =$ fifty hundredths $= 0.50$.

So 0.5 written in hundredths is 0.50.

1. Write 0.2 in hundredths.
   a. Write the fraction for 0.2. $\frac{2}{10}$
   b. Multiply the numerator and denominator by 10. Write the new fraction. $\frac{20}{100}$
   c. Write the new fraction as a decimal in hundredths. 0.20
2. Write 0.70 in tenths.
   a. Write the fraction for 0.70. $\frac{70}{100}$
   b. Divide the numerator and denominator by 10. Write the new fraction. $\frac{7}{10}$
   c. Write the new fraction as a decimal in tenths. 0.7

Write each decimal in hundredths.

3. 0.4 0.40
4. 0.7 0.70
5. 0.9 0.90

Write each decimal in tenths.

6. 0.60 0.6
7. 0.80 0.8
8. 0.30 0.3

Name ______________________

Another Look 11-3

Compare Strategies: Make an Organized List/Use Objects

Suppose you have 18 coins, all dimes and pennies, that total $1.26. How many of each coin do you have?

You can make an organized list to solve this problem. Then check your answer using objects.

Value	Dimes	Pennies	Number of Coins
$1.26	10	26	36
$1.26	11	16	27
$1.26	12	6	18

There are 12 dimes and 6 pennies.

12 dimes = $1.20 and 6 pennies = $0.06.
$1.20 + $0.06 = $1.26.
12 dimes and 6 pennies are 18 coins.
The answer is correct.

$1.20

$0.06

Suppose you have the same number of pennies and nickels. The coins total $0.18. How many of each coin do you have?

1. What do you know? The total amount is $0.18. There are equal numbers of pennies and nickels.
2. Make an organized list or draw a picture of the objects you can use to solve the problem. Possible answers:

   Organized list—

Nickels	Pennies	Value
1	1	$0.06
2	2	$0.12
3	3	$0.18

   Use objects—Student may draw a group of 3 nickels and a group of 3 pennies. 3 nickels = $0.15, 3 pennies = $0.03.
3. How many of each coin do you have? 3 nickels, 3 pennies

Name ______________________

Another Look 11-4

Comparing and Ordering Decimals

Order the following decimals from least to greatest: 9.43, 9.24, 9.40. Use a number line to help.

All of the decimals start with the whole number 9. Draw a number line from 9.0 to 10.0.

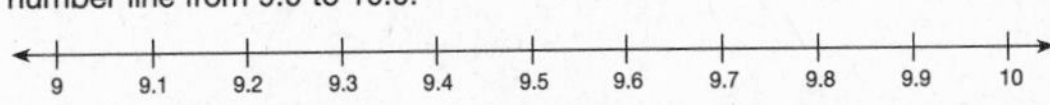

Look at the number in the tenths place in each decimal to help you find the order.
$2 < 3 < 4$, so 9.**2**4 is less than 9.**4**3 and 9.**4**0.

Now look at the number in the hundredths place in 9.43 and 9.40.
$0 < 3$, so 9.4**0** is less than 9.4**3**.

Write the decimals in order on the number line.

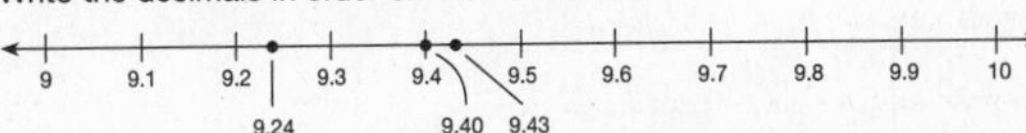

So, the order of the decimals from least to greatest is 9.24, 9.40, 9.43.

Order the decimals from least to greatest. Draw a number line to help.

1. 1.23, 1.01, 1.19
   a. Draw a number line from 1.0 to 2.0.

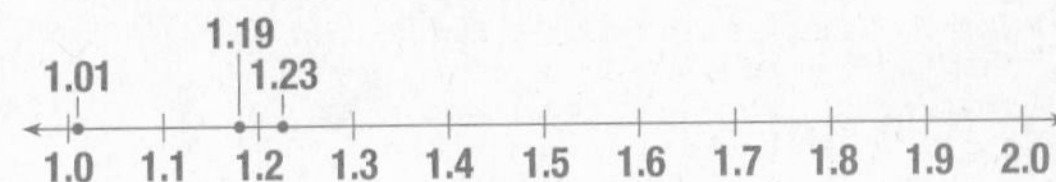

   b. Look at the number in the tenths place for each decimal to help find the order. Then look at the number in the hundredths place. Write the numbers on your number line above.
   c. Write the order of the decimals from least to greatest. 1.01, 1.19, 1.23
2. 5.34, 5.21, 5.64, 5.61, 5.21, 5.34, 5.61, 5.64

Name ______________________

Another Look 11-5

Rounding Decimals

You can round decimals to the nearest whole number by using a simple rule.

Rule: If the digit in the tenths place is less than 5, don't change the digit in the ones place. If it is 5 or greater, add 1 to the digit in the ones place.

Example 1 Round 24.28 to the nearest whole number.

Step 1 Look at the digit in the tenths place. Ignore all other digits!

$2 < 5$, so don't change the ones digit.

Step 2 Drop the decimal part and write the new whole number.

24.28 rounded to the nearest whole number is 24.

Example 2 Round 26.72 to the nearest whole number.

Step 1 Look at the digit in the tenths place.

$7 > 5$, so add 1 to the digit in the ones place.

Step 2 Drop the decimal part and write the new whole number.

26.72 rounded to the nearest whole number is 27.

Round each decimal to the nearest whole number.

1. 2.47
   a. What is the digit in the tenths place? 4
   b. Do you add 1 to the digit in the ones place or keep it as it is? Keep it as is.
   c. What is 2.47 rounded to the nearest whole number? 2
2. 11.51
   a. What is the digit in the tenths place? 5
   b. Do you add 1 to the digit in the ones place or keep it as it is? Add 1.
   c. What is 11.51 rounded to the nearest whole number? 12

Name ______________________

Another Look 11-6

Exploring Fractions as Decimals

In your book you used grids to show fractions as decimals. Here is another way to explore fractions as decimals.

Decimals and fractions both show parts of a whole. You can change a fraction to an equivalent fraction in tenths or hundredths. Then write the decimal.

Example 1 Find a decimal for $\frac{1}{2}$.

$2 \times 5 = 10$, so multiply the numerator and denominator by 5 to find an equivalent fraction in tenths.

$\frac{1 \times 5}{2 \times 5} = \frac{5}{10}$ So, $\frac{1}{2} = \frac{5}{10}$ = five tenths = 0.5.

Example 2 Find a decimal for $\frac{1}{4}$.

$4 \times 25 = 100$, so multiply the numerator and denominator by 25 to find an equivalent fraction in hundredths.

$\frac{1 \times 25}{4 \times 25} = \frac{25}{100}$ So, $\frac{1}{4} = \frac{25}{100}$ = twenty-five hundredths = 0.25

Find the decimal for each fraction. Use equivalent fractions to help.

1. $\frac{2}{5}$
   a. $\frac{2 \times 2}{5 \times 2} = \frac{4}{10}$
   b. What is the decimal for $\frac{2}{5}$? 0.4
2. $\frac{9}{20}$
   a. $\frac{9}{20} \times \frac{5}{5} = \frac{45}{100}$
   b. What is the decimal for $\frac{9}{20}$? 0.45
3. $\frac{3}{4}$
   a. $4 \times 25 = 100$
   b. What is the decimal for $\frac{3}{4}$? 0.75
4. $\frac{1}{25}$
   a. $25 \times 4 = 100$
   b. What is the decimal for $\frac{1}{25}$? 0.04

Name ______________________

Another Look 11-7

Estimating Sums and Differences

When estimating sums and differences with decimals, round each decimal to the nearest whole number. Then add or subtract.

> Tip: Do not change the whole number part if the decimal part is 0.49 or less. Add 1 to the whole number part if the decimal part is 0.50 or greater.

Estimate the sum of 29.49 and 31.50.

Step 1 Round 29.49 to the nearest whole number.

Round 29.**49** to 29.

Step 2 Round 31.50 to the nearest whole number.

Round 31.**50** to 32.

Step 3 Add the rounded numbers.
29 + 32 = 61

29.49 + 31.50 is about 61.

Round to the nearest whole number.

1. 4.1 __4__
2. 8.29 __8__
3. 35.62 __36__
4. 16.5 __17__
5. 17.99 __18__
6. 24.09 __24__

Estimate each sum or difference. Round to the nearest whole number.

7. 1.7 + 2.9 → [2] + [3] = __5__
8. 10.12 − 7.30 → [10] − [7] = __3__
9. 21.49 + 8.50 = __30__
10. 2.05 − 0.03 = __2__
11. 5.2 + 3.5 = __9__
12. 8.79 + 31.4 = __40__
13. 12.17 − 4.20 = __8__
14. 6.8 − 2.7 = __4__

Name ______________________

Another Look 11-8

Exploring Adding and Subtracting Decimals

In your book you used grids to add and subtract decimals. Here is another way.

Find the sum of 0.46 and 0.70.

Step 1 Write the numbers in a column, lining up the decimal points.

Step 2 Add as if you were adding whole numbers.

Step 3 Place a decimal point in the answer directly below where it occurs in the problem.

```
  0.46
+ 0.70
------
  1.16
```

The sum of 0.46 and 0.70 is 1.16.

Find each sum or difference.

1. 0.90 + 0.36
   a. Write the numbers in a column.
   b. Add and then place the decimal point.
   c. 0.90 + 0.36 = __1.26__

```
  [0].[9][0]
+ [0].[3][6]
  [1].[2][6]
```

2. 0.40 − 0.14
   a. Write the numbers in a column.
   b. Subtract. Regroup as needed. Then place the decimal point.
   c. 0.40 − 0.14 = __0.26__

```
  [0].[4][0]
− [0].[1][4]
  [0].[2][6]
```

3. 0.24 − 0.20 = 0.04
4. 0.48 + 0.15 = 0.63
5. 0.36 + 0.24 = 0.60
6. 0.43 − 0.20 = 0.23
7. 0.70 − 0.55 = 0.15
8. 0.98 − 0.76 = 0.22
9. 0.71 − 0.35 = 0.36
10. 0.69 + 0.35 = 1.04
11. 0.80 − 0.59 = 0.21
12. 0.85 + 0.35 = 1.20

Name ______________________

Another Look 11-9

Adding and Subtracting Decimals

Adding and subtracting decimals can be easy. Just follow these steps.

6.71 + 32.02 + 8.4

A Line up the decimal points.	B Write zeros as needed.	C Add. Regroup if necessary.
6.71 32.02 + 8.4	6.71 32.02 + 8.40	6.71 32.02 + 8.40 47.13

28.7 − 17.92

A Line up the decimal points.	B Write zeros as needed.	C Subtract. Regroup if necessary.
28.7 − 17.92	28.70 − 17.92	28.70 − 17.92 10.78

Find each sum or difference. Estimate to check your answer.

1. 7.3 + 3.45 = 10.75
2. 18.32 + 1.05 = 19.37
3. 44.27 + 32.78 = 77.05
4. 17.39 + 14.82 = 32.21
5. 15.03 + 16.7 = 31.73
6. 7.89 − 0.15 = 7.74
7. 10.42 − 3.03 = 7.39
8. 25.28 − 18.32 = 6.96
9. 55.47 − 15.49 = 39.98
10. 65.3 − 18.91 = 46.39

Name ______________________

Another Look 11-10

Exploring Centimeters, Decimeters, and Meters

In your book you explored metric measurement by finding the distance around balls of different sizes. Here is another way to explore centimeters, decimeters, and meters.

Here are benchmarks you can use to estimate centimeters, decimeters, and meters.

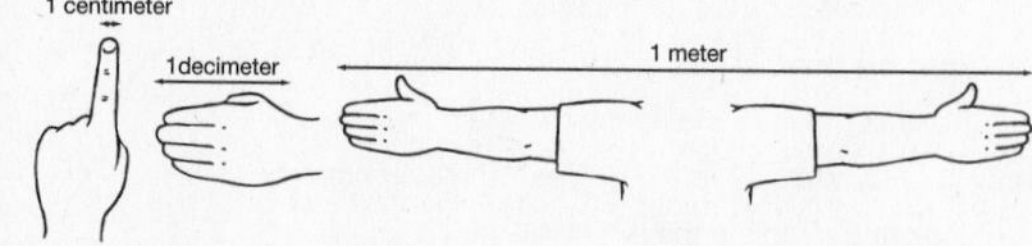

Which unit of measure would you use to measure the length of this page?

The page isn't as long as your outstretched arms, so meters would be too large.

You could measure this page with your finger, but that would take a lot of time. So, centimeters would be too small.

Decimeters is the best unit of measure.

Circle the better unit of measure for each object.

1. 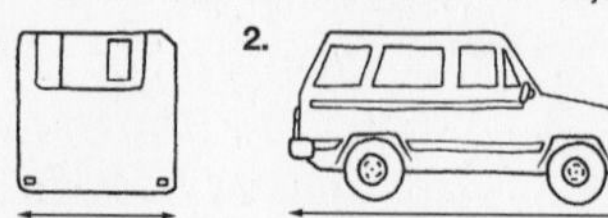
(centimeters) or meters

2. 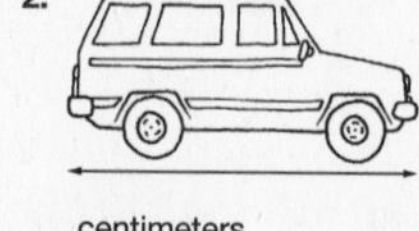
centimeters or (meters)

3. 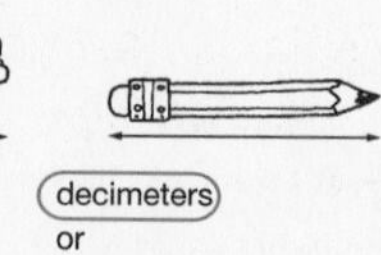
(decimeters) or meters

Name ______________________

Another Look 11-11

Meters and Kilometers

The meter (m) and kilometer (km) are units of length in the metric system. A kilometer measures longer distances.

1 km = 1,000 m

2 km = ▩ m	7,000 m = ▩ km
Meters are shorter than kilometers.	Kilometers are longer than meters.
To change to a lesser unit, *multiply*. Think: 1 km = 1,000 m 2 × 1,000 = 2,000	To change to a greater unit, *divide*. Think: 1,000 m = 1 km 7,000 ÷ 1,000 = 7
2 km = 2,000 m	7,000 m = 7 km
There are 2,000 meters in 2 kilometers.	7 kilometers are the same as 7,000 meters.

Compare 2 km and 7,000 m.
2 km = 2,000 m
Since 2,000 m < 7,000 m

2 km (<) 7,000 m

Complete the table.

Multiply →

1.	1 km	1,000 m
2.	2 km	2,000 m
3.	3 km	3,000 m
4.	10 km	10,000 m

← Divide

Complete. Write >, <, or =.

5. 7 km (=) 7,000 m
6. 5 m (<) 5 km
7. 140 m (<) 14 km
8. 6 km (=) 6,000 m
9. 1 km (>) 100 m
10. 40 m (<) 40 km
11. 300 km (>) 3,000 m
12. 86 km (=) 86,000 m

Name ______________________

Another Look 11-12

Exploring Length and Decimals

In your book you measured your arm span and height in centimeters and meters. Here is another way to explore length and decimals.

Centimeters and meters are used to measure length.

To change meters to centimeters, multiply by 100.

To multiply by 100, *move the decimal point 2 places to the right.*

4.35 m = ▩ cm

4.35 m   4.35.   435 cm

move 2 places right

4.35 m = 435 cm

To change centimeters to meters, divide by 100.

To divide by 100, *move the decimal point 2 places to the left.*

330 cm = ▩ m

330 cm   3.30.   3.30 m

move 2 places left

330 cm = 3.3 m

Write the letter of the measurement that matches.

1. 2.36 m __b__
   a. 23.6 cm
   b. 236 cm
2. 272 cm __a__
   a. 2.72 m
   b. 27.2 m

Complete.

3. 32 cm = __0.32__ m
4. 1.4 m = __140__ cm
5. 45.7 cm = __0.457__ m
6. 0.07 m = __7__ cm
7. 33.8 m = __3,380__ cm
8. 19 m = __1,190__ cm
9. 2.1 cm = __.021__ m
10. 3.2 m = __320__ cm

Name ______________________

Another Look 11-13

Exploring Mass

In your book you used a balance scale to explore mass. Here is another way to explore mass.

Grams and kilograms are metric units used to measure mass.

A gram is used to measure light objects.

To change grams to kilograms, divide by 1,000.

3 grams

3 g = ▩ kg

Think: 3 ÷ 1,000 = 0.003   *Move the decimal 3 places to the left.*

3g = 0.003 kg

A kilogram is used to measure heavy objects.

To change from kilograms to grams, multiply by 1,000.

3 kilograms

3 kg = ▩ g

Think: 3 × 1,000 = 3,000   *Move the decimal 3 places to the left.*

3 kg = 3,000 g

Choose a reasonable unit of mass for each. Ask yourself if the mass of each object is closer to the mass of a penny or the mass of a dog. Write g or kg.

1. a cookie __g__
2. a truck __kg__
3. a turkey __kg__
4. an apple __g__
5. a horse __kg__
6. a dime __g__
7. a teaspoon __g__
8. a bowling ball __kg__

Write the letter of the measurement that matches.

9. 5 kg __a__ g
   a. 5,000 g b. 0.005 g
10. 30,000 g __b__ kg
   a. 3 kg b. 30 kg

Complete.

11. 8 kg = __8,000__ g
12. 2,300 g = __2.3__ kg
13. 0.3 kg = __300__ g
14. 230 kg = __230,000__ kg

Name ______________________

Another Look 11-14

Exploring Capacity

In your book you explored capacity by filling containers with water. Here is another way to explore capacity.

Liters and milliliters are metric units used to measure liquids. The amount of liquid a container holds is its capacity.

Milliliters are used to measure the liquid in small containers. Liters are used to measure the liquid in large containers.

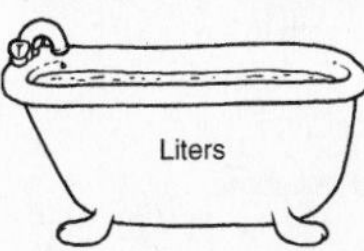

To change liters to milliliters, multiply by 1,000.

To multiply by 1,000, move the decimal point 3 places to the right.

7.2 L = ▩ mL

7.2 L   7.200.   7,200 mL

7.2 L = 7,200 mL

To change milliliters to liters, divide by 1,000.

To divide by 1,000, move the decimal point 3 places to the left.

4,500 mL = ▩ L

4,500 mL   4.500.   4.500 L or 4.5 L

4,500 mL = 4.5 L

Write the letter of the measurement that matches.

1. 3.2 L __a__
   a. 3,200 mL b. 32,000 mL
2. 650 mL __b__
   a. 6.5 L b. 0.65 L

Complete.

3. 5 L = __5,000__ mL
4. 62,000 mL = __62__ L
5. 8.2 L = __8,200__ mL
6. 510 mL = __0.51__ L

Name ______________________________

Another Look 11-15

Temperature

Follow these steps to read a thermometer.

1. Find the top of the liquid in the thermometer.
2. Find the number on the thermometer that is closest to the top of the liquid.

   The closest number is 80.
3. The marks between the numbers indicate 2 degrees. So count those marks up or down by 2's to the top of the liquid.

   Point to each mark as you count down. Say, "80, 78, 76." Stop at the liquid. What is the temperature?

   The thermometer shows a temperature of 76°F.

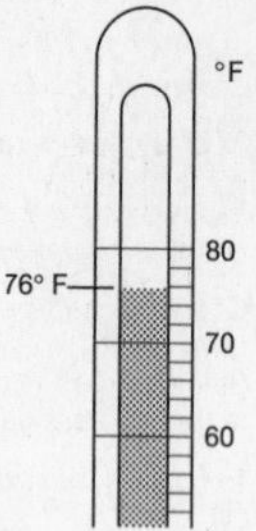

Read each thermometer. Write the temperature on the line.

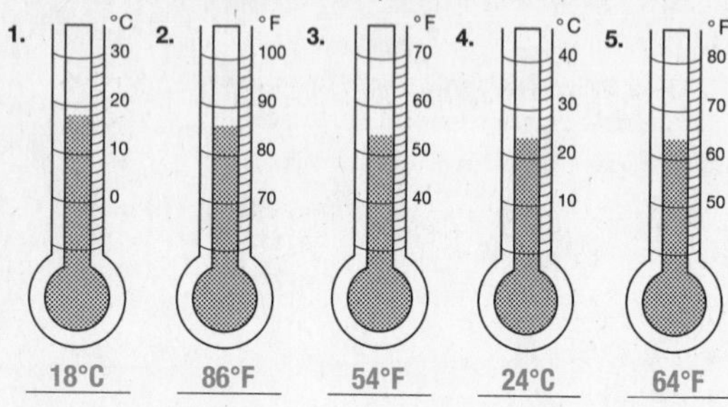

1. 18°C
2. 86°F
3. 54°F
4. 24°C
5. 64°F

Name ______________________________

Another Look 11-16

Decision Making

In your book you created your own track model. Here, you will complete a track model that has already been started. You will need string and scissors. Follow these steps:

Step 1 Cut a piece of string the same length as the perimeter of the inner oval.

Step 2 Holding one end of the string at the finish line in lane 1, lay the string clockwise along the center of the lane. Mark where it ends. Draw a line across the lane at the mark. This is the starting point for lane 1.

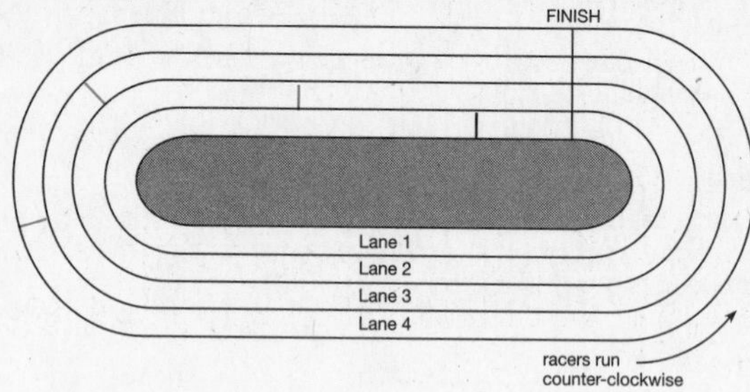

Complete the track.

1. Hold one end of the string at the finish line in lane 2. Lay it clockwise along the center of that lane, and mark where it ends. Draw the starting line for lane 2.
2. Do the same for lanes 3 and 4.

Name ______________________________

Another Look 12-1

Exploring Division Problems

In your book you used place-value patterns to help divide greater numbers. Here is another way.

Cross off an equal number of zeros in the divisor and the dividend, starting from the ones place and moving to the left. Then divide the smaller numbers.

For example, to divide 1,800 by 60, follow these steps:

Step 1 Cross off an equal number of zeros from both the divisor and the dividend.

1,80Ø ÷ 6Ø

Step 2 Rewrite the problem without the crossed out zeros.

180 ÷ 6

Step 3 Solve.

180 ÷ 6 = 30

Find each quotient by crossing off an equal number of zeros. Show the new problem. Then solve.

1. 3,500 ÷ 70 = 350 ÷ 7 = 50
2. 35,000 ÷ 70 = 3,500 ÷ 7 = 500
3. 4,800 ÷ 60 = 480 ÷ 6 = 80
4. 48,000 ÷ 60 = 4,800 ÷ 6 = 800
5. 8,100 ÷ 90 = 810 ÷ 9 = 90
6. 81,000 ÷ 90 = 8,100 ÷ 9 = 900
7. 2,400 ÷ 80 = 240 ÷ 8 = 30
8. 24,000 ÷ 80 = 2,400 ÷ 8 = 300
9. 4,800 ÷ 40 = 480 ÷ 4 = 120
10. 48,000 ÷ 40 = 4,800 ÷ 4 = 1,200
11. 3,000 ÷ 60 = 300 ÷ 6 = 50
12. 30,000 ÷ 60 = 3,000 ÷ 6 = 500

Name ______________________________

Another Look 12-2

Estimating Quotients with 2-Digit Divisors

Estimate 372 ÷ 72

Step 1 372 ÷ 72 — Look at the two front digits of the dividend. What one-digit number divides 37 evenly? Only 1 and 37 divide 37 evenly.

Step 2 372 ÷ 72 — Look at the front digit of the divisor.

Step 3 372 ÷ 72 — Compare 37 and 7. Is there a division fact that uses values close to these numbers? You know 36 ÷ 6 = 6

Step 4 Estimate the division by using fact.

36 ÷ 6 = 6, so 360 ÷ 60 = 60

372 ÷ 72 is about 60.

Estimate each quotient.

1. 492 ÷ 68
   - **a.** 49 can be divided evenly by 7.
   - **b.** Change the problem to 490 ÷ 70.
   - **c.** Estimate: 7
2. 814 ÷ 89
   - **a.** 81 can be divided evenly by 9.
   - **b.** Change the problem to 810 ÷ 90.
   - **c.** Estimate: 9
3. 238 ÷ 61

   240 ÷ 60 = 4
4. 718 ÷ 91

   720 ÷ 90 = 8
5. 561 ÷ 79

   560 ÷ 80 = 7
6. 627 ÷ 87

   630 ÷ 90 = 7

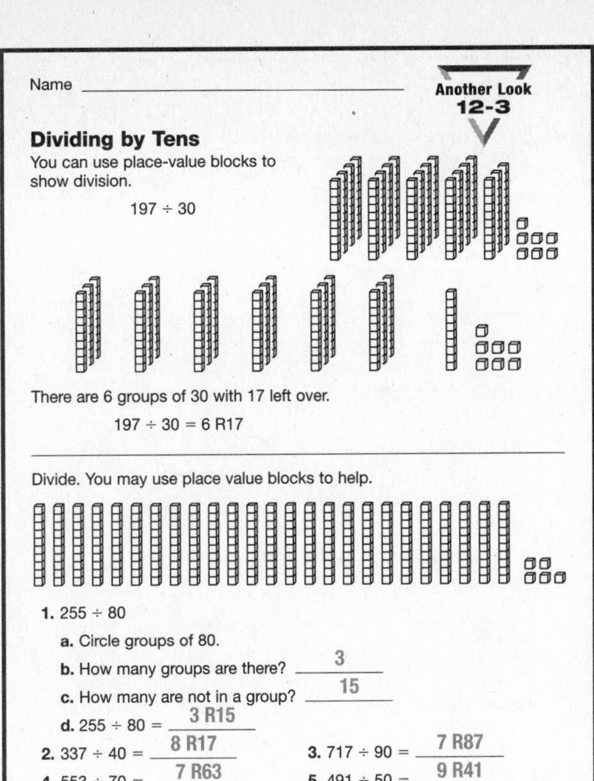

Name ______________________

Another Look 12-3

Dividing by Tens

You can use place-value blocks to show division.

197 ÷ 30

There are 6 groups of 30 with 17 left over.

197 ÷ 30 = 6 R17

Divide. You may use place value blocks to help.

1. 255 ÷ 80
   - a. Circle groups of 80.
   - b. How many groups are there? 3
   - c. How many are not in a group? 15
   - d. 255 ÷ 80 = 3 R15
2. 337 ÷ 40 = 8 R17
3. 717 ÷ 90 = 7 R87
4. 553 ÷ 70 = 7 R63
5. 491 ÷ 50 = 9 R41
6. 241 ÷ 30 = 8 R1
7. 896 ÷ 60 = 14 R56

Use with pages 532–533. 153

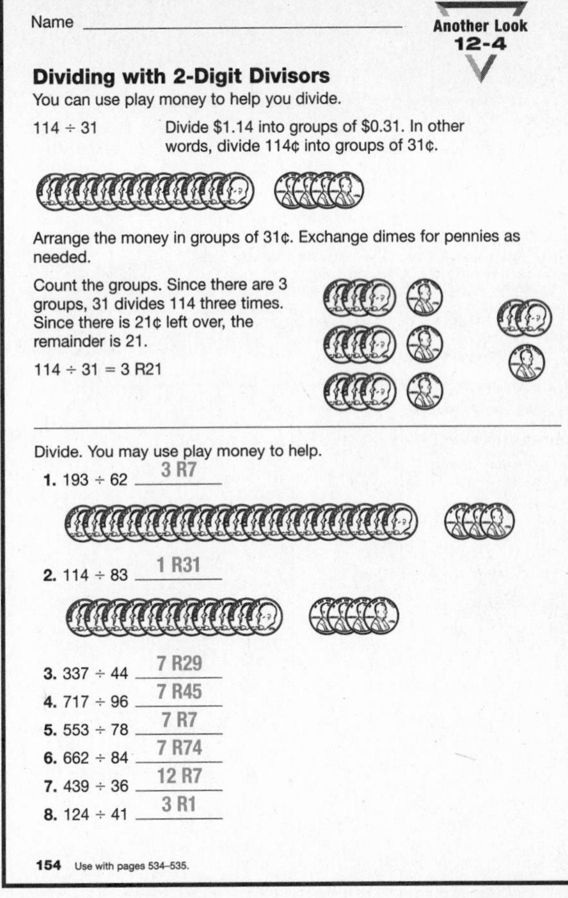

Name ______________________

Another Look 12-4

Dividing with 2-Digit Divisors

You can use play money to help you divide.

114 ÷ 31 Divide $1.14 into groups of $0.31. In other words, divide 114¢ into groups of 31¢.

Arrange the money in groups of 31¢. Exchange dimes for pennies as needed.

Count the groups. Since there are 3 groups, 31 divides 114 three times. Since there is 21¢ left over, the remainder is 21.

114 ÷ 31 = 3 R21

Divide. You may use play money to help.

1. 193 ÷ 62 3 R7
2. 114 ÷ 83 1 R31
3. 337 ÷ 44 7 R29
4. 717 ÷ 96 7 R45
5. 553 ÷ 78 7 R7
6. 662 ÷ 84 7 R74
7. 439 ÷ 36 12 R7
8. 124 ÷ 41 3 R1

154 Use with pages 534–535.

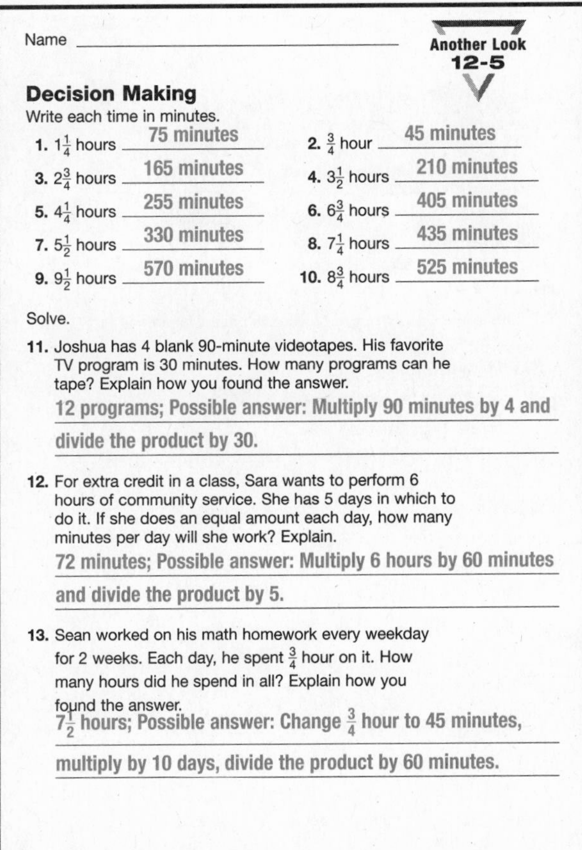

Name ______________________

Another Look 12-5

Decision Making

Write each time in minutes.

1. $1\frac{1}{4}$ hours 75 minutes
2. $\frac{3}{4}$ hour 45 minutes
3. $2\frac{3}{4}$ hours 165 minutes
4. $3\frac{1}{2}$ hours 210 minutes
5. $4\frac{1}{4}$ hours 255 minutes
6. $6\frac{3}{4}$ hours 405 minutes
7. $5\frac{1}{2}$ hours 330 minutes
8. $7\frac{1}{4}$ hours 435 minutes
9. $9\frac{1}{2}$ hours 570 minutes
10. $8\frac{3}{4}$ hours 525 minutes

Solve.

11. Joshua has 4 blank 90-minute videotapes. His favorite TV program is 30 minutes. How many programs can he tape? Explain how you found the answer.
    12 programs; Possible answer: Multiply 90 minutes by 4 and divide the product by 30.
12. For extra credit in a class, Sara wants to perform 6 hours of community service. She has 5 days in which to do it. If she does an equal amount each day, how many minutes per day will she work? Explain.
    72 minutes; Possible answer: Multiply 6 hours by 60 minutes and divide the product by 5.
13. Sean worked on his math homework every weekday for 2 weeks. Each day, he spent $\frac{3}{4}$ hour on it. How many hours did he spend in all? Explain how you found the answer.
    $7\frac{1}{2}$ hours; Possible answer: Change $\frac{3}{4}$ hour to 45 minutes, multiply by 10 days, divide the product by 60 minutes.

Use with pages 536–537. 155

Name ______________________

Another Look 12-6

Exploring Likely and Unlikely

In your book you explored likely and unlikely with miniature golf. Here is another way to understand likely and unlikely.

Sometimes you need to predict if an event can happen. You make predictions based on experiences you have had. Each statement shows the different ways you can think about an event.

You will eat. → certain
Think: You have to eat to live.

You have milk in your cereal. → likely
Think: Most people eat cereal with milk.

Your dinner will be served hot. → equally likely as unlikely
Think: You could have cold food instead.

Your dinner cost $100 to prepare. → unlikely
Think: Most meals do not cost this much.

You eat 100 pounds of beef for dinner. → impossible
Think: No one can eat this much.

Read each statement. Write whether the event is impossible, unlikely, equally likely as unlikely, likely, or certain.

1. Your school serves 1,000,000 lunches a day. Impossible
2. The hamburgers cost $20.00 a pound. Unlikely
3. You eat a sandwich for lunch. Equally likely as unlikely
4. You will have something new to eat this year. Likely
5. Cows produce milk. Certain
6. You eat a 2-pound steak for dinner. Unlikely
7. You have a drink with your lunch. Likely
8. You eat popcorn at the movies. Equally likely as unlikely
9. Ice cream is made from hot dogs. Impossible
10. The sun will rise in the east. Certain

156 Use with pages 540–541.

Name ______________________________

Exploring Fairness

In your book you explored fairness using a number cube. Here is another way to explore fairness.

The **possible outcomes** of both spinner A and spinner B are 1, 2, 3, and 4.

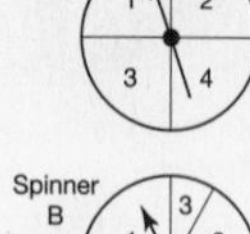

Example 1: Spinner A is divided into four equal parts. There is an **equally likely** chance of every possible outcome.

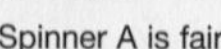

Spinner A is fair.

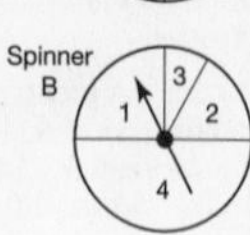

Example 2: Spinner B is divided into four parts but the parts are not equal. You have a greater chance of spinning 4 because that section is largest.

Spinner B is unfair.

Circle fair or unfair for each situation.

1. Spin the spinner.

   (fair) or unfair

2. Spin the spinner.

   fair or (unfair)

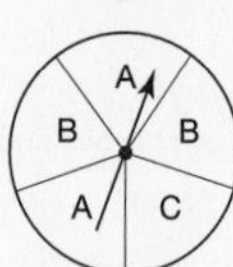

3. Pick a marble without looking.

   fair or (unfair)

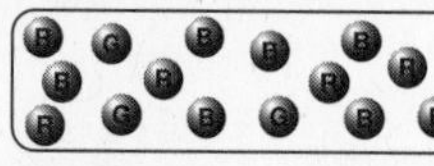

4. Toss a coin.

   (fair) or unfair

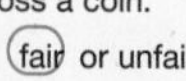

Name ______________________________

Listing Possible Outcomes

Spin each spinner once. How many different sums are possible?
You can spin a 1 or a 2 on spinner A.
On spinner B you can spin either a 3, 4, 5, or 6.

Spinner A: 1, 2

Spinner B: 3, 4, 5, 6

What are the possible combinations for both spinners together?

Pair up one number from each spinner and find the sums.

Spinner A	1	1	1	1	2	2	2	2
Spinner B	3	4	5	6	3	4	5	6
Sum	4	5	6	7	5	6	7	8

The **possible outcomes** (sums) are 4, 5, 6, 7, and 8.

A sum of 5, 6, or 7 is more likely than a sum of 4 or 8.

1. What are the possible outcomes for Spinner C?
   2, 4, 6

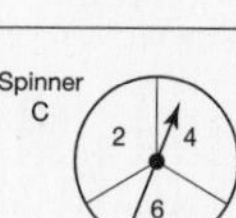

2. What are the possible outcomes for Spinner D?
   1, 3, 5

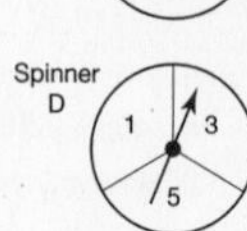

3. Write the possible combinations for both spinners together.

   $2 + 1 = 3$ $4 + 1 = 5$ $6 + 1 = 7$

   $2 + 3 = 5$ $4 + 3 = 7$ $6 + 3 = 9$

   $2 + 5 = 7$ $4 + 5 = 9$ $6 + 5 = 11$

4. How many different sums are possible? 5

5. List all the ways you can get a sum of 7.
   $2 + 5, 4 + 3, 6 + 1$

Name ______________________________

Another Look
12-9

Exploring Probability

In your book you used a number cube to explore probability. Here is another way to explore probability.

The spinner has 6 equal sections.
So, the total number of different spins is 6.

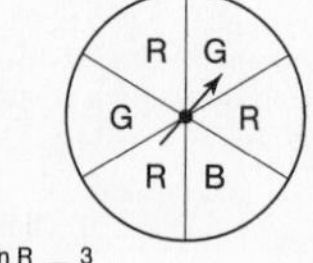

You can spin an R, B, or G on this spinner.

What is the probability of spinning R?

There are 3 ways to spin R.
The probability of spinning R is $\frac{\text{number of ways to spin R}}{\text{total number of outcomes}} = \frac{3}{6}$

So, the probability is $\frac{3}{6} = \frac{1}{2}$.

Use the spinner above to answer **1–2**.

1. What is the probability of spinning B? $\frac{1}{6}$
2. What is the probability of spinning G? $\frac{2}{6}$ or $\frac{1}{3}$

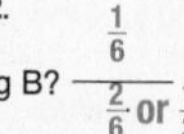

Use the spinner to find each probability.

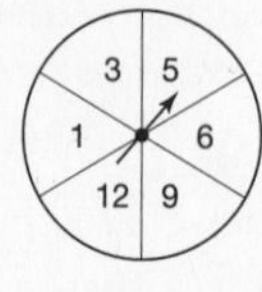

3. What is the probability of spinning a 3? $\frac{1}{6}$
4. What is the probability of spinning an even number? $\frac{2}{6}$ or $\frac{1}{3}$
5. What is the probability of spinning a number less than 3? $\frac{1}{6}$

Name ______________________________

Exploring Predictions

In your book you played a guessing game to explore predictions. Here is another way to explore predictions.

In a survey, 20 students were asked their favorite breakfast food. The table shows the results.

Breakfast Food	
Cereal	10
Muffin	8
Bagel	2

Ten students like cereal.

The probability that someone likes cereal is 10 out of 20 or $\frac{10}{20}$.

Simplify: $\frac{10}{20} = \frac{1}{2}$.

The probability of an event can be used to predict future events.

You can use probability of $\frac{1}{2}$ to predict how many students out of 100 will like cereal.

Use equivalent fractions.

$$\frac{1}{2} \xrightarrow{\times 50} \frac{\square}{100}$$

You predict that 50 out of 100 students will like cereal.

Use the table.

1. What is the probability that a student likes bagels? $\frac{2}{20} = \frac{1}{10}$

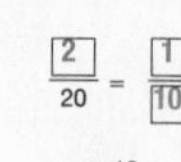

2. How many students out of 100 will like bagels? $\frac{1}{10} \xrightarrow{\times 10} \frac{10}{100}$
3. What is the probability that a student likes muffins? $\frac{8}{20}$ or $\frac{2}{5}$
4. Predict how many students out of 500 will like muffins.
   200 students
5. Predict how many students out of 300 will like cereal.
   150 students

Name ______________________________

Another Look
12-11

Analyze Strategies: Solve a Simpler Problem

Ellen has enough ribbon to wrap 12 gift boxes. How many cuts will she have to make to have 12 ribbons?

Think of a simpler problem to help find a solution.

Find the number of cuts needed to have 2 ribbons.

2 ribbons, 1 cut needed

Now try 3 ribbons.

3 ribbons, 2 cuts needed

Now try 4 ribbons.

4 ribbons, 3 cuts needed

Look for a pattern.

The number of cuts needed is always 1 less than the number of ribbons needed.

If 12 ribbons are needed, there must be 11 cuts.

Solve. Try finding a simpler problem.

1. Mrs. Wilson has enough ribbon to decorate 24 door wreaths. For 24 pieces of ribbon, how many cuts will she have to make? 23
2. Eight boys and 8 girls are in a tennis tournament. Each boy plays each girl once. How many games are played? 64
3. In a bag of mixed nuts, there is one Brazil nut for every 3 cashews. If there are 48 cashews, how many Brazil nuts will there be? 16